ESSAYS IN MODERN BIOLOGY

This is life

ESSAYS IN MODERN

Holt,

Rinehart

and

Winston,

New York

BIOLOGY

This is life

Edited by

WILLIS H. JOHNSON
Wabash College

WILLIAM C. STEERE
Director, New York Botanical Garden

Library of Congress Catalog Card Number: 62–8422
24695–0512
Printed in the United States of America

Preface

Many things are being done these days to improve both teaching and learning in each of the sciences, and biologists have been especially active. Although many good college and high school biology texts are available, it is not possible, within the limits of a single text, to develop many aspects of modern biology to the satisfaction of the able and interested student. It occurred to the editors of this volume that this problem might be solved, at least in part, by a book in which each of a series of chapters deals with a particular aspect of modern biology having great current interest and importance, and is written by a person active in that area. With this aim, we planned the present volume.

Each author has written with the beginning college student in mind. Although the volume was designed primarily as collateral reading for college students in a general biology or introductory biology course, it should also prove useful to students in beginning botany and beginning zoology courses, and to advanced high school students. Furthermore, we believe that many of the chapters can be read with interest and profit by more advanced students in biology, by those in other fields of science who want up-to-date information on biology, and by the interested layman.

There are so many areas of great activity in biology today that it is not possible in a single volume to include a separate chapter for each. The areas selected, in the opinion of the editors, stand among the more important ones in modern biology.

Although the chapters may be read in any order, a rationale for their arrangement here is apparent. Certainly, one of the most important syntheses in all nature is the storage of energy by green plants in basic carbohydrates, and this is dealt with in the first chapter, on *Photosynthesis.* To be useful to organisms, this stored energy must be released and utilized, and the second chapter discusses *Energy Release and Utilization.* Among the important contributions to modern biology come those from the field of electron microscopy. The chapter on *Ultrastructure and Function* is placed next because of the knowledge we now have about the nature of the ultrastructures involved in both photosynthesis and cell respiration. The nutrition of organisms, the area involved with the determination of the specific compounds required for normal growth and reproduction, and the possible evolution of these requirements are important. Since the nutritive requirements found in unicellular plants and animals are so varied, the next chapter considers *Nutrition of Protists.*

Among the most notable advances made in biology during the past century are those in the field of genetics, and this is a very active field today. Chapters 5, 6, and 7 are devoted to genetics. Chapters 5 and 6 on *Viruses: Reproduction and Heredity* and *Bacteria: Reproduction and Heredity* are included because of the great contributions to genetic theory made by studies on viruses and on bacteria. Chapter 7 summarizes the present status of basic genetic concepts under the title, *Structure of the Genetic Material and the Concept of the Gene.* In moving from the gene to the definitive organism, one must consider the phenomena of growth and differentiation. The next three chapters treat these areas—one on *Plant Growth and Plant Hormones,* one on *Plant Morphogenesis,* and one on *Animal Morphogenesis.* The principle of organic evolution ties together and integrates all biological knowledge, and without some treatment of this area our volume would not be complete.

Although the role of hybridization is usually presented in advanced classes in biology, the editors are convinced that this aspect of the study of evolution can properly be presented to beginning students. The subject of Chapter 11, then, is *The Role of Hybridization in Evolution.* For a long time biologists lacked a good working hypothesis covering the origin of life. Information now available makes possible a reasonable working hypothesis. The concluding chapter, therefore, is on *The Origin of Life.* We have placed it at the end instead of at the beginning because both the author and the editors feel that the materials presented in the other chapters will make the materials in this chapter easier to follow.

The editors were gratified by the responses of the authors to their invitations to write the chapters, and we want to thank each one of them for joining in this venture. A brief biographic account of each author is placed at the beginning of his chapter.

W. H. J.
W. C. S.

Crawfordsville, Indiana
New York City
February, 1962

WILLIS H. JOHNSON, *Chairman*

Department of Biology
Wabash College

Willis Hugh Johnson was born at Parkersburg, Indiana, in 1902. He attended Wabash College where he was awarded the A.B. degree in 1925. His graduate training was obtained at the University of Chicago; M.S., 1929 and Ph.D., 1932. Except for the period of his graduate training he was a member of the Department of Zoology at Wabash College from 1925 to 1935. In 1935 he joined the staff in biology at Stanford University where he served as assistant professor, associate professor, and then professor until 1946. He returned to Wabash College, where he is now located, in 1946 as Chairman of the Science Division and Chairman of the Department of Biology.

Professor Johnson has long been interested in the teaching of introductory biology at the college level. He served as Chairman of the Biology Examination Committee and Chief Reader in Biology in the Advanced Placement Program from its inception until 1960. He served as Chairman of the Conference on Undergraduate Curricula in the Biological Sciences held in 1957 under NRC auspices and is coauthor of the report of that conference "Recommendations on Undergraduate Curricula in the Biological Sciences," NAC–NRC publication 578. At present he is Chairman of the subcommittee on Standards of the Education Committee of the American Institute of Biological Sciences. He is a past president of the Indiana Academy of Science and of the Midwest Conference of College Biology Teachers.

Professor Johnson is the author of numerous research articles among which are: "A purine and pyrimidine requirement for *Paramecium multimicronucleatum*" (with C. A. Miller), *J. Protozool.*, 1957, 4:220–224; "Nutrition of *Paramecium:* A fatty acid requirement" (with C. A. Miller), *J. Protozool.*, 1960, 7:297–301; "Induced loss of pigment in planarians" (with C. A. Miller and J. H. Brumbaugh), *Physiol. Zool.*, 1962, 35:18–26. He is a member of the editorial board of the *Journal of Protozoology and of Physiological Zoology*. He is also coauthor (with R. A. Laubengayer and L. E. DeLanney) of the text *General Biology*, Holt, Rinehart and Winston, 1961.

WILLIAM C. STEERE, *Director*

The New York Botanical Garden, and
Professor of Botany, Columbia University
New York

William Campbell Steere was born in Muskegon, Michigan, in 1907. After graduation from the University of Michigan in 1929, in plant physiology, he carried on graduate studies in cytology at the University of Pennsylvania for two years. In 1931 he became an instructor at the University of Michigan, receiving the Ph.D. degree there in 1932; he became Professor of Botany in 1946 and Chairman of the Department in 1947. Between 1950 and 1958 he was Professor of Biology and, from 1955 on, also Dean of the Graduate Division at Stanford University. He has held his present position since 1958. Other professional activities have been, while on leave, Exchange Professor at the University of Puerto Rico, 1939–40; Senior Botanist, Board of Economic Warfare, with quinine-procurement missions in Colombia, 1942–43, and Ecuador, 1943–44; and Program Director for Systematic Biology at the National Science Foundation in Washington, D.C., 1954–55. He is a past president of the Botanical Society of America, the American Bryological Society, the American Society of Naturalists, the American Society of Plant Taxonomists, the California Botanical Society, and the Torrey Botanical Club. In 1959, during official ceremonies of the IX International Botanical Congress, he received the degree of Docteur ès-Sci. (honoris causa) from the University of Montreal.

His research interests center about the geographical distribution of plants, especially mosses, and he has investigated problems involving their systematics, ecology, cytology, and paleobotany. These studies, based on extensive field work in many parts of the Western Hemisphere, have resulted in more than 150 published research papers, of which the following are illustrative: "Chromosome number and behavior in arctic mosses," *Botan. Gaz.*, 116(1954): 93–133; "The mosses of Porto Rico and the Virgin Islands," (with H. A. Crum) New York Acad. Sci., *Sci. Survey P. R. and the V. I.*, 1957, 7(4): 393–599; "A preliminary review of the bryophytes of Antarctica," Nat. Acad. Sci., *Nat. Research Council Publ.*, 1961, 839: 20–33.

Contents

1. *Photosynthesis* **3**
C. Stacy French, *Carnegie Institution of Washington*

2. *Energy Release and Utilization* **41**
Arthur C. Giese, *Stanford University*

3. *Ultrastructure of Cells in Relation to Function* **79**
Ruth V. Dippell, *Indiana University*

4. *Nutrition of Protists* **109**
S. H. Hutner, *Haskins Laboratory*

5. *Viruses: Reproduction and Heredity* **139**
Albert Siegel, *University of Arizona*

6. *Bacteria: Reproduction and Heredity* 169
H. R. Garner, *Purdue University*

7. *Structure of the Genetic Material and the Concept of the Gene* 185
George W. Beadle, *University of Chicago*

8. *Plant Growth and Plant Hormones* 213
Frits W. Went, *Missouri Botanical Garden*

9. *Plant Morphogenesis* 255
Ian M. Sussex, *Yale University*

10. *Animal Morphogenesis* 271
M. V. Edds, Jr., *Brown University*

11. *The Role of Hybridization in Evolution* 287
Edgar Anderson, *Missouri Botanical Garden and Washington University*

12. *The Origin of Life* 317
Stanley L. Miller, *University of California, San Diego*

Index 343

CHAPTER 1

C. STACY FRENCH, *Director*

Department of Plant Biology
Carnegie Institution of Washington
Stanford, California

C. Stacy French was born in Lowell, Massachusetts, in 1907. He attended Harvard University where he was awarded the B.S. degree in 1930 and the Ph.D. degree in 1934, with general physiology as his special field. In 1934–35 he was a Research Fellow at California Institute of Technology with Robert Emerson. He was Guest Investigator at the Kaiser Wilhelm Institute in Berlin in 1935–36 with Otto Warburg. In 1936–38 he was Austin Teaching Fellow in the Department of Biochemistry of Harvard Medical School. During 1938 to 1941 he was Research Instructor in the Department of Chemistry of the University of Chicago with James Franck. From 1941 to 1946 he was Assistant and Associate Professor of Botany at the University of Minnesota. He has been in his present position since 1947.

His research interests have centered on photosynthesis, particularly the nature and function of the relevant pigments and the development of specialized spectroscopic equipment for such work. Among his numerous technical papers are the following: "Fluorescence spectrophotometry of photosynthetic pigments," in *Luminescence of Biological Systems* (Frank H. Johnson, ed.), American Association for the Advancement of Science, 1955; "The variability of chlorophyll in plants," in *Photobiology,* Biology Colloquium, Oregon State College, 1958; "Action spectra and optical properties of cellular pigments," in *Photoperiodism and Related Phenomena in Plants and Animals,* AAAS, 1959; "Evidences from action spectra for a specific participation of chlorophyll *b* in photosynthesis," *J. Gen. Physiol.,* 1960, 43:723–736 (with J. Myers); "Light, pigments, and photosynthesis," in *Light and Life* (W. D. McElroy and B. Glass, eds.), Johns Hopkins Press, 1961; "Computer solutions for photosynthesis rates from a two-pigment model," *Biophysical Journal,* 1961, 1:669–681 (with D. C. Fork).

Photosynthesis

CHAPTER 1

C. S. FRENCH

Carnegie Institution of Washington

The food we eat and the oxygen we breathe are both formed by plants through the process of photosynthesis. The power to drive the photosynthetic reaction comes from sunlight absorbed by chlorophyll in plants. Although all life depends directly or indirectly on photosynthesis, the chemical nature of this remarkable energy-converting process is not at all well understood. No known chemical system can be made to serve as substitute for this ability of plants to turn carbon dioxide into organic matter and free oxygen, using energy from sunlight. Furthermore, chlorophyll, in its functional form in plants, is a different substance from extracted chlorophyll. The chemistry of chlorophyll, in its natural state of combination as a protein complex, is almost completely unknown, even though that material is the most obvious organic substance on earth. The reason for our ignorance about this extraordinary natural process is not so much due to lack of scientific effort as to the inherent complexity of the system.

This chapter will survey some of the things that are known about the nature and function of chlorophyll in plants. We shall see why research on photosynthesis has continued to be a subject of major importance to many different kinds of scientists ever since the subjects of biology, chemistry, and physics began to be recognized.

For the moment, we will forget that there is an elaborately developed knowledge of chemistry and that biology is a vigorous, flourishing subject of research, involving thousands of highly trained investigators using the techniques of modern physics, chemistry, and mathematics. For a clearer understanding of how present-day ideas of photosynthesis came about, let us think back a few hundred years to a time when much of the material included in this book was completely unknown.

Some Early Discoveries about How Plants Live

One of the early experiments in plant physiology was a very simple and beautiful experiment with a willow tree, undertaken by van Helmont (1577–1644). Somewhat ahead of his time, van Helmont had the idea that one could find out about things better by making measurements and observations than by studying the literature. Scientific literature then consisted almost entirely of Aristotle's writings, which even at that time were over a thousand years old.

Van Helmont's historical experiment was to weigh a small willow shoot and also a tub of soil. He then planted the willow in the soil and watered it carefully for five years. When he removed the tree it had gained 164 pounds while the soil had lost only a few ounces. Therefore he came to the conclusion that the extra weight of the tree had come from the water. This conclusion, like most scientific conclusions of our own day, was partly right and partly wrong. We know now that, in addition to the water, much of the weight of this tree had come from atmospheric carbon dioxide. In van Helmont's time no one knew that such a thing as carbon dioxide existed. His experiment was the beginning of the story of photosynthesis—the story of how plants produce their own food and ours by using carbon dioxide and sunlight.

Interdependence of plants and animals. In those days the rate of scientific progress was somewhat less bewildering than it is today. In fact, 125 years went by before the next experiment bearing on our subject was tried. In 1774, Joseph Priestley published a description of some experiments that uncovered a new and startling effect. He found that air in which mice had been kept until they died was in some strange way regenerated and again made usable for the mice by the insertion of green plants. It is obvious to us today that Priestley's mice had used up the oxygen and produced carbon dioxide, and that the plants converted the carbon dioxide back to oxygen again through the process of photosynthesis. In Priestley's time oxygen and carbon dioxide were unknown, so that his experimental observation lacked a rational scientific explanation. Nevertheless, it opened the way to a very important development in understanding the carbon cycle in nature.

Classification and physiology of plants. In work with plants during Priestley's time a major emphasis was placed on their description and classification. It happened to follow the most productive period of Linnaeus, who proposed the first workable system of classification. Although Linnaeus himself performed and strongly advocated experiments with plants, many of his successors paid little attention to this aspect of his work. They had become too engrossed in using the new tool provided by the simplification in classification.

This enthusiasm for classification, the academic counterpart of stamp collecting, has remained a major part of botanical research since the time of Linnaeus. Even to this day the study of how plants function, as compared with the study of their shapes and taxonomic relationships, is generally a small part of elementary botany courses. The process of photosynthesis, however, has continued to attract the attention of scientists with many different kinds of training and experience.

A Dutch physician, Ingenhousz, who traveled widely about Europe and enjoyed a prosperous career as a Royal physician, somehow found time in his busy and urbane life to carry on experiments on photosynthesis. The great contribution Ingenhousz made in about 1780 was to find that light was necessary for the purification of air by plants. Three years later, Senebier made another great advance in the understanding of the basic principles of photosynthesis in terms of plant physiology. He found that only the green parts of plants were active and, furthermore, that the volume of good air plants produced was dependent on the amount of bad air they received. In the next year, 1784, Lavoisier, who discovered oxygen (and later lost his head over politics), worked out the composition of carbon dioxide and the nature of its formation by burning carbon compounds. The basic chemistry was now available for a clear understanding of the process of photosynthesis, which is the conversion of carbon dioxide and water into organic material.

Although the first textbook of plant physiology was published in 1795 by the Danish botanist C. G. Rafn, the entire process of photosynthesis was not clarified and described in chemical terms until 1804. In that year de Saussure showed by gas analysis that carbon dioxide was used up during the formation of organic matter and oxygen was produced.

In 1818, Pelletier and Caventou gave the name of "chlorophyll" to the green stuff that could be extracted from plants by alcohol. Yet even at the present time no one knows how chlorophyll works in photosynthesis. In 1840, the German agricultural chemist Liebig clearly showed that it was the inorganic salts in soil that were necessary for plant growth and not the organic matter. He understood that humus in the soil had its source in plants, in contrast to the old idea that plants were dependent upon the humus in the soil for their growth.

Discovery of energy transformation. The quantitative aspect of the utilization of light by plants was first considered seriously in 1845, when Robert Mayer formulated the law of conservation of energy. Although this law seems clearly self-evident now, it was a most important discovery in its time. The concept that energy can be changed from one form to another but does not disappear had an immediate bearing on the subject of photosynthesis in plants. Mayer realized that photosynthesis is a conversion of light energy to the form of stabilized chemical energy stored in organic substances.

Photosynthesis and plant physiology. Thus after 75 years, from the time when Priestley discovered that air used up by mice could be freshened by leaving plants in it, the energy conversion concepts of Mayer completed the clarification of the overall picture of just what photosynthesis is and what it does. Photosynthesis can be summarized by the equation

$$6CO_2 + 6H_2O + 112{,}000 \text{ cal} \rightarrow C_6H_{12}O_6 + 6O_2$$

This says that 112,000 calories of absorbed light energy convert 6 moles of CO_2 and water into 1 mole of carbohydrate and 6 moles of oxygen. The equation only tells what goes in and what comes out. This basic chemical reaction of photosynthesis was as well recognized a hundred years ago as it is today. The problem then became the more difficult one of finding out what different chemical steps take place to produce this overall result. Today we ask not what photosynthesis is, but rather how it is carried on. We are still unable to duplicate photosynthesis by any known chemical system.

Up until a hundred years ago, botanists were chiefly concerned with classification of plants, and so knowledge of photosynthesis was advanced more by chemists than by botanists. After about 1860, however, plant physiology as a part of botany began to develop under the influence of Sachs, Pfeffer, Timiryazev, and others who were primarily students of plant life rather than of chemistry.

One of the important discoveries regarding the photosynthetic system of plants was made by a physicist. This was Stokes, an Englishman who was concerned with the process of fluorescence—that is, the re-emission of absorbed light as a particular color determined by the chemical structure of the material. Chlorophyll is highly fluorescent, and the effect is easy to see. A leaf mashed in alcohol gives a green solution that can be clarified by filtering through cloth. This green extract will show red fluorescence if placed under a bright light in a moderately dark room (a slide projector is a good light source). Stokes, in purifying chlorophyll to study its fluorescence, found there were two forms of chlorophyll, which he called chlorophyll *a* and chlorophyll *b*. About one fourth of the chlorophyll in plants is chlorophyll *b*. This discovery was made in 1864, and we have only recently begun to have a reasonably good idea as to why plants need to have both kinds of chlorophyll.

From 1895 to 1911 a great deal of research on the rate of photosynthesis was carried on at the University of Cambridge by Blackman and his group. They studied the effects of environmental factors, such as light intensity and temperature, as well as internal factors controlled by the nature and previous treatment of the plant. The effects of these different factors were found to be interrelated, and the level of one variable was seen to determine how the other variables influence the speed with which plants carry on photosynthesis.

Following the Blackman period Willstätter and Stoll produced two monumental volumes, one on chlorophyll in 1913 and one on the process of photosynthesis in 1918. Both books were based on many years of intensive laboratory investigation. About 1920, Warburg introduced improved measuring methods and the use of unicellular algae, thus vastly extending the quantitative study of the process. Most present-day investigations of photosynthesis and of pigment function reflect the methodology, the standards of precision, and the clear thought brought to bear on photosynthesis by Warburg.

Although Priestley's last days were spent in the United States, photosynthesis otherwise remained an entirely European research activity until 1911, when Spoehr, who with Warburg had studied under Emil Fisher in Berlin, started his career in this country. In 1926 Spoehr published a monograph summarizing everything known about photosynthesis up to that time. His was to remain the major source of reference on the subject for twenty years. The next American, Emerson, returned from Warburg's Berlin laboratory in 1927, and for some years photosynthesis research in this country was almost entirely the province of Spoehr, Emerson, and their collaborators.

About the middle of the 1930 to 1940 decade the European tradition of photosynthesis investigation was reinforced and diversified by the immigration of such men as van Niel, Franck, Gaffron, and Rabinowitch, and later Kok. They, as well as Spoehr, Emerson, and Burk, established laboratories, trained students, and developed active groups of investigators in the United States. European interest also continued to expand. A few of the active centers of photosynthesis research and the names of some of those now actively interested in the mechanism of photosynthesis are listed in an appendix at the end of this chapter.

The preceding historical survey and the mention of a few names of currently active investigators will emphasize the point that research on photosynthesis has kept many men busy for a long time, and that workers from very different scientific disciplines have been concerned with this basic process. It is worthwhile to realize that the recent new discoveries reported in newspapers usually represent only a small amount of information added to a large pre-existing accumulation of knowledge; it is this knowledge that endows the new discoveries with significance.

The Role of Photosynthesis

Regulation of the atmosphere. The energy by which all animals live is generated by the oxidation of plant-produced foods—either directly by eating plants, or indirectly by eating plant-fed animals. This oxidation of organic compounds by respiration or fermentation gives off carbon dioxide to the air. Man's use of organic matter produced by plants ages ago and stored as coal or oil also continuously pours CO_2 into the air. Yet despite the enormous CO_2 production on a worldwide scale, the concentration of CO_2 in air has remained very nearly constant since it was first measured. Evidently the total rate of CO_2-consuming photosynthesis is just about in balance with the total CO_2 production over the whole earth. How does it happen that the two opposing processes, going on entirely independently of each other, remain so nearly equal in their overall volume of production?

A partial answer to this question illustrates a basic principle of biology: the automatic control of environmental factors within or around living things at a level favorable to their survival. Fortunately for the continuance of life on earth, the rate of photosynthesis of all plants is nearly proportional to the CO_2 concentration prevailing in air. Because of this relation (which is illustrated later in Fig. 1.3), the level of CO_2 in the atmosphere is very hard to change appreciably. In other words, the more CO_2 that is available, the more rapidly it is turned back into oxygen. Conversely, the lower the CO_2 concentration, the smaller its conversion rate to oxygen.

The regulation of the atmospheric CO_2 level by photosynthesis is not at all thoroughly understood. It is, nevertheless, of great importance in affecting the earth's temperature and hence, by variation of the polar ice caps, in determining the level of the oceans.

Production of food. Whether the current explosion of the human population will have a serious effect on the CO_2 level of the air, or whether worldwide photosynthesis will increase enough to offset the imbalance, has not been given much consideration. However, the total of the earth's food production by photosynthesis is a matter of serious concern to anyone attempting to compile a balance sheet showing food-supply potential and human population estimates in the near future. The fact that well over half the people of the world are hungry all the time, even now, is often brushed aside by writers who have particular motives for obscuring basic facts about the overpopulation problem. Because all food is derived from photosynthesis either directly or indirectly, an understanding of this process is of basic importance to humanity. Yet direct application of research in photosynthesis to increased food production is still a vague hope rather than a present reality.

Kinetics of Photosynthesis

Measurement of photosynthesis in plants

In order to study any natural process or effect, some method for measuring it in quantitative terms must be available. Furthermore, we need to know what degree of accuracy can be attained by the procedures available. The progress possible in any scientific investigation is entirely dependent on the reliability and convenience of the method of measurement used.

In studying the process, photosynthesis is most frequently followed by calculating either the CO_2 used up or the O_2 evolved. The way this is done depends on whether the plant grows in air or under water. A few of the many methods that have been used for studying photosynthesis will be mentioned.

Bubble counting. Inverted sprigs of some submerged water plants will give off bubbles of oxygen from cut stems. The number of bubbles produced per minute can be used as a very rough measure of the photosynthetic rate. The method survives because of its simplicity, and its main use is in elementary teaching. A curve can be plotted showing relative rate of photosynthesis for various light intensities. The experiment is done with a sprig of *Elodea* in a jar of water. The light intensity is adjusted by putting the light source at various distances and is measured with a photographic exposure meter. Machlis and Torrey give directions for an improved version of this experiment (see References).

Titration of oxygen. In sealed bottles full of partly deoxygenated water supplied with dissolved CO_2 or bicarbonate, the amount of oxygen produced by submerged water plants can be determined by the Winkler titration procedure. Details of the operation are given in books on analytical chemistry. Except for use in ecological studies, this method has been superseded by others requiring less trouble but more equipment.

Determination of CO_2 by pH change. This venerable procedure passed out of fashion long ago; but it has recently been revived and improved for modern research by Blinks and by Gaffron, who describes the procedure in his chapter on "Energy Storage: Photosynthesis" (see References). The simplicity, convenience, and speed of commercial glass electrode pH meters make this a useful procedure for studying photosynthesis of algal suspensions.

Manometry. Most photosynthesis research for the past forty years has been done with Warburg manometers. The details of procedure are to be found in all textbooks of laboratory biochemistry. Measurements of both O_2 and CO_2 exchange can, without much difficulty, be made with a precision approaching 1 percent on small volumes of algal suspensions, although the equipment is expensive. Except for experiments in which the time lag of a minute, more or less, causes trouble, this procedure is probably to be preferred over most others since its capabilities and limitations have been so thoroughly studied.

Platinum electrodes. In stirred solutions a platinum electrode measures the concentration of dissolved oxygen with speed and precision. A great advance in the art of measuring photosynthesis was made by Blinks and Skow, who used a platinum electrode in direct contact with the plant tissue. This can be done in such a way that current through the electrode gives a nearly instantaneous measure of the rate of photosynthesis rather than a measure of the oxygen concentration in the bulk of the solution. For studies of rapid changes in photosynthetic rate and for determining action spectra of water plants, this method is the best available.

Radioactive CO_2. Counts of the radioactivity of C^{14} (as initiated by Ruben and Kamen) taken up by plants have also been used to study photosynthetic rates. The primary purpose of this method is to follow carbon atoms through the intermediate compounds between

CO_2 and carbohydrate. The elucidation of a pathway of carbon fixation by Calvin and his collaborators was made possible by this procedure, combined with chemical separation of the intermediate compounds by paper chromatography.

CO_2 absorption by alkali. Early plant physiologists made good progress by flowing a gas stream through a closed container with a plant in it, and absorbing the remaining CO_2 in alkali. Titration of the alkali and of a control with the same amount of gas flow, but without the plant, is used to measure CO_2 fixation.

Infrared absorption by CO_2. The previous method has been rendered obsolete by modern commercial instruments that give a continuous record of CO_2 concentration in a gas stream. Concentration is determined by the capacity of the CO_2 to absorb specific wavelengths of infrared. This procedure is the best currently available for the study of photosynthesis by leaves.

The efficiency of photosynthesis

Crop production. One of the more obvious questions one might ask about photosynthesis is: How efficient a process is it? This question can be put in still another way: How efficiently does a plant growing out-of-doors use the energy available from sunlight?

The wavelength of much of the energy is too long to be absorbed by chlorophyll, and this energy is wasted. About 20 percent of the incident energy is reradiated as long-wavelength infrared, and about 30 percent of the light goes right through the leaf, unabsorbed, and without having any effect at all. About half the energy of sunlight falling on a normal leaf is used up as heat in the evaporation of water. The answer, then, is that only about 2 percent of the total sunlight is used for photosynthesis by crop plants growing in direct sunlight.

One reason for this low efficiency is that sunlight is very bright and leaves cannot take advantage of very bright light, as discussed below and illustrated in Fig. 1.2. Furthermore, the small amount of light that is actually used for photosynthesis goes to make a whole plant, not only the useful parts: a large fraction of a typical plant consists of inedible fibers. Finally, much of the energy captured by photosynthesis is used up again in respiration.

If a crop is eaten as a vegetable the food is converted directly into animal or human tissue, although with a low efficiency. About 90 percent of the energy in the crop fed to cattle is wasted in producing the animals. This means that eating meat gives us only about 10 percent of the energy which was originally in the feed used in raising the meat.

Underdeveloped and overpopulated countries are therefore primarily bound to vegetarianism.

Quantum yield. A second measure of photosynthetic efficiency is the maximum yield of photosynthesis obtainable from plants under their optimum conditions. By shining beams of light of measured intensity into suspensions of single-celled algae like *Chorella,* the maximum obtainable efficiency of photosynthesis has frequently been determined. In measurements of this type it is convenient to express the light intensity, not in terms of energy, but in number of quanta—the smallest unit package of light. This is done so that the results may be compared directly with the number of carbon dioxide molecules reduced. This experiment was carried out by Warburg and Negelein in Berlin in 1922. They found that it took about 4 quanta of light to reduce a carbon dioxide molecule. This experiment was repeated in about 1938 by Emerson and Lewis, who found a requirement of 8 to 12 quanta per CO_2. In spite of a great number of investigations by many different people, the results of such measurements still vary widely for reasons that are not yet clear.

Factors affecting the rate of photosynthesis

To simplify the subject of photosynthesis it is convenient to represent the part of a leaf that does the work by a black box, as in Fig. 1.1.

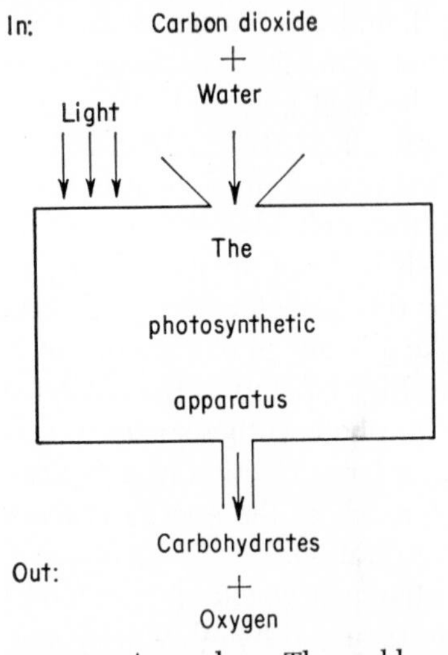

Fig. 1.1. An analogy. The problem of photosynthesis is to find out what the mechanism in the box is and how it works.

Our basic question is: What does the black box contain and how do its components work? Our investigation is hindered by the fact that if, figuratively speaking, we pry off the cover to look inside our box its wheels stop turning. We can, however, pour carbon dioxide and water into this box and, while shining light on it, take out carbohydrates and oxygen. We can study the way things go on in the black box by making precise measurements of the rate of CO_2 uptake, O_2 evolution, and product formation. Thus by using water labeled with the O^{18} isotope it has been found that the oxygen of photosynthesis is derived from the water, not from the CO_2. The study of the way in which these measurable photosynthetic rates depend on the temperature of the box, the light intensity supplied, and the concentration of CO_2 fed to it has been a major part of photosynthetic research. Many theories regarding the mechanisms within the box have been developed from observations of the way these controllable factors influence the rate of photosynthesis.

Light intensity. The detailed study during the last fifty years of the rate of photosynthesis under different conditions has been of no help in identifying the type of compounds involved, but it has furnished

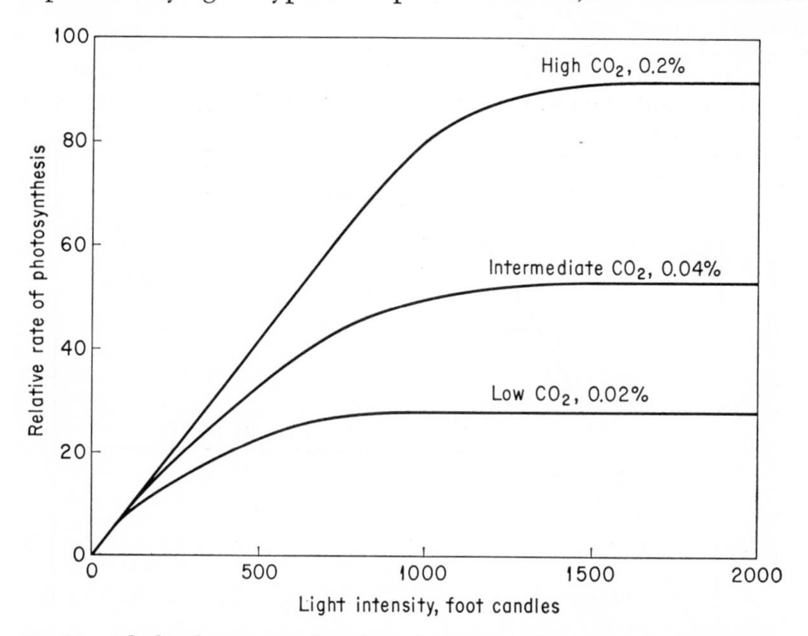

Fig. 1.2. Idealized curves to show how the rate of photosynthesis is influenced by light intensity. When the light is weak, the rate is directly proportional to intensity and is independent of the carbon dioxide concentration and of temperature. By contrast, when the light is very bright, photosynthesis is not influenced by small changes of intensity but is then dependent on the carbon dioxide concentration and on the temperature.

some information as to the complexity of the process. For instance, if we measure the amount of photosynthesis produced by a leaf or a suspension of algae at different light intensities, it is found that the photosynthetic rate increases in proportion to intensity while the light is weak, as shown in Fig. 1.2. However, when the light is strong, the addition of more light does not produce any more rapid photosynthesis. This means that there must be some step, not dependent on light, whose rate becomes limiting when the strictly photochemical part of the mechanism is going as rapidly as it can. The effect of varying the color of the light depends on the pigments that are present and so will be discussed after the pigments have been described.

CO_2 concentration. In Fig. 1.3 it can be seen that CO_2 concentration influences the rate of photosynthesis in much the same way as does the light intensity. At low pressures of carbon dioxide, such as are present in normal air (about 0.03 percent), the rate of photosynthesis increases proportionally with the supply of carbon dioxide. Further increases above 0.2 percent CO_2 in the air have no influence on photosynthetic rates until toxic effects appear, at concentrations of about 10 percent.

Temperature. When the light intensity is high enough so that the photochemical part of the process is not limiting the rate, the effect

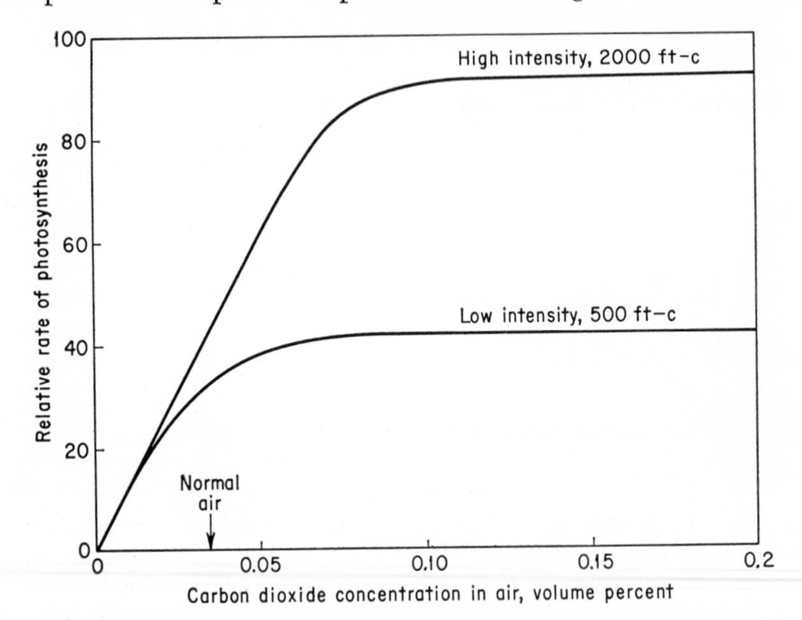

Fig. 1.3. Idealized curves showing how the carbon dioxide concentration influences photosynthesis at high and at low light intensities.

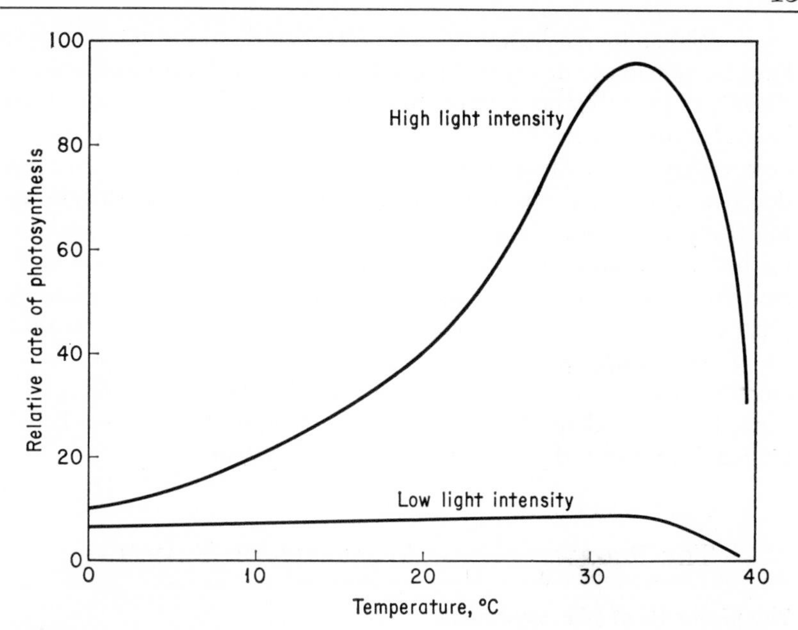

Fig. 1.4. The variation of photosynthesis with temperature. At high intensity the rate increases about twice for a 10° temperature rise from zero to about 25 to 30° C. Above this range it reaches a maximum value at about 30 to 35°, then drops steeply because the mechanism is damaged by high temperature. At low intensity the rate rises only about 10 percent for a 10° C temperature increase. These are idealized curves typical of various measurements.

of temperature on photosynthesis is much like its effect on other enzymatic reactions. Thus in bright light the photosynthetic rate increases exponentially with temperature in the low temperature range (Q_{10} = ca 2.0), reaches an optimum at about 30 to 35° C, and then drops rapidly to zero at temperatures around 40 to 50° C that inactivate the enzymes. At low light intensity, however, the photosynthetic rate rises very slowly with temperature (Q_{10} = ca 1.1), goes over a broad optimum, and then drops down to zero at inactivating temperatures. Fig. 1.4 shows these relations between photosynthesis and temperature.

Some particular strains of algae that can tolerate unusually hot weather have been found to occur in hot springs and in Texas. The temperature necessary to inactivate their enzymes is higher than that of the more common algae. In these algae the rate of photosynthesis keeps on going up as the temperature is raised above the optimum for normal algae. As a consequence, much higher rates of photosynthesis than are usual can be produced at the temperature optimum of these special algae.

Elaborate mathematical attempts based on detailed theories have been made to describe the combined effects of various factors on the rate of photosynthesis; at one time this approach was thought capable of leading to a hypothetical mechanism that would account for the observed reaction. These attempts have, however, largely been abandoned in favor of the actual separation of chemical components and the study of separate steps in the reaction by biochemical isolation methods. The reason the straightforward kinetic approach used in the study of simple photochemical reactions was not successful when applied to photosynthesis is that too large a number of steps constitute the photosynthetic process. This does not mean that attempts to find kinetic explanations were wasted; it simply means that the results proved the actual mechanism to be too complicated for the kinetic approach to give a definitive picture of the system.

The Photochemical Apparatus of Plants

The pigments of photosynthesis

Photochemistry in plants. Photochemistry is the study of the interaction of light and matter. A basic principle of photochemistry is that light must be absorbed in order to have any effect on a substance. Since light passing through an object cannot cause any chemical change in it, plants must have pigments if they are to use light. Pigments are colored because they absorb some colors more than others, and the reason for this selective absorption is that certain parts of their molecules have a natural vibration frequency corresponding to the wavelength of specific colors of light.

A quantum is the smallest unit package of light. Each quantum coming near a molecule is either entirely absorbed or moves on without being changed at all. If absorbed, it no longer exists as light and the energy of the light quantum is now within the absorbing molecule, giving it a higher energy content than that molecule had before the light absorption took place. The pigment molecule activated with this extra energy may do any one of the following things:

1) It may lose the extra energy by transfer to another molecule, thus leaving the second molecule activated.

2) It may cause a chemical change within the pigment itself.

3) It may waste the energy as heat and so speed up the random motion of the neighboring molecules.

4) It may re-emit a quantum of light as fluorescence. If this happens, the color of the emitted fluorescence will not be the same as

that of the original quantum absorbed, but will be the specific color characteristic of the pigment molecule.

The possibility of a pigment molecule's performing any of these acts must be taken into account in the investigation of pigment function in plants.

The color of leaves. The amount of light absorbed or reflected by a leaf depends on the color of the light. More of the light is reflected in the green part of the spectrum than in either the red or the blue. This is why leaves look green. Typical measurements of the reflection and absorption spectra of leaves are illustrated in Fig. 1.5.

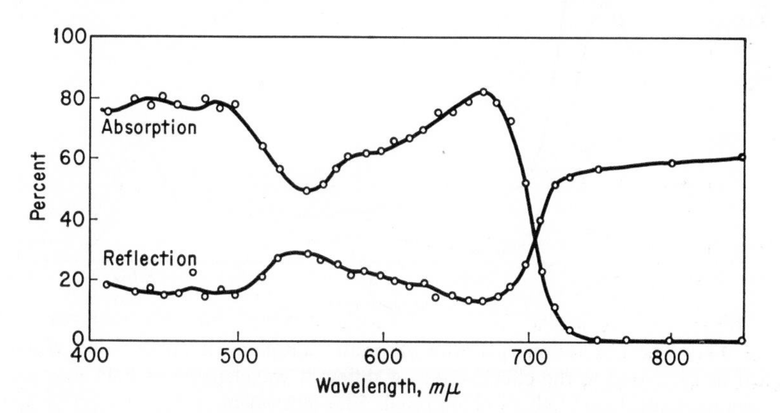

Fig. 1.5. The absorption and reflection of a cabbage leaf for different wavelengths of light. Leaves look green because they both transmit and reflect green light more than other colors.

It is evident from the curve that the reflection of leaves is high in the infrared and that there is almost no absorption at all by the leaf pigments beyond about 725 mμ. This high reflectivity of leaves in the infrared makes them look white in infrared photographs. The absorption peak in red light at a wavelength of 678 mμ is characteristic of chlorophyll in the special complex form that makes it able to do photosynthesis.

Chlorophyll formation. Light is essential not only for photosynthesis but also for the production of chlorophyll necessary to the process. The light that is used to form chlorophyll is absorbed by protochlorophyll. This is a pale green substance which needs only 2 hydrogen atoms to become chlorophyll but does not add them until it is illuminated. This reaction has been studied by J. H. C. Smith. Fig. 1.6 shows the effectiveness of different wavelengths of light in forming chlorophyll from protochlorophyll in illuminated corn seedings. The

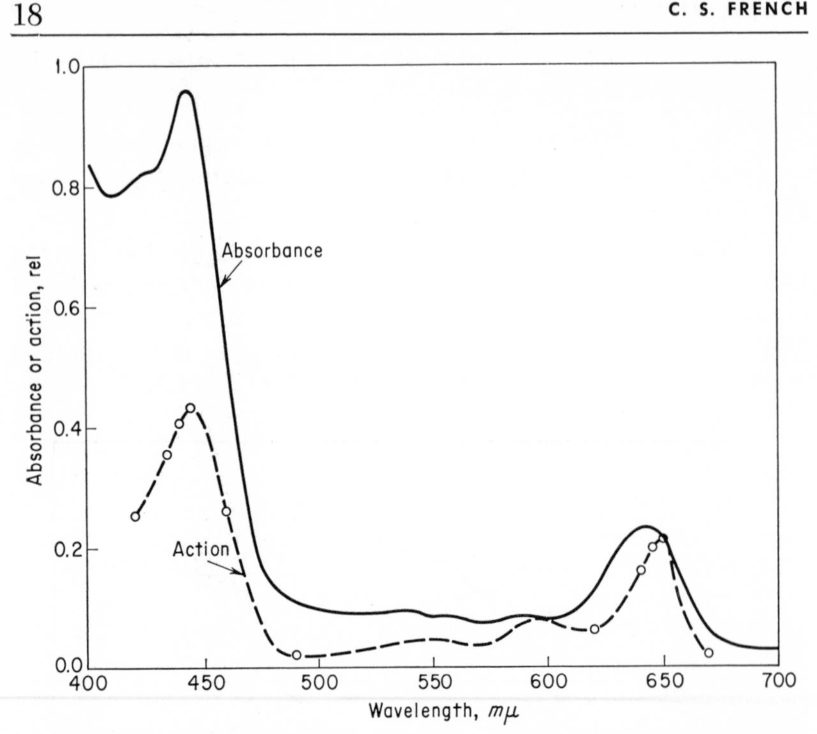

Fig. 1.6. The absorption spectrum of protochlorophyll in an etiolated albino leaf as compared to the effectiveness of different wavelengths of light in transforming protochlorophyll to chlorophyll. The agreement in wavelength of the peaks for the two curves shows that light absorbed by protochlorophyll causes its transformation to chlorophyll. (From J. H. C. Smith.)

effectiveness is the reciprocal of the amount of incident light needed to turn a certain fraction of the protochlorophyll into chlorophyll. The wavelength position of the peaks very nearly matches the absorption peaks for protochlorophyll *in vivo.* This comparison shows that it is protochlorophyll which absorbs the light for its own transformation into chlorophyll.

Experiments have been made by means of growing plants in the dark and then exposing them to light until various amounts of chlorophyll are formed. When the leaves have only a very small amount of chlorophyll, the rate of photosynthesis increases directly in proportion to the amount of chlorophyll available. However, when an adequate supply of chlorophyll is available, an excess of it does not increase the capacity of leaves for photosynthesis. Some step other than the absorption of light by chlorophyll must therefore be limiting the rate of photosynthesis when plenty of chlorophyll is on hand. The photosynthetic system of plants has many other components in addition to

appear to act in large units of several hundred chlorophyll molecules, so arranged that light absorbed by any one molecule can transfer its energy at random to another chlorophyll molecule within a single unit. Eventually this energy reaches an active center, possibly a place where a chlorophyll molecule is attached to an enzyme. This process of energy transfer is very important because it enables chlorophyll to use light with a high degree of efficiency. That is, light absorbed by any chlorophyll molecule is transferred directly to the spot where it is needed, instead of being wasted as heat if it happens to be absorbed by a molecule which is not attached to an enzyme.

This energy transfer not only takes place between chlorophyll molecules, but energy may also be transmitted from other pigments to chlorophyll. Some of the accessory pigments may accomplish this by transferring their absorbed light energy to chlorophyll, probably C_a673.

Chloroplasts of green plants contain two cytochromes, *f* and b_6, that are not found elsewhere. It seems likely that these cytochromes are closely bound with chlorophyll. Recent work of Chance has shown that even at extremely low temperatures the absorption spectrum of these cytochromes changes immediately when the chlorophyll is illuminated. It may be that the first chemical change in photosynthesis produced by light is a change in the oxidation level of these cytochromes effected by energy transferred from chlorophyll.

Accessory pigments. Not all the color in plants is due to chlorophyll; all photosynthetic plants contain some carotenoid pigments as well. Carotenoids are unsaturated hydrocarbons, though some of them may contain a few oxygen molecules. The name for this class of pigments is taken from the common carrot. Carrots are highly colored by beta-carotene, a pigment also present in leaves.

Red and blue-green algae, besides having chlorophyll *a*—though not *b*—and carotenoids, are often spectacularly colored by mixtures of the red pigment, phycoerythrin, and the blue pigment, phycocyanin. There are a number of different phycoerythrins and phycocyanins which as a class are called phycobilin proteins. The phycobilin pigments, like chlorophyll, are found as complexes with proteins and are also, like them, made of four pyrole groups. However, these phycobilin protein complexes are unlike chlorophyll in that they are water soluble, and their pigmented components cannot be separated from the protein as easily as chlorophyll is extracted from its protein complex. The absorption bands of various plant pigments are shown in Fig. 1.9.

Given a specific plant, it is possible to find out which pigments are participating in photosynthesis. This information is obtained by

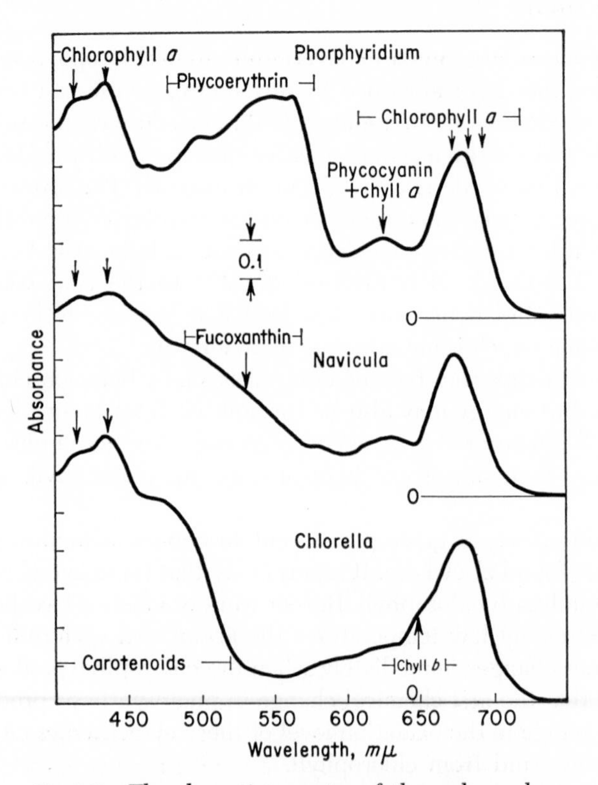

Fig. 1.9. The absorption spectra of three algae, showing the regions of absorption due to the different kinds of photosynthetic pigments. The large band at 675–680 is due to chlorophyll *a* in all the species. Three arrows show the positions of the separate forms of chlorophyll *a*, C_a673, C_a683, and C_a695 that overlap to make this composite absorption band. Chlorophyll *a* also has a small band around 620 mμ and two large bands in the blue region, marked with arrows. Nothing is known about the contribution of the different forms of chlorophyll *a* to these blue bands. *Chlorella vulgaris* is a green alga that has much the same pigment system as ordinary leaves. Chlorophyll *b* shows as a shoulder in the *Chlorella* spectrum and its blue band also causes part of the absorption in the carotenoid region at about 480 mμ. *Navicula minima,* a diatom, shows the absorption of the carotenoid fucoxanthin, which is at longer wavelengths than most other carotenoids. *Porphyridium cruentum* is a red salt-water alga with phycoerythrin and a very little phycocyanin.

comparing the action spectrum of photosynthesis in the plant with the absorption spectra of the different pigments that are present. An action spectrum is determined by plotting the photosynthesis produced by a given number of incident quanta against the wavelength of light used.

Action spectra made by Engelmann in 1887 showed that the phycobilins and some carotenoids can use the light they absorb for photosynthesis. Anthocyanin pigments—those water-soluble glucosides that color red cabbage, beets, copper beech leaves, and many flowers—are not active in photosynthesis. All photosynthetic plant pigments other than chlorophyll have come to be known as "accessory pigments" —a name with unfortunate connotations that for a long time helped to obscure the very important function of these colored substances.

The two-pigment theory. Quite apart from the unsolved problem of how chlorophyll does its work we may ask whether the accessory pigments serve the same purpose as chlorophyll or whether they have an entirely different function. Within the last few years it has become evident that the accessory pigments do indeed have a specific role different from that of chlorophyll *a*. Furthermore, chlorophyll *b* and the shortest wavelength form of chlorophyll *a*, C_a673, have been found to have the same function as the accessory pigments.

Photosynthesis is now believed to depend on two different photochemical reactions driven by different pigments. Just what the chemistry of the two reactions may be is not clear, but there are biochemical reasons favoring the idea that one of them might be photophosphorylation and the other the formation of a reducing substance.

In green plants one of the reactions is driven specifically by chlorophyll *b*, by carotenoids, or by the 673 mμ form of chlorophyll *a*. The other reaction is powered by the 683 mμ form of chlorophyll *a*. In red algae it seems that whereas phycoerythrin and phycocyanin drive one of the reactions, all the chlorophyll *a* forms drive the other.

The existence of two separate photochemical reactions is deduced from the striking increase in photosynthesis obtained when two pigments both absorb light as contrasted with illumination of either pigment alone. This enhancement effect of two colors of light, each chosen to be absorbed by a specific pigment, was discovered by Emerson: it is at present one of the aspects of photosynthesis attracting much attention from a number of laboratories.

The study of action spectra and the enhancing effects of different wavelengths, as illustrated in Fig. 1.10, seems to be the most direct way to investigate the discrete functions of the different pigments in photosynthesis.

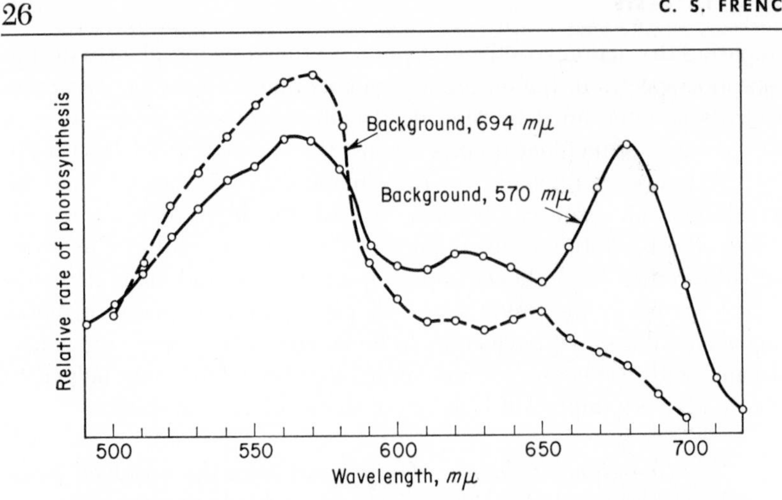

Fig. 1.10. The effectiveness of different wavelengths of light on photosynthesis in the blue-green alga, *Phormidium.* There are two separate sets of measurements made with different colors of supplementary background light. The solid line shows the action spectrum with green background light (570 mμ), which is absorbed by phycoerythrin. When phycoerythrin is thus activated the light absorbed by chlorophyll is effective, as is shown by the peak in this curve at 680 mμ. The dotted curve was measured with red background light, 694 mμ, which is absorbed only by chlorophyll. This curve by comparison with the other shows enhancement of the effectiveness of the green light absorbed by phycoerythrin. It is evident that neither chlorophyll nor phycoerythrin can work at maximum effectiveness unless the other pigment is also activated. This means that there are two different photochemical reactions in photosynthesis. (From an experiment of G. C. McLeod.)

Chloroplasts

All the chlorophyll of plants is in chloroplasts. Although these small bodies have different shapes in various species of plants, they are frequently oval. They vary in size as well as in shape, but a typical chloroplast is about 5 mμ in length. The chloroplasts seem to have membranes around them and complex structures within. The chlorophyll is stored in small packages called grana. These are made up of alternate layers of the chlorophyll complex between layers of material without chlorophyll. The internal structure of chloroplasts is studied largely by electron microscopy.

Many detailed schematic drawings of stacked chlorophyll molecules showing one end attached to a protein and their phytol tails lined up with carotenoid molecules have been published, and even reproduced in textbooks. Such schemes are necessarily based largely on hypothesis rather than on direct observation, because the individual molecules are smaller than the limit of resolution of the electron microscope.

Some of the partial reactions of photosynthesis

The equation on page 6 summarizes the stochiometric relationship of the CO_2 and the H_2O used by photosynthesis to produce organic matter and O_2. This equation is a gross oversimplification even when we think of it only as an overall result of many separate steps. In actuality the assimilatory quotient O_2/CO_2 is not often exactly 1.0, as the equation implies. It is perhaps better to think of photosynthesis as the photochemical production of two materials, one a reduced material, presumably $TPNH_2$, and the other high-energy phosphate, ATP. These two substances, probably made by separate systems, provide the chemical driving power for the formation and interconversion of the vast number of assorted chemical substances in plants by very complex and interlocked biochemical pathways.

We know no sharply defined or generally accepted dividing line between the process of photosynthesis and the innumerable synthetic, degradative, and interconversion reactions of cellular metabolism. Most living organisms can fix carbon dioxide and make organic matter, provided they are supplied with adequate driving power in the form of a reducing agent or of a high-energy phosphate compound. What makes green plants unique and gives them their key position in nature is the fact that they can use light for the formation of these essential materials.

When detailed information is available on how plant pigments use light energy for $TPNH_2$ and ATP formation, it may be that the synthetic reactions following the strictly light-dependent steps will more naturally appear as general metabolic reactions common to all living cells. The study of limited phases of the overall process, now called photosynthesis, has already been very successful. We shall now discuss briefly some of the partial reactions that are already well known.

Photochemical reducing activity of isolated chloroplasts. In 1937, Hill found that it was possible to study the photochemical reduction of some chemicals added to a suspension of isolated chloroplasts.

Chloroplasts can easily be isolated from leaves. The leaves are either ground in a mortar or in a Waring blender until the cells are broken up, but not long enough to cause many of the chloroplasts to disintegrate. The grinding is done in the presence of a suitable aqueous medium such as 0.5M sucrose. The osmotic effect of the sucrose is to keep the chloroplasts from swelling and disintegrating. The fibers and large leaf particles are strained out through cloth. Gentle centrifuging of this leaf macerate will separate starch grains, other solid particles, and whole cells from the suspended chloroplasts. The chloroplasts may then be centrifuged out at higher speeds and thus collected in a reasonable state of purity.

Hill's discovery has turned out to be extremely important because it shows that the formation of reducing power by the action of light is independent of the rest of the photosynthetic system. Many investigations have been made of the Hill reaction, using different kinds of chemical additives to measure the reducing ability of the chloroplast material under illumination.

A good classroom demonstration experiment can be performed by adding the blue dye 2,6-dichlorophenol-indophenol to a chloroplast suspension and illuminating part of it. (Refer to Machlis and Torrey for details of procedure.) Experiments of this type have been used to investigate the photochemical part of the photosynthetic mechanism. This part of photosynthesis is the step by which reducing power is obtained by splitting water. The oxygen from water is given off as a gas and the combined hydrogen becomes available for driving the carbon dioxide reduction system.

In living cells the substance acquiring the energy is not a blue dye, ferricyanide, quinone, or any other of the test substances that have been used for studying the Hill reaction, but rather some biochemical intermediate normally present in the cells—presumably TPN.

Photophosphorylation. Arnon and his group at the University of California have shown that isolated chloroplasts under the influence of light can also make high-energy organic phosphate, ATP, from inorganic phosphate. This process is called photophosphorylation and is more sensitive to impairment from mistreatment of the chloroplasts than is the Hill reaction.

CO_2 fixation by chloroplasts. Fager found that isolated chloroplasts could fix small amounts of CO_2, although the activity was very low. Arnon and his collaborators noted that the addition of some of the cellular components that are washed out during isolation of chloroplasts can restore this activity to a reasonably high level. It is now possible, therefore, to separate and study the processes of CO_2 fixation, oxygen evolution, and phosphorylation in isolated chloroplasts.

The path of carbon. Another part of photosynthesis has been successfully investigated by Calvin and his associates at the University of California. By the use of radioactive C^{14} they were able to identify and trace many of the intermediate compounds through which the carbon passes from CO_2 to carbohydrates.

These experiments are begun by illuminating a suspension of the alga *Chlorella* or other photosynthetic material in the presence of radioactive CO_2 which is taken up by photosynthesis. Then, after a few seconds or minutes, the whole suspension is diluted with boiling alcohol, which stops the reaction and extracts the organic substances. The products are then separated from each other by paper chromatography, and the relative amount of radioactivity from the labeled CO_2 in the different fractions is determined on separate parts of the paper chromatogram. The first carbon compound formed by the CO_2 is believed to be phosphoglyceric acid.

Microscopic Algae

Use in photosynthesis experiments. For laboratory studies of photosynthesis it is often more convenient to use algae than leaves. Unicellular algae are useful because they are about the size of yeast cells and remain suspended in water. Thus it is possible to divide a suspension of algae into different parts with a pipette just as if it were a chemical solution. Another useful property of unicellular algae is the speed with which they can be grown under entirely reproducible conditions.

The most popular of all unicellular algae used for photosynthesis experiments has been *Chlorella,* which is a small green alga that grows wild in most parts of the world. It is a very resistant organism and has been called an algal weed because under natural conditions it outgrows many other algae. In the laboratory, *Chlorella* is grown in a dilute solution of the necessary nutrient salts and gets its carbon entirely from CO_2 through photosynthesis. It can also be grown in the dark if supplied with organic matter such as sugar.

The fact that the algae have a far greater variety of pigments than the leaves of land plants, nearly all of which have the same functional pigment system, also makes them of particular value for experimental work. In addition to the microscopic algae, there are some marine algae growing as thin sheets; these are excellent experimental material, especially for optical measurements.

Use as food. The rapid and predictable growth of single-celled algae led to the idea that they might be cultivated for food purposes in a controlled environment. The accumulated experience of many people who have been culturing them in the laboratory and in small outdoor model pilot plants has shown that it is perfectly feasible, but very expensive, to grow various green unicellular algae like *Chlorella* and *Scenedesmus* in large quantities.

The most advanced work on practical algal culture for food purposes is being done in Japan as an outgrowth of the photosynthesis research of Tamiya. A factory with about an acre of culture surface is producing *Chlorella* on an experimental basis as a supplement to the protein diet. In the United States, where material, labor, and construction costs are so high, growing algae for food would seem to be a very good way to lose money rapidly. The economic conditions and advanced technical skills found in Japan make it far more likely that such an undertaking will be a commercial success there. The algae are grown in shallow ponds that are stirred and given additional carbon dioxide. The algae are then collected by centrifuging and processed to a dry powder, which may be eaten in various ways. It is extremely good when mixed into ice cream or added to the flour used in making bread. It has a rather pleasant vegetable taste with a touch of the odor of violets.

Potential use in space travel. In this country there is much current interest in the use of controlled algal culture for the replenishing of oxygen in inhabited spaceships and submarines. To convert the CO_2 expired by one man appears to require about 600 square feet of an illuminated algal culture. A man in a closed chamber uses up O_2 and produces a nearly equivalent amount of CO_2. The accumulated CO_2 reaches a poisonous concentration long before the O_2 is used up.

The problem of maintaining an exact balance in the atmospheric composition of a closed system containing a man and an algal culture is not simple. Part of the difficulty is that the respiratory quotient—that is, the volume of CO_2 produced per volume of O_2 used up—is not exactly 1.0 (unity), nor is the corresponding assimilatory quotient, O_2/CO_2, of algae. Therefore, after the cycle has run for a time the atmospheric composition drifts. By appropriate adjustment of the algal nutrients, however, it is possible to introduce corrections to improve the balance.

As with other aspects of the large-scale rocket and space travel programs there is a great diversion of interest, money, and trained personnel to projects like this, that would be of far greater long-range value if concentrated on basic rather than developmental research.

Controlled Photosynthesis as an Energy Source

Photosynthesis is a supplier of energy as well as of food. Modern industry and, in fact, the maintenance of our industrial civilization are dependent upon the reserves of coal and oil which we are removing from the earth at a rapid rate. Whether this period of profitable exploitation of stored natural reserves will come to an end during the lifetime of those who are now children, or whether it can last another generation or two beyond that, is a subject being hotly debated. However, everyone agrees that when the stored supplies of coal, oil, and nuclear energy are used up, a continuing source of energy will have to be found.

There is abundant solar energy available for future practical use. One and one-half square miles of the earth's surface receives in a day approximately the same amount of energy as is released by the explosion of one of the earlier atomic bombs. The problem is that as yet we cannot make use of sunshine directly as a form of energy except for heat. It has to be converted to some stable form from which it can be released under controlled conditions.

Water power in the United States can provide only a very small fraction of the electric power that will be needed in the future. Atomic energy, which presumably will eventually be a source of much of our electricity, is itself dependent on an adequate supply of ores which, in their turn, may become exhausted or uneconomical. The great abundance of solar energy that blankets the earth will have to be utilized effectively before many generations have passed. About 1/40,000 of the solar energy falling on the earth is now used by man. The methods at present available for the direct conversion of sunlight into power through heat engines or into electricity by photocells do not yet hold the promise of application on a large scale.

The need for power sources is one reason for the great interest in photosynthesis, which captures light energy in storable chemical form by a reasonably efficient and large-scale process. Photosynthesis takes place over the surface of the earth at the rate of about one million tons of carbon fixed per minute. Unfortunately, we do not yet know any chemical systems that can be utilized to perform photosynthesis or an equally useful reaction.

An artificial system for converting solar energy to power might operate very differently from the mechanism of green plants. However, the fact that photosynthesis does carry on this reaction reliably is one reason for studying the natural process. It seems reasonable to expect that unless more progress is made in solar-energy-conversion research during the next hundred years than has been made in the last fifty, we may again be dependent on the horse and buggy for transportation.

Some Objectives of Photosynthesis Research

There is a distant hope that with a more detailed understanding of how photosynthesis is carried on by plants it may be possible to increase their growth efficiency. This thought is at the back of the minds of all investigators in photosynthesis, but there is still no obvious means by which the data accumulating in photosynthesis laboratories can be applied directly to crop production. At present our understanding of photosynthesis is a part of the body of science that is almost pure and unapplied, and like all basic science has potential future applications, but in ways that are highly unpredictable. It is therefore premature to say that the reason for carrying on photosynthesis research is that the knowledge gained thereby will be of direct value to agriculture or to power production.

Understanding, as an objective in itself, has frequently become useful later from a practical point of view. Therefore it is clearly unnecessary to hunt for long-range applications to justify fundamental research on any significant scientific problem. Scientific understanding of natural processes has to be well developed long before the information can be applied to man's immediate needs. Certainly one thing that should be known about life on earth is how the food for living organisms is manufactured.

The history of photosynthesis well illustrates one important principle of scientific progress—namely, the limitation that incomplete knowledge in surrounding fields imposes on the possible development of any particular subject. In 1804, for instance, Saussure had clarified the nature of the photosynthetic process; he showed that carbon dioxide was used up, oxygen was produced, light was necessary, and organic matter was synthesized. The point is, that by 1804 the problem of photosynthesis had been solved—that is, solved in terms of the chemistry and physics known at the time. In 1845, the problem of photosynthesis was solved again by showing that it is really a conversion of energy in the form of light into a form of bound chemical energy. This transformation-of-energy aspect of photosynthesis could not even have been discussed before 1845 because the nature of the different forms of energy was not yet known.

A frequently raised question is: How long will it take to solve the problem of photosynthesis? To answer this question we must be clear as to what we mean by solving a problem. It is very likely that many of the questions we can now ask about how photosynthesis works will be answered within relatively few years. However, at such time as these answers are at hand it will also be possible to ask far more penetrating and detailed questions that cannot now be formulated. The continual expansion in the scope of questions that may be raised is one of the more important aspects controlling the advancement of any particular branch of science. In one sense no scientific problem has ever been completely solved, and in another sense, in terms of the state of knowledge at the time and the type of solution that would then have had meaning, most scientific questions have found their answer again and again—but each time within the limits of contemporary knowledge and vocabulary.

REFERENCES

The following two references are probably best to start with for a further general acquaintance with photosynthesis:

HILL, R., AND C. P. WHITTINGHAM, 1955, *Photosynthesis.* London: Methuen.

GAFFRON, H., 1960, "Energy storage: Photosynthesis," in *Plant Physiology,* a Treatise, Vol. 1 B, F. C. Steward, ed. New York: Academic Press.

These more specialized books are best read selectively for certain aspects of the subject:

ALLEN, M. B., ed., 1960, *Comparative Biochemistry of Photoreactive Pigments.* New York: Academic Press.

BURLEW, J. S., ed., 1953, *Algal Culture from Laboratory to Pilot Plant.* Washington: Carnegie Institution of Washington, Publ. 600.

FOGG, G. E., 1953, *The Metabolism of Algae.* London: Methuen.

FULLER, R. C., *et al.*, eds., 1958, *The Photochemical Apparatus.* Brookhaven, N. Y.: Brookhaven Natl. Lab.

GAFFRON, H., *et al.*, eds., 1957, *Research in Photosynthesis.* New York: Interscience.

HOLLAENDER, E., ed., 1956, *Radiation Biology,* Vol. III. New York: McGraw-Hill.

MACHLIS, L., AND J. G. TORREY, 1956, *Plants in Action, a Laboratory Manual of Plant Physiology.* San Francisco: Freeman.

PRINGSHEIM, E. G., 1946, *Pure Cultures of Algae.* Cambridge: Cambridge University Press.

RABINOWITCH, E. I., 1956, *Photosynthesis and Related Processes.* 3 Vols. New York: Interscience (1946, 1951).

RUHLAND, W., ed., 1960, "The assimilation of carbon dioxide," in *Handbook of Plant Physiology,* Vol. 5. Berlin: Springer.

SOC. EXP. BIOL., 1951, *Carbon Dioxide Fixation and Photosynthesis.* Cambridge: Cambridge University Press.

WITHROW, R. B., ed., 1959, *Photoperiodism and Related Phenonema in Plants and Animals.* Washington, D.C.: AAAS.

The following periodicals often contain original articles on photosynthesis: *American Journal of Botany; Annual Reviews of Biochemistry; Annual Reviews of Plant Physiology; Arch. Biochemistry and Biophysics; Biochemica et Biophysica Acta;* Carnegie Institution of Washington, *Yearbook; Doklady,* Academy of Science, USSR. (English translation); *Journal of General Physiology; Nature; Physiologia Plantarum; Plant Physiology* (also the English translation of the Russian journal—*Plant Physiology*); *Proceedings of the National Academy of Science; Science; Studies from the Tokugawa Institute.*

APPENDIX *Some Laboratories Currently Investigating the Mechanism of Photosynthesis**

Institution	Location	Scientists	Main Areas of Investigation
CANADA			
Nat. Res. Council	Ottawa	Mortimer, Holt	Path of carbon, chemistry of chlorophyll
Science Service Lab.	London	Good	Hill reaction
Queen's U.	Kingston	Krotkov	Path of carbon
FRANCE			
Center of Nuclear Studies	Saclay	Roux	O_2 from phosphate
Nat. Sci. Res. Center	Gif-sur-Yvette	Moyse, Lavorel, Kouchkovsky	Pigment function and algal culture
Sorbonne	Paris	Wurmser, Joliot	Pigment function
GERMANY			
Technical Univ.	Munich	Kandler	Photophosphorylation
U. Cologne	Cologne	Menke	Optical properties of choroplasts
U. Göttingen	Göttingen	Pirson, Harder	Algal physiology
U. Frankfurt	Frankfurt	Egle	Pigment function

* This list covers primarily those workers whose interests are closely related to the aspects of photosynthesis covered in this article. The following fields, and individuals associated with them, have been omitted; ecological aspects of photosynthesis; structural chemistry of chlorophyll; biochemical studies related, but not exclusively, to photosynthesis; algal culture laboratories not primarily concerned with the mechanism of photosynthesis; plant physiologists with a general but not exclusive interest in photosynthesis; workers active in the field for less than ten years; older workers now specializing in other fields. The author apologizes to any colleagues who may have been omitted inadvertently or for some inadequate reason.

Institution	Location	Scientists	Main Areas of Investigation
U. Heidelberg	Heidelberg	Seybold, Falk	Leaf absorption, pigment function
U. Wurzburg	Wurzburg	Simonis	Photophosphorylation
Max Planck Inst.	Berlin	Warburg	Quantum yield, kinetics, mechanism
Max Planck Inst.	Marburg	Witt	Absorption changes of pigments, induction effects
Inst. for Silica Chem.	Marburg	Kautsky	Chlorophyll fluorescence
GREAT BRITAIN			
Queen Mary College	London	Whittingham	Kinetics, mechanism
Imperial College	London	Porter, James	Carbon, path mechanism
U. Cambridge	Cambridge	Hill, Briggs	Chloroplast cytochromes, kinetics
U. Oxford	Oxford	Lascelles	Bacterial photosynthesis
University College	Galway	ÓhEocha	Phycobilin pigments
JAPAN			
Tokugawa Institute	Tokyo	Tamiya, Shibata	Kinetics, algal culture, pigment absorption
ITALY			
U. Milan	Milan	Marre, Forti	Chloroplast reactions
NETHERLANDS			
Phillips Lamp Works	Eindhoven	van der Veen, Massini, Wessels	Induction effect, Hill reaction
U. Leiden	Leiden	Duysens, Amesz	Pigment function
U. Utrecht	Utrecht	Thomas, Goodheer, Brill	Pigment function, *in vivo* chlorophyll
U. Wageningen	Wageningen	Wassink	Light reactions, pigments

Institution	Location	Scientists	Main Areas of Investigation
SCANDINAVIA			
Agricultural College	Ultuna	Virgin	Chlorophyll formation, fluorescence
Technical College	Copenhagen	Gabrielsen, Velby	Action spectra, induction effects
U. Copenhagen	Copenhagen	Müller	Light intensity effects
Technical College	Trondheim	Larsen	Photosynthesis and pigments of green bacteria
U.S.A.			
Associated Universities	Brookhaven, N.Y.	Bergeron, J. W. Olsen	Nature of *in vivo* chlorophyll
U. Arizona	Tucson, Ariz.	Tollin	Semi-conductor nature of chlorophyll
Brandeis U.	Waltham, Mass.	Linschitz	Chyll photochemistry
U. Cal.	Berkeley, Cal.	Arnon, Whatley	Reactions of chloroplasts
U. Cal.	Berkeley, Cal.	Calvin, Bassham	Path of carbon, O_2 evolution process
U. Cal.	Berkeley, Cal.	Stanier	Carotenoid function, bacterial pigments
U. Cal.	La Jolla, Cal.	Haxo, Clendenning, Kamen	Nature and function of pigments, marine algae, induction effects
U. Cal.	Los Angeles, Cal.	Benson	Path of carbon
Carbide and Carbon Corp.	Oak Ridge, Tenn.	Arnold, Clayton	Chloroplasts as semi-conductors
Carnegie Inst. of Wash.	Stanford, Cal.	J. H. C. Smith, Milner, French	Chyll formation, forms of *in vivo* chyll, pigment function
Cornell U.	Ithaca, N.Y.	Gibbs	Path of carbon
U. Chicago	Chicago, Ill.	Vennesland	Enzymes of chloroplasts
U. Chicago	Chicago, Ill.	Bogorad	Chyll formation
Dartmouth College	Hanover, N.H.	L. Smith, Fuller	Pigment interaction

Institution	*Location*	*Scientists*	*Main Areas of Investigation*
Duke U.	Durham, N.C.	Franck	Physical theories of photosynthetic mechanism
U. Florida	Tallahassee, Fla.	Gaffron, Bishop	Biochemistry of photosynthesis
U. Illinois	Urbana, Ill.	Rabinowitch	Pigment function, action spectra
Int. Business Machines	New York, N.Y.	Brody	State of chlorophyll
Kaiser Research Foundation	Richmond, Cal.	Allen	Pigment distribution and function in algae
Kettering Foundation	Yellow Springs, Ohio	Vernon	Pigments, cytochromes
Johns Hopkins U.	Baltimore, Md.	Jagendorf, San Pietro	Hill reaction, enzymes of photosynthesis
U. Minnesota	Minneapolis, Minn.	Livingston, Lumry, Brown, Frenkel	Photochemistry of chyll, Hill reaction, O_2 evolution, photophosphorylation
Nat. Inst. Health	Bethesda, Md.	Burk, Brackett R. A. Olsen	Quantum yield
U. Penn.	Philadelphia, Pa.	Chance, W. Bonner	Pigment interaction with cytochromes
U. Pittsburgh	Pittsburgh, Pa.	Wolken	Structure and function of chloroplasts
RIAS	Baltimore, Md.	Kok	Pigments, kinetics
Stanford U.	Pacific Grove, Cal.	Blinks, van Niel	Action spectra, induction effects, purple bacteria
U. Rochester	Rochester, N.Y.	Vishniac, Bannister, Punnett	Chlorophyll function
U. Texas	Austin, Texas	Myers	Algal physiology
U. Utah	Salt Lake City, Utah	Spikes, van Norman	Hill reaction, kinetics, fluorescence
U. Wisconsin	Madison, Wisc.	Daniels	Quantum yield, energy conversion

Institution	Location	Scientists	Main Areas of Investigation
Vanderbilt U.	Nashville, Tenn.	Latimer	Light absorption and scattering by pigments
U.S.S.R.			
	ACADEMY OF SCIENCE		
Biochemistry	Moscow		Photoreduction of chlorophyll
Biochemistry	Moscow	Evstigneev	Photoreduction of chlorophyll
Biochemistry	Moscow	Doman	Path of carbon
Plant Physiology	Moscow	Nichiporovich	Wavelength influence on path of carbon
Plant Physiology	Moscow	Bell	Kinetics
Physical Chemistry and Rad. Biol.	Moscow	Tumermann	Chlorophyll function
Geochemistry	Moscow	Boichenko, Kutyurin, Vinogradov	Isotope studies
University of Moscow	Moscow	Litvin	Chlorophyll fluorescence
Bot. Garden	Leningrad	Sapozhinkov	Carotenoid function
Bot. Garden	Leningrad	Zalensky	Kinetics
Optical Institute	Leningrad	Terenin	Chlorophyll spectroscopy
Acad. of Sciences	Kiev	Godnev	Chlorophyll formation
Acad. of Sciences	Kiev	Shlyk	Chlorophyll formation

CHAPTER 2

ARTHUR C. GIESE

Professor of Biology
Stanford University, California

Arthur C. Giese was born in Chicago in 1904. He was educated at the University of Chicago (B.S., 1927), the University of California, and Stanford University (Ph.D., 1933). He has been a member of the Department of Biology at Stanford University since 1933, serving as Instructor, Assistant and Associate Professor, and Professor. In 1939–40 he was a Rockefeller Fellow at Princeton University and the Marine Biological Laboratory at Woods Hole, Massachusetts. He held a Guggenheim Fellowship at the California Institute of Technology and Northwestern University in 1947 and at various Marine Stations in Europe in 1959. He has served as Summer Instructor at Cold Spring Harbor (1935), at the M.B.L. at Woods Hole (1942, 1944, and 1945), and as Acting Professor at the California Institute of Technology (1950).

His research interests involve the effects of radiations upon cells and the reproductive physiology of invertebrates. Among his research papers are the following: "Ultraviolet radiations and life," *Physiol. Zool.*, 1945, 18:223–250; "Protozoa in photobiological research," *Physiol. Zool.*, 1953, 26:1–22; "Annual reproductive cycles of marine invertebrates," *Ann. Rev. Physiol.*, 1959, 21:547–576. In addition to his numerous technical papers, Dr. Giese is the author of the text *Cell Physiology*, 2d ed., Saunders, 1962. He is Associate Editor of the *Annual Review of Physiology*.

Energy release and utilization

CHAPTER 2

ARTHUR C. GIESE
Stanford University
California

Life is a steady state in which energy—the capacity to do work—must be continuously liberated to maintain the cells of the organism in a state of readiness to react. Energy release is a cellular activity and must, of necessity, be studied at the cell level. It is the purpose of this chapter to inquire into the principles governing energy release, the reactions by which it is released in the cell, and the ways in which the energy released is utilized (8, Ch. 15).

Energy may be classified as: a) kinetic, and b) potential. Kinetic energy is energy of motion. Heat is kinetic energy of molecules, atoms, and aggregates in random motion, such as is visualized in Brownian movement. All other forms of energy are called potential energy. Potential energy is stored energy which can be liberated to do work—for example, positional, photic (light), electrical, chemical, and atomic energy. Potential energy is considered high-grade energy, that is, capable of doing work more effectively than kinetic energy, which consequently is thought to be lower-grade energy.

Potential energy is easily converted into kinetic energy—that is, positional, electrical, light, chemical, and atomic energy may all be easily and completely converted to heat—but the process is not reversible. For example, the heat obtained from a definite amount of electrical energy cannot be completely reconverted into electricity, since if this heat is used to run a generator to produce electricity, only a small fraction of it (about 20 percent) can be recovered as electricity. The degradation of energy from a high-grade to a low-grade form is part of the everyday experience of mankind and is embodied conceptually in the *second law of thermodynamics* which states that natural processes are irreversible. However, when potential energy is converted to kinetic energy, the total amount of energy remains the same; that is, energy has neither been created nor destroyed, but has only been converted from one form to another. This is one statement of the *first law of thermodynamics.*

Proof of the first law of thermodynamics came from a study of energy changes in an isolated system, which is a system insulated in such a manner that heat can neither enter nor leave it. (Although complete insulation of a system is not possible, the small residual leaks can be measured and a correction made for them.) When a given amount of electrical, light, chemical, or positional energy is liberated in an isolated system, it can be completely recovered as heat (kinetic energy) and the heat equivalent then can be measured. Thus when the combustion of chemicals in a calorimeter is complete the potential chemical energy is converted into heat, and if no work is done by the system the potential energy of the compounds may be measured by the amount of heat produced. This method is known as *calorimetry* (Fig. 2.1) and has been extensively used to determine the heat of combustion of various organic compounds of biological interest. The heat of combustion of a few such compounds are given in Table 2.1.

TABLE 2.1

Heats of Combustion of Various Organic Compounds

(in calories per mole)

Stearic acid	2,711,000
Sucrose	1,349,000
Glucose	673,000
Glycerol	397,000
Alanine	387,000
Ethyl alcohol	327,000
Lactic acid	326,000
Acetaldehyde	279,000
Acetic acid	209,000
Pyruvic acid	279,100

From Giese, 1957, *Cell Physiology,* Saunders, p. 314.

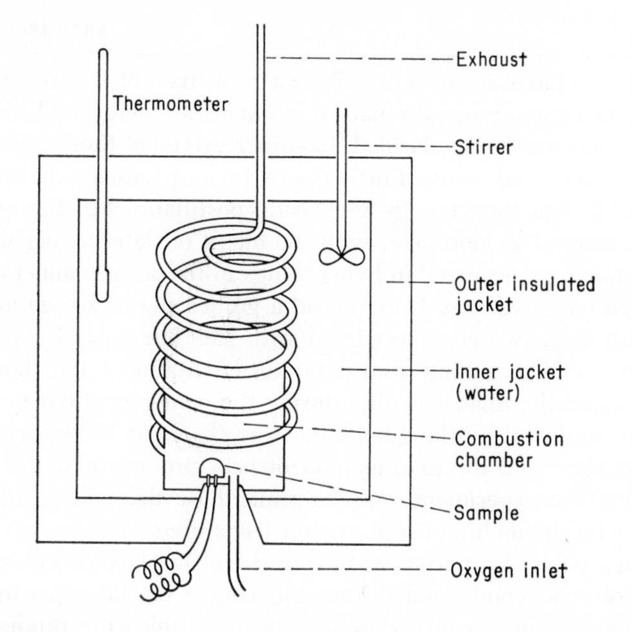

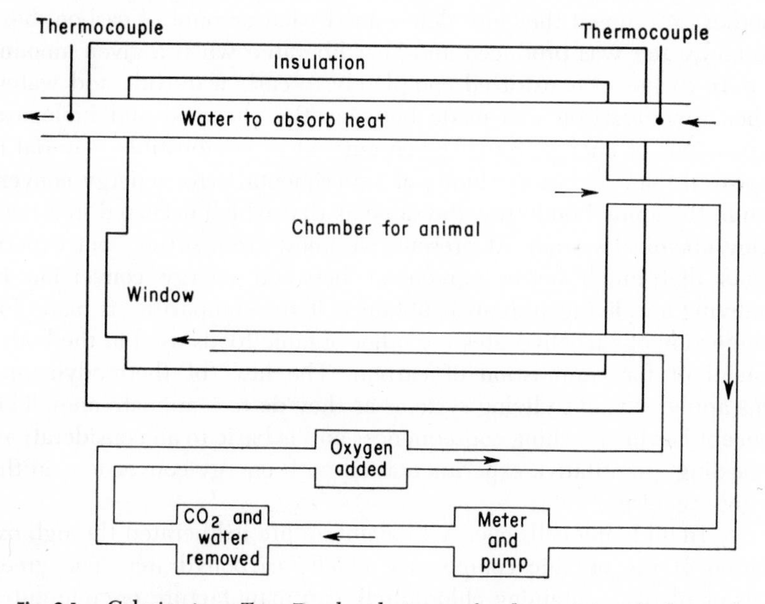

Fig. 2.1. Calorimeters. *Top:* Bomb calorimeter for determining the heat of combustion of organic compounds. *Bottom:* A modern calorimeter for use with animals. The heat produced is determined by the rise in temperature of water passing through the insulated chamber. The oxygen consumption and CO_2 production are determined from the gas flow through the chamber. (Redrawn from A. C. Giese, *Cell Physiology*, Saunders, 1957. With permission.)

It was Lavoisier who in 1779 first conceived of life as oxidation. He lived in an age when the nature of chemical energy and its use in machines was just being clarified. Lavoisier extended these concepts to include animals and plants. Furthermore, he and Laplace designed experiments to test their energy-conversion postulates. For this purpose they constructed a calorimeter with the intent of determining whether energy exchanges occurred in living things in the same manner as they did in nonliving systems. They placed a guinea pig in a cage and surrounded it with two chambers filled with ice. The outer ice chamber absorbed any heat coming from the outer environment and thus effectively isolated the inner chamber during the course of the experiment. The heat produced by the guinea pig was absorbed by the ice in the inner chamber, and the total amount of heat produced by the guinea pig during the experiment was determined by the volume of water produced by the melting ice in the inner chamber (7).

In a parallel experiment, Lavoisier and Laplace determined the amount of food combusted during the course of the experiment by measuring the amount of carbon dioxide the guinea pig produced. In another experiment they also determined what amount of carbon dioxide and water was produced and heat liberated when a given amount of pure carbon was oxidized completely to carbon dioxide and water. When a comparison was made between the chemical and biological conversions of energy from a given amount of combustible material it appeared that, within the limits of experimental error, energy conversion in the animal body was the same as that which occurred in a nonliving chemical system. At present, we know from subsequent experiments that much better agreement between energy conversion in nonliving and living systems is obtained if the comparison is made for combustion of carbohydrates (or other organic foods used in the body) instead of for combustion of carbon. The laws of thermodynamics thus apply as well to living systems as they do to inanimate ones. This concept has far-reaching consequences and is basic to all considerations regarding quantitative experimentation with energy conversions in the living organism.

In all living cells energy to maintain life is liberated through oxidation of the organic compounds, chiefly carbohydrates. The green cells of plants, containing chlorophyll, can manufacture organic nutrients from inorganic compounds, binding the energy of sunlight in photosynthesis and storing it thus as potential chemical energy (see Chapter 1). But cells lacking chlorophyll must depend upon such organic compounds as are made by green cells and must be supplied with them as food. Many animals are also dependent upon green plants for vitamins.

Fermentation and Respiration

The oxidation of organic compounds that takes place in the chemical reactions (metabolism) of the cell can be carried on either in the absence of oxygen (fermentation) or in its presence (respiration). The term "oxidation" is used here in its most generalized sense, to mean loss of electrons. In cells this usually occurs along with the loss of hydrogen from a nutrient (dehydrogenation). Conversely, "reduction" is taken to mean the gain of electrons. In cells this usually occurs with the addition of hydrogen.

In the nineteenth century it was thought that only intact cells could carry on fermentation and respiration, and to some investigators this indicated the need for a vital force found only in living protoplasm. However, in 1904 Buchner ruptured yeast cells by grinding them with abrasive, and found that the cell-free "zymase" preparation which he filtered from the ground cells was capable of fermenting glucose, producing alcohol and carbon dioxide in much the same manner as did intact yeast cells (7). This experiment indicated that fermentation, and presumably other oxidative activities of cells, are catalyzed by biocatalysts called enzymes, which can carry on their activities even in the absence of cells. Hydrolytic enzymes, which aid in the digestion of food, were already known at the time to operate outside the cell and the body, but Buchner's experiment opened the way to a similar analysis of the chemistry of energy-yielding reactions. Since that time many of the enzymes participating in fermentation and in respiration have been isolated and characterized and their specific functions in the chain of reactions have been determined.

Organisms which can oxidize organic compounds in the absence of oxygen are called anaerobes; those which must have oxygen are called aerobes.

Yeast, kept in a vat of nutrient solution containing sugar and essential nitrogenous compounds or salts, will ferment the sugar and accumulate alcohol, a fact known far back in history as evidenced by the great variety of fermented drinks used by mankind: cider, beer, ale, wine, pulque, saki, etc. In bread making, the carbon dioxide evolved during fermentation of sugar is used to raise the dough, yeast being the leaven spoken of in the Bible. Yeast, then, can grow and carry on all of its life activities in the absence of oxygen; that is, it is capable of anaerobic existence (8, Ch. 19; 26).

Lactic acid bacteria used in the preparation of koumiss, kephyr, yoghurt, Bulgarian sour milk, sauerkraut, and ensilage are also anaerobic microorganisms. During fermentation they produce lactic acid, which gives the sour taste to their products. The lactic acid acts as a preservative because in the absence of oxygen no other organisms can tolerate the high acidity produced by the lactic acid bacteria. In fact, the acidity eventually kills the bacteria themselves.

Some anaerobes, such as the dreaded *Bacillus botulinus* that causes botulism, are *obligate anaerobes;* that is, they cannot tolerate oxygen and die if exposed to it. Other anaerobes, like yeast, can tolerate oxygen and are called *facultative anaerobes.* In the presence of oxygen yeast oxidizes the alcohol to carbon dioxide and water. Therefore, fermented liquors in which yeast is present can be preserved only if oxygen is excluded.

Animals are usually considered to be aerobes, and certainly higher animals are dependent upon oxygen for survival. However, all animals are able to work beyond the capacity of the body to supply oxygen needed for immediate purposes and they thus develop an oxygen debt: that is, by anaerobic processes they liberate the energy required for the work in progress and extra oxygen is subsequently used to repay the "debt" when the period of violent exertion is over. This means that some, at least, of the tissues and cells of aerobic animals can tolerate relatively anaerobic conditions for a time. On the other hand, certain animals, such as the protozoans in the rumen of a cow or the roundworms in the intestine of an animal, live under anaerobic conditions and may be injured by exposure to air.

Plants, like animals, are essentially aerobes, but many are capable of tolerating considerable periods of anaerobiosis. Anaerobic, energy-yielding reactions have been identified in plant as well as in animal cells. It is such reactions which make plants and animals, or parts of them, capable of tolerating anaerobiosis, at least for a time.

Measurement of fermentation and respiration

Many methods have been devised for measuring rates of fermentation and respiration, based on the volume of carbon dioxide evolved or oxygen consumed during oxidation. One may measure carbon dioxide output by trapping the gas in limewater. From the amount of carbonate thus formed the amount of carbon dioxide produced may be ascertained. One may, on the other hand, determine the carbon dioxide output manometrically by measuring the rise of pressure as the gas is emitted during oxidations. The manometric method has the advantage that determinations of carbon dioxide production can be made at frequent intervals of time; thus the rate of carbon dioxide production and its variation with changes in conditions can be ascertained (33). One type of manometer is shown in Fig. 2.2.

In the measurement of oxygen consumption it is possible to use

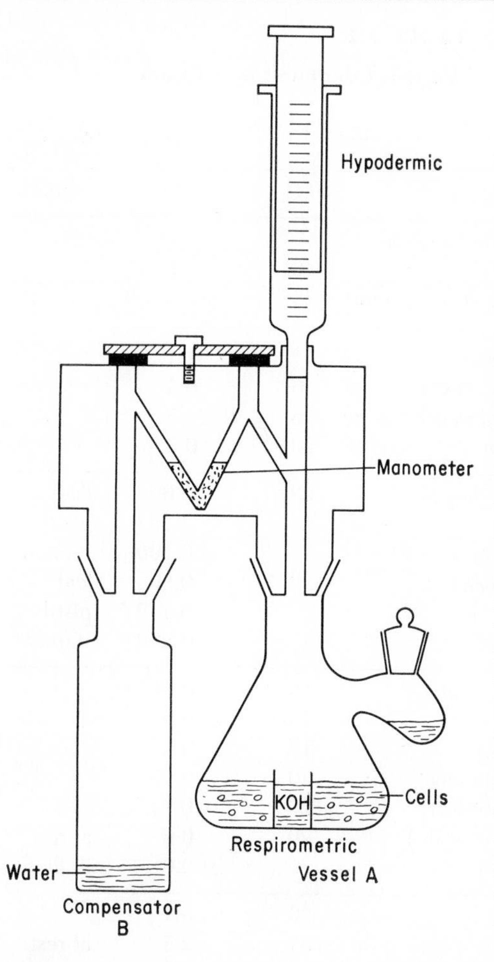

Fig. 2.2. A respirometer. After thermal equilibration the manometer level is set at the same level on both sides and the vessel is closed from the exterior. If oxygen is consumed by the cells or organisms in the right-hand vessel, the level of the manometer rises on the right side and falls on the left, since the KOH in the well absorbs any CO_2 produced during respiration. The volume of oxygen consumed may be determined by the volume of gas which must be added from the calibrated syringe to level the manometer. If fermentation or glycolysis is to be studied, no KOH is used and the manometer is leveled by withdrawing gas with the calibrated syringe, thus measuring the volume of gas produced. Since thermal or other changes affect the compensator vessel on the left, their effect on the respirometric vessel is canceled out. (Redrawn from A. C. Giese, *Cell Physiology*, Saunders, 1957. With permission.)

chemical methods (for instance, Winkler method) but again, the manometric method offers more flexibility as well as the possibility of determining the reaction rate at frequent intervals of time and the effects of poisons or other agents added from the side arms of the vessel (see Fig. 2.2) on the respiration rate. The rate of respiration (or fermentation) is usually given in terms of unit volume per unit weight (wet or preferably dry) per unit time (usually per hour). Some data on the rates of respiration of various organisms and tissues are given in Table 2.2.

Examination of the data in Table 2.2 discloses that plants and animals have lower respiration rates than microorganisms. This is probably because plants and animals have a large amount of nonrespiring extracellular skeletal material. Furthermore, it is the respiration of rest-

TABLE 2.2

Respiration Rates of Various Organisms and Tissues

(Qo_2 is given in milliliters per gram of wet weight per hour.)

Group	Organism	°C	Qo_2	Remarks
Microorganisms	*Bacillus mesentericus vulgatus*	16	12.1	
	Azotobacter chroococcum	28	500–1000	
	Bacillus fluorescens non liquefaciens		4100	
	Neurospora crassa	26	6.4	
	Saccharomyces cereviseae	26	8–14.5	
	Paramecium	20	0.5	
Plants	*Verbascum thapsus*	23	0.093	leaf
			0.204	pistil
			0.190	stamen
	Papaver rhoeas	22	0.803	leaf
			0.172	pistil
			0.280	stamen
Invertebrates	*Anemonia sulcata*	18	0.0134	
	Asterias rubens	15	0.03	
	Nereis virens	15	0.026	
	Mytilus (mussel)	20	0.02	
	Astacus (crayfish)	20	0.047	
	Vanessa (butterfly)	20	0.6	at rest
			100.0	in flight
Vertebrates	carp	20	0.1	
	mouse	37	2.5	at rest
			20.0	running
	man	37	0.2	at rest
			4.0	maximal work
Animal tissues	rat liver	37.5	2.2–3.3	
	rat kidney cortex	37.5	5.2–9.0	
	rat brain cortex	37.5	2.7	
	rat voluntary muscle	37	1.5	at rest
		37	10.0	active
	frog nerve	15	0.02	at rest
		15	0.75	active
	rabbit nerve	37	0.29	at rest

From Giese, 1957, *Cell Physiology*, Saunders, p. 314.

ing animals and plants that is generally given in tables, while, in contrast, the respiration of active microorganisms is generally measured. When animals are most active—for example, when running or flying—their rate of respiration is comparable to the rate of respiration of yeast or of some bacteria. Tissues such as muscle, nerve, and kidney, when active, have rates of respiration much higher than the average value for the entire animal.

The rate of fermentation and of respiration increases with a rise in environmental temperature by a factor of two or more for each 10° C rise in temperature within the viable range. In birds and mammals where the body temperature is regulated, the environmental temperature has little effect on their rate of respiration. Temperature regulation is achieved by various means. Normally heat resulting from muscular contraction is more than sufficient to maintain the body temperature of warm-blooded animals—in fact, ways have been evolved to help dispel the heat which tends to accumulate in such animals. Thus, evaporation of water from the surface of part or all of the skin serves this purpose. In addition, some mammals have sweat glands which secrete onto the surface of the skin; evaporation of the sweat lowers the temperature of the surface blood, thus cooling the body. On the other hand, when the body is chilled, shivering or involuntary rapid contraction of various muscles supplies heat (27).

Some warm-blooded animals, on the other hand, have difficulty maintaining the high temperature characteristic of the species. Thus the shrew loses heat so rapidly that it must have a continuous supply of food to maintain its body temperature; it therefore eats day and night throughout its life span (24). The hummingbird is confronted with a similar problem: it loses heat so rapidly that its reserves of food in the stomach do not suffice to maintain the temperature overnight. As a consequence, its temperature drops to that of the surroundings and it becomes torpid during the night, its respiration and other activities falling to a low level. In the morning it must go through setting-up exercises to warm itself up before it can fly (23).

The rate of respiration rises as the size of the animal declines, and the greater the ratio of surface area to volume the greater the rate of respiration. Small animals like the hummingbird and the shrew have a very large surface in relation to the volume and their rate of respiration is the highest known in the vertebrates. Somewhat similar relations have been found among the invertebrates as well.

Respiration falls to a very low level or ceases when the organism is dried, as happens in seeds, cysts and spores. This is because hydrolysis and oxidation cannot occur in the absence of water. In some

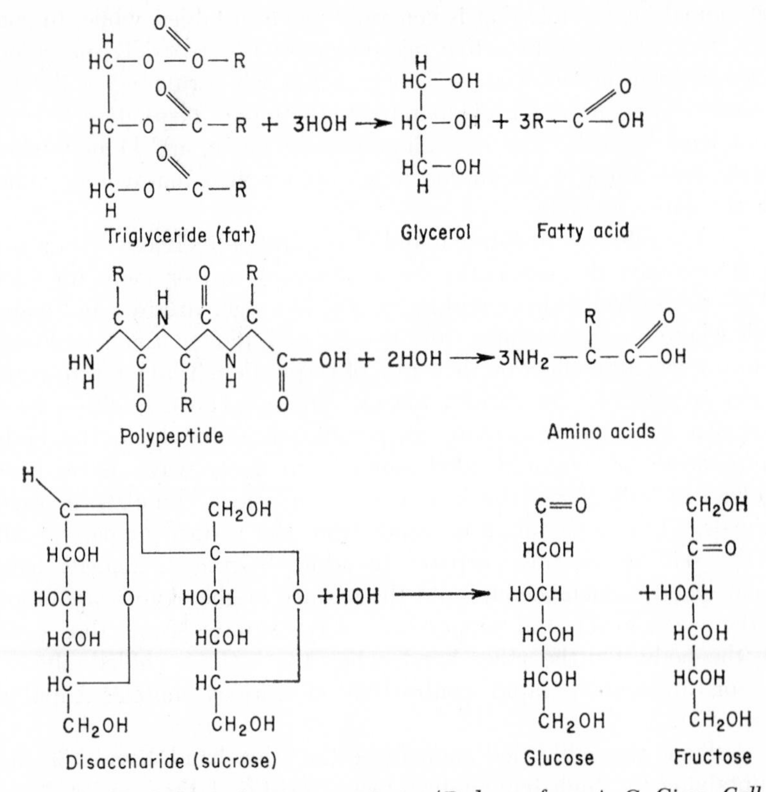

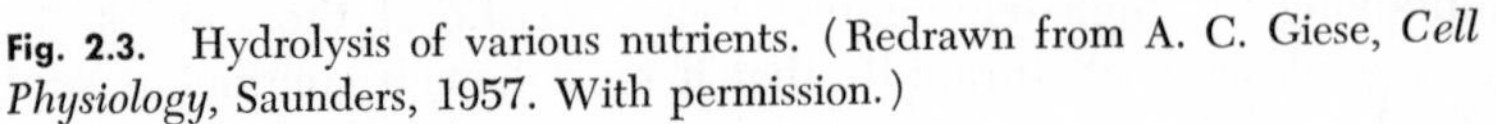
Fig. 2.3. Hydrolysis of various nutrients. (Redrawn from A. C. Giese, *Cell Physiology,* Saunders, 1957. With permission.)

organisms such as lichens, respiration rises to a normal level within thirty minutes after adding water to the dried specimen.

The Role of Enzymes in Biological Reactions

Enzymes are proteinaceous substances which act as catalysts of biological reactions. It is a common experience to find that a sterile starch solution does not hydrolyze to glucose in a finite time nor does a sterile glucose solution oxidize noticeably even though oxygen is available. Both hydrolyses and oxidations in cells occur at an appreciable rate only in the presence of specific enzymes which accelerate the rate of the reactions.

When yeast is provided with sucrose it digests the sucrose to dextrose (glucose) and levulose (fructose). This occurs by the splitting of the disaccharide sucrose into the two monosaccharides as shown in Fig. 2.3. Similarly, when a person digests a piece of bread, the starch in the flour is split into maltose by the ptyalin (salivary amylase) in the saliva. With the aid of appropriate enzymes, the maltose is split into glucose, proteins are split into amino acids, and fats into fatty acids and glycerol. Digestion always occurs by the insertion of water between constituent molecules of the larger molecules. The process is therefore known as *hydrolysis,* or a splitting by the addition of water (8, Ch. 16; 20).

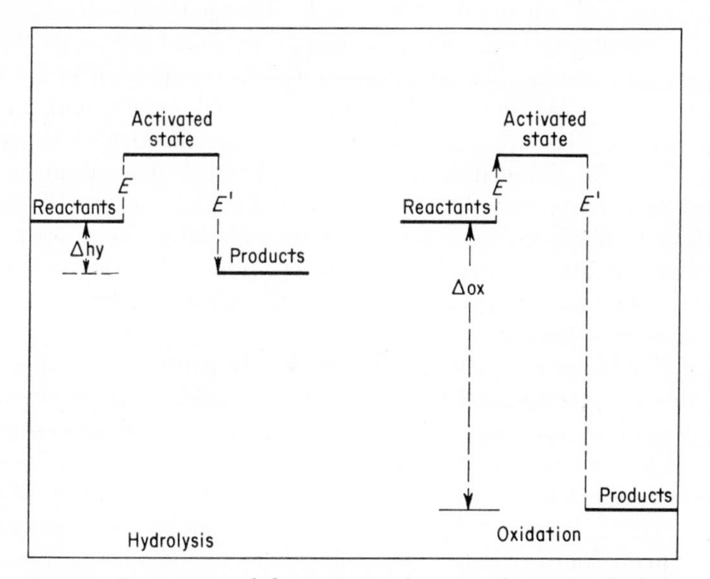

Fig. 2.4. Comparison of the amounts of energy liberated in hydrolysis and in oxidation. The molecules are first raised to an activated state before reacting. Note the small energy change (Δ hy) in hydrolysis, compared with the large change (Δ ox) in oxidation. (Redrawn from A. C. Giese, *Cell Physiology,* Saunders, 1957. With permission.)

Digestion is accompanied by a very small loss of energy; that is, the products of digestion (put together) have almost as much energy as the original molecules. It is understandable, therefore, that with but little energy input the process of hydrolysis is reversed. However, the enzyme required for synthesis is not the same as that which catalyzes the hydrolysis. Also a source of energy is necessary, usually from a high-energy phosphate compound (see below).

In contrast to hydrolysis, the amount of energy liberated in oxidations is generally quite large (Fig. 2.4) and the overall reaction series, each step of which requires a specific enzyme, is essentially irreversible; that is, the addition of a considerable amount of energy is necessary to reverse certain steps in the process. However, individual oxidative steps are often reversible. Since oxidation proceeds with considerable liberation of energy, oxidations supply most of the energy for performing the work of the cell.

Hydrolytic enzymes are unconjugated proteins and they require the presence of certain salts for their activity. For example, salivary diastase requires the presence of chloride. In the absence of chloride it becomes inactive; activity is regained as soon as chloride is added.

Enzymes are usually irreversibly damaged by heating above 60° C, presumably because the protein is denatured (altered). Some exceptional enzymes, like taka-diastase (a diastase present in a mold, *Aspergillus oryzae*), withstand boiling for several minutes without being destroyed. Taka-diastase, however, becomes inactive at temperatures above 60° C but once it is cooled below this temperature it resumes its activity, unmodified by the heat. Enzymes are usually quite sensitive to the hydrogen ion concentration of the solution, operating at a maximal rate only in a limited zone of acidity. Thus pepsin is most active at an acidity equivalent to 0.1N HC1 while pytalin is most effective near neutrality.

Hydrolytic enzymes usually attack only particular linkages and are, therefore, considered to be substrate specific. Thus pepsin from the stomach of vertebrates is specific to the amino side of a peptide bond between tyrosine and other amino acid residues, whereas chymotrypsin (present in pancreatic juice) is specific to the carboxy side of such residues. However, lipases which digest fats lack specificity and attack many kinds of esters or combinations of the alcohol, glycerol, and various fatty acids.

Oxidases and other enzymes participating in the oxidations and reductions in the cell are quite specific to their substrates. Thus pyruvic acid dehydrogenase acts only on pyruvic acid, succinic acid dehydrogenase only on succinic acid, and fumarase only on fumaric acid. Occasionally the same enzyme will attack two or more closely related substrates. Thus xanthine oxidase acts upon hypoxanthine, converting it to xanthine, and acts upon xanthine, converting it to uric acid. The specificity of an enzyme is determined by a steric relationship to the bonds in the molecule.

Oxidative enzymes consist of a protein carrier and a prosthetic group attached to the protein (8, Ch. 16; 9). The prosthetic group is usually an organic molecule, often of considerable complexity. The prosthetic group of an oxidative enzyme usually contains one of the members of the vitamin B group (Table 2.3). A prosthetic group is called a coenzyme when it dissociates readily from the protein. Metal ions required for activity of an enzyme are best called activators rather than coenzymes (20).

Because oxidases show such a high degree of specificity, they

TABLE 2.3

Vitamins in the Prosthetic Groups of Various Enzymes

Vitamin	*Chemical nature*	*Found in:*
B_1	Thiamin	Coenzyme involved in pyruvate metabolism
Protogen	Thioctic acid	Coenzyme involved in pyruvate metabolism
Pantothen	Pantothenic acid	Coenzyme A
Niacin	Nicotinic acid amide	Dehydrogenases
B_2	Riboflavin	Flavoprotein enzyme
B_6	Pyridoxin	Coenzyme for amino acid conversions
H	Biotin	Coenzyme for CO_2 fixation in C_4 acids
Folic acid	Pterolyglutamic acid	Coenzyme functioning in use of single carbon units in syntheses
B_{12}	Cyanocobalamin	Coenzyme of an enzyme involved in methyl transfer and nucleic acid metabolism

are often poisoned (or inactivated) by molecules which resemble the substrate upon which they work. Thus succinic acid dehydrogenase, which affects succinic acid (a 4-carbon dicarboxylic acid), is poisoned by malonic acid, which has two carboxyl groups like succinic acid but has only three carbon atoms. Enzymes are also inactivated in other ways, as by the addition of a poison to an active center of the molecule. For example, cyanide, when added, binds itself to the iron of the cytochrome oxidase molecule. This renders the iron incapable of changing valency, which is essential if it is to act as an electron transporter in oxidation-reduction reactions of the cell (32).

Energy Release, Transfer, and Storage in Fermentation and Glycolysis

When glucose is added to a suspension of yeast which has exhausted the supply of glucose in the medium, a hissing noise is heard, the result of carbon dioxide emission during the rapid fermentation suddenly induced. It might therefore appear that fermentation is a relatively simple reaction. On the contrary, the process of fermentation is now known to consist of many steps, involving a number of enzymes and cofactors as summarized in Fig. 2.5.

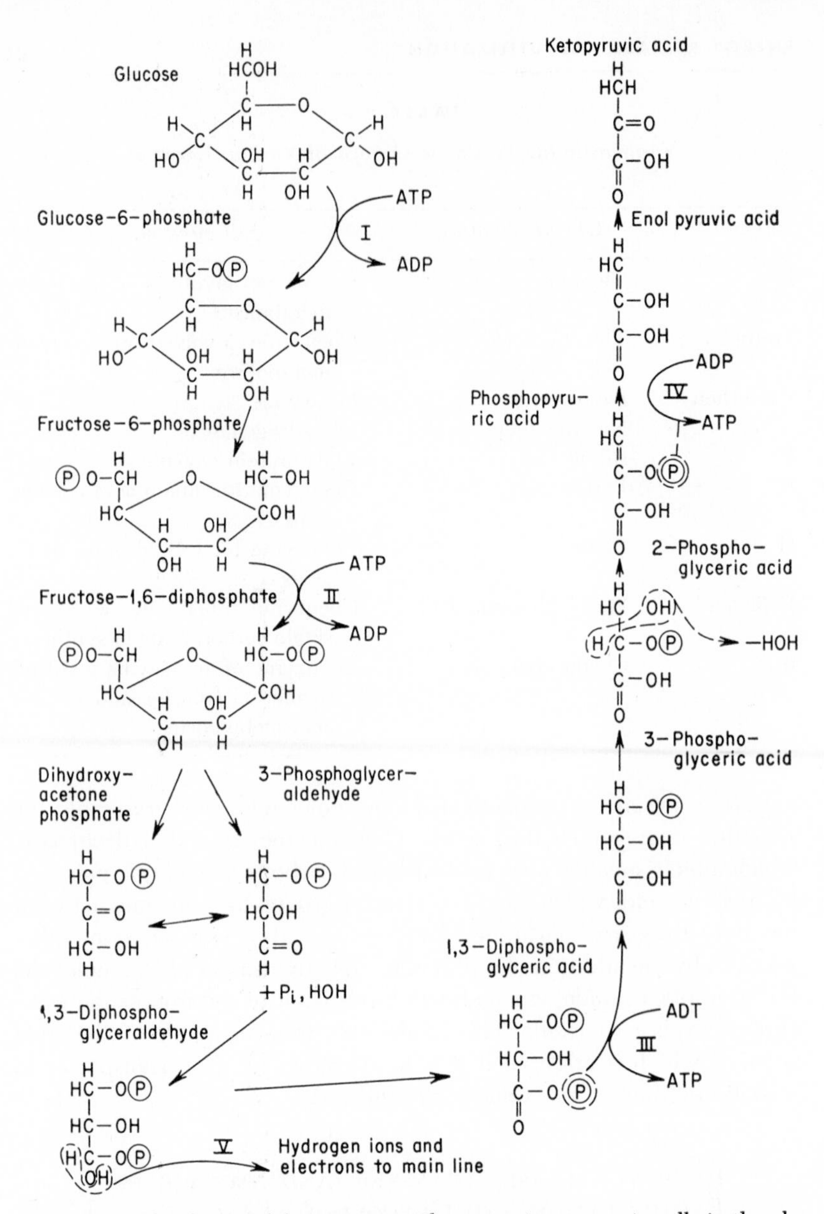

Fig. 2.5. Glycolysis and fermentation. These reactions go on in cells in the absence of oxygen but in the presence of various enzymes. Note that in reactions I and II high-energy phosphate is used up but that it is regenerated in reactions III and IV. Since each glucose molecule (C_6) gives rise to two triose molecules (C_3) each of which gives rise to two ATP from ADP, there is a net gain of two high-energy phosphates (in ATP) during the anaerobic breakdown of glucose. In the presence of oxygen the hydrogens split from 1-3-diP-glyceraldehyde are passed through the main line of enzymes giving rise to three more ATP (or six per glucose molecule). Ⓟ, phosphate; P_i, inorganic phosphate; ADP, adenosine diphosphate; and ATP, adenosine triphosphate.

During fermentation glucose is first phosphorylated; it then undergoes internal rearrangements and is finally split into two triose phosphates. These undergo oxidation to form a phosphorylated pyruvic acid during which high energy phosphates are produced. The pyruvic acid is in turn decarboxylated, as a result of which carbon dioxide is liberated and acetaldehyde is formed. The acetaldehyde, by combining with

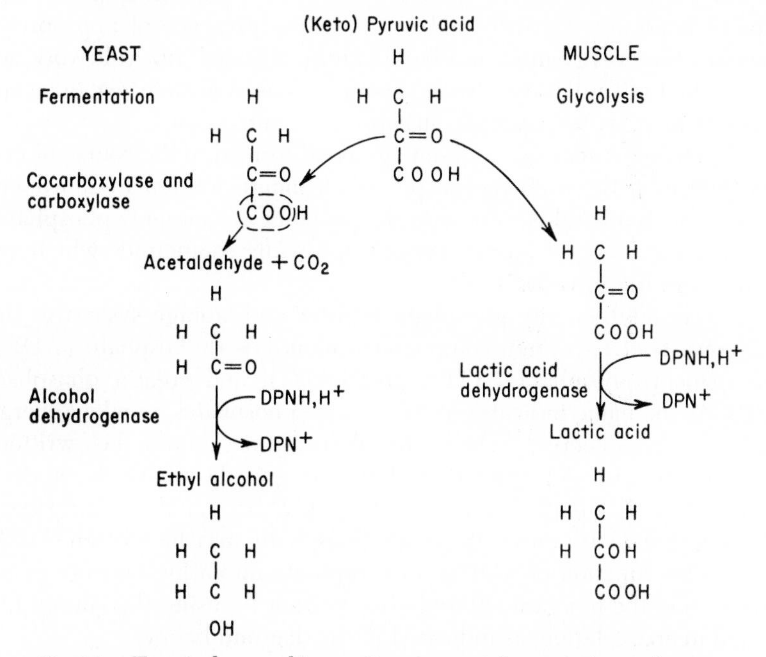

Fig. 2.6. Terminal anaerobic reactions in yeast fermentation and muscle glycolysis. The hydrogen for the reduction of acetaldehyde and pyruvic acid comes from the dehydrogenation (oxidation) of 1,3-diphosphoglyceraldehyde to 1,3-diphosphoglyceric acid in Fig. 2.5. When oxygen is present the hydrogen is passed to the enzymes of the main line (see Fig. 2.8).

hydrogen, is now reduced to form alcohol (Fig. 2.6). The whole series of events is known as the Embden-Meyerhof-Parnas pathway in honor of three of the investigators who contributed much to our knowledge of fermentation in yeast (3).

While the details of the process of fermentation are beyond the scope of this discussion, certain aspects of the process have general importance. It is clear that the oxidation of glucose is accomplished in a series of small steps. Some of these oxidations involve considerable energy liberation, but the amount of energy evolved per mole is always small compared to the amount of energy liberated in a bomb calorimeter when a mole of glucose is completely oxidized to carbon dioxide and water (673,000 calories per mole). In fact, there is no mechanism by which the cell could use so much energy released at once. As a rule something of the order of 20,000 to 50,000 calories per mole are liberated in the oxidative dehydrogenations during fermentation. Some of this energy is bound, or stored, in high-energy bonds. These bonds can be transferred from one compound to another. Compounds having this type of bond are relatively stable; yet in the presence of appropriate enzymes the energy in such a bond can be released and cell work accomplished (31). Ultimately, the energy released in such reactions appears as heat, as for example, in muscular contraction.

The most common high-energy bond formed in the course of cell metabolism is the high-energy phosphate bond, written in shorthand as $\sim$ P. Such a bond is formed in the presence of inorganic phosphates and at the expense of energy present in organic compounds which are oxidized in the process.

The high-energy phosphate transfer and storage system in the cell consists of four main compounds: adenosine diphosphate (ADP), adenosine triphosphate (ATP), creatin (C), and creatin phosphate (CP). As the name indicates, ADP has two phosphates, one low-energy and one high-energy, which, in abbreviation, could be written: $A \cdot P \sim P$. In ATP another high-energy phosphate is added: $A \cdot P \sim P \sim P$. Creatin, an organic base, is abbreviated as C and creatin phosphate, with one high-energy phosphate, may be written $C \sim P$.

One function of ADP is to incorporate into a high-energy phosphate bond the inorganic phosphorus, written P_i, using the energy liberated in an oxidation, as indicated in the diagram below:

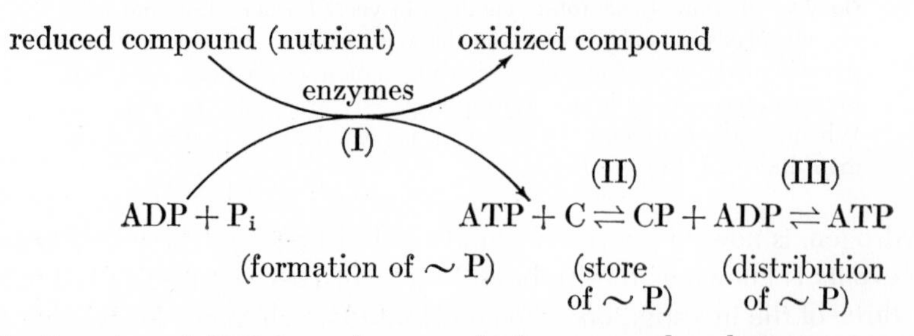

The function of ATP is to donate a high-energy phosphate to a compound, enabling it to react as for example, in the phosphorylation of glucose and of fructose-6-phosphate in the early reactions of the fermentation scheme shown in Fig. 2.5.

The function of creatin phosphate (CP), also called phosphagen, is to serve as a store of high-energy phosphates. Creatin phosphate is formed from creatin (C) by the uptake of a high-energy phos-

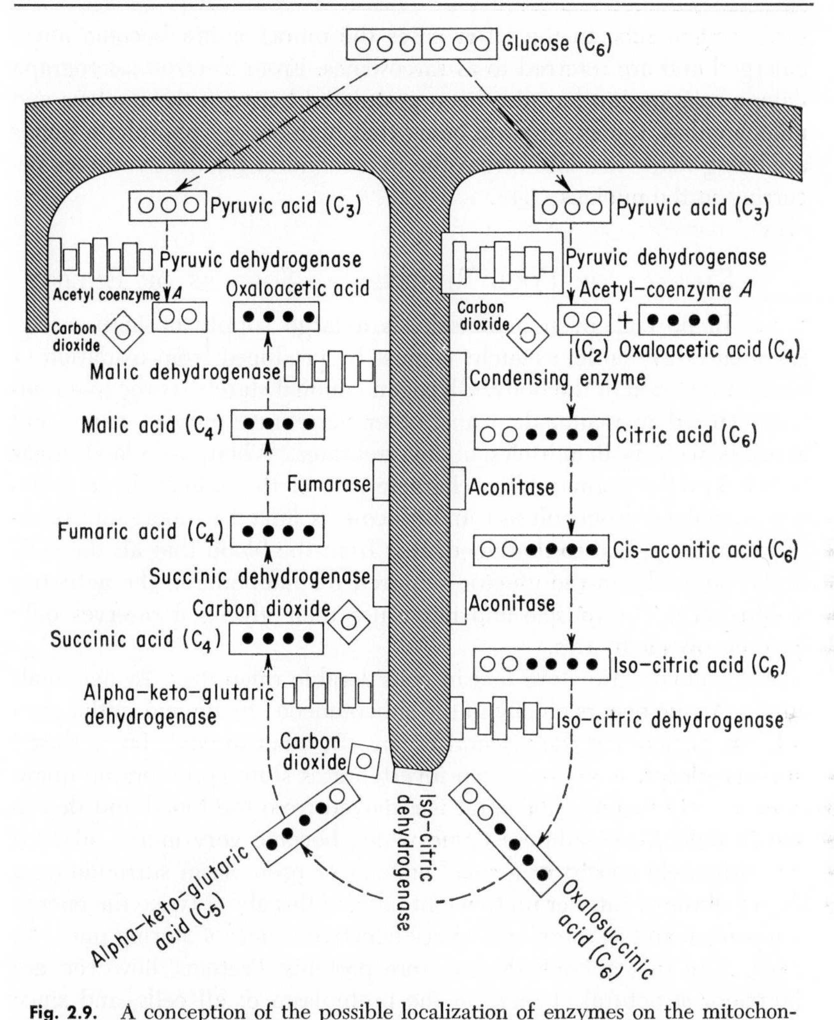

Fig. 2.9. A conception of the possible localization of enzymes on the mitochondrial shelf. Piles of discs represent hydrogen ion and electron transfer systems; rectangles, other enzymes. For convenience the four carbons contributed by oxaloacetic acid are labeled as black circles and those added by the acetyl fragment as white circles. For details of the chemical reactions as they occur, see Fig. 2.7. (Adapted from *The Cell, A SCOPE Monograph,* The Upjohn Company, 1960. With permission.)

not only of the reactions of the Krebs cycle but of oxidative phosphorylations as well, often can be observed in electron micrographs, concentrated where the work of the cell has to be done; for example, at the synapses of nerves, at the nodes of Ranvier (where the impulses of the myelinated neurons are thought to be propagated), around the spindle of a cleaving egg, and among the fibers of active muscles of birds and insects. In the latter cases the mitochondria become much enlarged and are referred to as sarcosomes. From electron micrograph data, a relationship has also been postulated between the nucleus and mitochondria, the assumption being that high-energy phosphate bonds are being made available from the mitochondria for the syntheses occurring in the nucleus (34).

Storage of Food Reserves as Sources of Energy

In no cell, even in muscle, is a large supply of high-energy phosphates available, as such: it must be produced from oxidation of foodstuffs stored in the body. Glycogen (animal starch) is the main nutrient stored in mammalian and other vertebrate muscle, nerve and liver, as well as in muscles of invertebrates. When the blood sugar falls below the normal value characteristic of the animal, liver glycogen is split (glycogenolysis) and glucose is linked to inorganic phosphate and supplied to the blood. It is from the blood that all the cells of the body obtain the glucose required for maintaining the activities of life (27). The muscle and nerve use their glycogen reserves only for their own activities.

Animals also store fats in considerable quantities. In mammals adipose tissue occurs chiefly in the subcutaneous tissue and in the mesenteries suspending the visceral organs. In other animals fat is stored in other places. However, even invertebrates store considerable quantities of fatty materials. The fat is removed from the blood and deposited in the cells of adipose tissue which become very much enlarged and ultimately consist of a small amount of protoplasm surrounding a large globule of fat. Per unit weight fat contains about twice the energy of glycogen and is, therefore, a very effective means of storing nutrient.

As a rule animals do not store proteins. Proteins, however, are the major structural element in the protoplasm of all cells, and since this undergoes slow degradation, a certain amount of protein is always required in the animal diet (28). In the absence of nitrogenous food in the diet or during severe starvation, however, proteins of the protoplasm are attacked and utilized.

Plants store various nutrients in different organs, the storage organ and the type of nutrient stored depending upon the species. Thus carrots and beets store sugar in the root, potatoes store starch in large quantities in the tubers, and many plants store oils or fats in the fruit (castor bean, olive, avocado, and various nuts). Some plants—for example, beans and grains—store considerable quantities of protein in the seeds. It is interesting to note that much of the storage in plants is related to the next growing season or the next generation.

Utilization of Stored Food—Respiratory Quotient

Even when an animal, plant, or microbe is not moving or growing, a certain amount of nutrient is consumed in the very process of keeping the cells alive and, in the case of a warm-blooded animal, keeping up its temperature. Animals chiefly make use of carbohydrates in doing work but usually some protein and fat is combusted as well. Some of the protein in the protoplasm of the cell is degraded in the course of various life activities and must be replaced. By using radioactive elements as markers in amino acids incorporated into proteins of the cells, it has been shown that destruction and replacement of protein molecules continually takes place. This is called "turnover." In some tissues, as the liver, turnover is quite rapid, while in others, such as connective tissue, it is very slow (28).

By using labeled precursors for the fatty compounds of the cell, it has been demonstrated that they, too, show a characteristic turnover rate. Consequently, fatty substances synthesized by the organism or supplied in its diet seemingly replace those destroyed during metabolic activities of the cell.

It is possible to determine the relative amount of protein, fat, and carbohydrate being utilized by an animal from an analysis of the *respiratory quotient.* The respiratory quotient (R.Q.) is the ratio of the carbon dioxide produced to the oxygen consumed.

The respiratory quotient is measured by placing the animal in a respiratory chamber for a number of hours and determining both the amount of carbon dioxide produced and the amount of oxygen consumed. Presumably the oxygen is consumed in the combustion of carbohydrate, fat, and protein and the carbon dioxide is produced from the decarboxylation of intermediate breakdown products of all three nutrients. The problem, then, is to determine for each of the three nutrients, its share in the total oxygen consumption and carbon dioxide production which results from this combustion (29).

To determine how much oxygen is consumed as a result of protein metabolism it is necessary to catch all the urine produced during a period of study and determine its content of nitrogen—for example, by the Kjeldahl method. Assuming that all the nitrogen in the urine is derived from the protein consumed, the amount of protein combusted during the experiment can be calculated by multiplying the nitrogen content of the urine by the factor 6.25, since only 1/6.25 of the protein consists of nitrogen. The amount of oxygen consumed by the oxidation of this amount of protein in the mammal can now be calculated since a gram of protein consumes 0.95 liter of oxygen. When the calculated oxygen consumed by protein is subtracted from the total experimental oxygen consumption, the remainder represents the oxygen consumed by the combustion of both fat and carbohydrate (O_2^{FC}) during the course of the experiment.

Since each gram of protein combusted by the mammal liberates 0.78 liter of carbon dioxide, the carbon dioxide production during the experiment is the product of this factor and the calculated total of protein combusted during the experimental period. When the carbon dioxide produced by combustion of protein is subtracted from the total experimental carbon dioxide production, the remainder represents the carbon dioxide produced by combustion of both fat and carbohydrate (CO_2^{FC}). The ratio of CO_2^{FC}/O_2^{FC} is the R.Q. resulting from fat and carbohydrate combustion.

The problem then remaining is to determine the fraction of oxygen consumed and the fraction of carbon dioxide produced as a result of combustion of fat on the one hand and of carbohydrate on the other. This can be done using a graphical method as follows: When only carbohydrate is utilized, the amount of carbon dioxide produced is equal to the volume of oxygen consumed and the respiratory quotient is 1.0. This is evident from the equation for carbohydrate oxidation:

$$\text{R.Q.} = \frac{CO_2}{O_2} = \frac{1}{1} = 1$$

However, when fat alone is consumed the respiratory quotient is approximately 0.7, as may be seen, for example, from the equation for the oxidation of the fat tripalmitin:

$$(C_{15}H_{31}COO)_3C_3H_5 + 72.5O_2 \rightarrow 51CO_2 + 49H_2O$$

$$\text{R.Q.} = \frac{CO_2}{O_2} = \frac{51}{72.5} = 0.7$$

When mixtures of fat and carbohydrate of various proportions are used, the R.Q. will vary linearly between these two extremes, as shown in Fig. 2.10. From this graph the relative amounts of carbohydrates and fats consumed may now be determined by approximation. For example, if R.Q.^{FC} is 0.8, the corresponding proportion of oxygen utilized in carbohydrate consumption is 34 percent. The proportion used in fat combustion is then 66 percent.

Similar calculations, with such modifications as are called for by differences in metabolism, may be made for various animals. For plants and microorganisms this procedure is not satisfactory since these organisms usually synthesize nitrogenous compounds to suit their immediate need and usually re-use the nitrogen of waste products. The respiratory quotient of a microbe's consumption of carbohydrates in the presence of adequate oxygen is usually 1.0, if no fermentative reactions occur. The same organism utilizing amino acids or fatty acids as a source of carbon is likely to have an R.Q. of less than 1.0 and approximating the theoretical value based on calculations for the substrate being used.

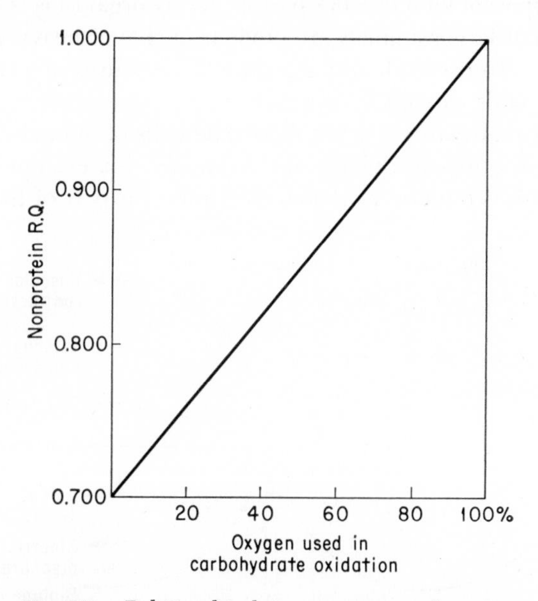

Fig. 2.10. Relationship between percent of oxygen used in carbohydrate oxidation and nonprotein R.Q. (Redrawn from Ruch and Fulton, *Medical Physiology and Biophysics,* Saunders, 1960. Courtesy of Dr. John C. Brobeck and Dr. Theodore C. Ruch.)

When, let us say, a well-fed goose is storing fat, the R.Q. is greater than 1.0 because as carbohydrate is converted to fat, oxygen becomes available from the carbohydrate. Such oxygen is, therefore, available to receive the hydrogen ions liberated during oxidation reductions. Consequently, less oxygen need be taken up from the atmosphere.

In some strains of yeast capable of carrying on some fermentation even in the presence of an excess of oxygen for respiration, the R.Q. may be greater than 1.0—in fact, values of 2.0 to 4.0 are sometimes obtained.

Utilization of Energy in Maintaining Life Activities

Cells use the energy liberated during the combustion of nutrients to do various types of work. A few of those mentioned below are shown in Fig. 2.11. The readiness of organisms to respond to changes in environment results only from the continuous expenditure of energy. The most apparent kind of work performed by organisms is locomotion, and muscles of larger animals are obvious agents of heavy work. However, nerves also do work and the growth responses of plants require work of the cells as well.

Many materials enter and leave the cells of animals, plants, and microbes at the expense of metabolic energy—for example, by active transport. This is osmotic work and the process is part of the metabolic

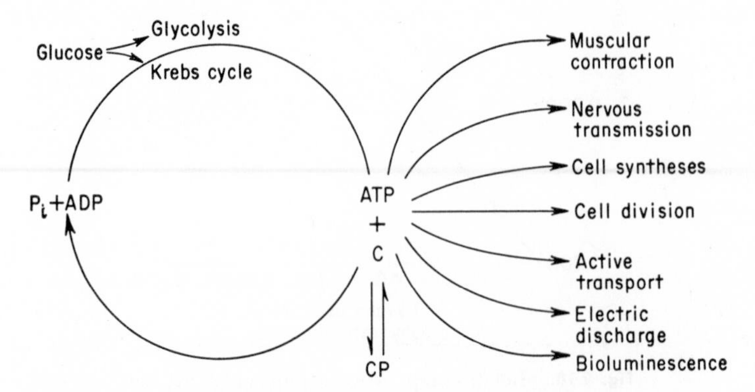

Fig. 2.11. Use of high-energy phosphates in cell work. It is important to note that some cell syntheses occur without intermediation of high-energy phosphates, and proof for use of high-energy phosphates is incomplete for active transport and for some types of bioluminescence. Moreover, high-energy bonds other than the phosphates referred to exist.

activities of the cell and ceases when these activities are inhibited by metabolic poison. Similarly, the kidney performs osmotic work as it transports many materials against concentration gradients. The uptake of salts by the root hairs of plants is by active transport. In a number of microbes, uptake of organic materials has been shown to occur only when metabolism was possible, and to cease in the presence of metabolic poisons (8), indicating an active transport process.

In a few instances a special kind of work may be done by a cell. For example, in luminous organisms chemical energy is converted to light, which in many species is of importance to location of mates (fireflies) or as a lure in predators (certain fishes), but in other cases has no apparent purpose (luminous bacteria).

Another specialized type of work found in only a few species is emission of electric shocks for predation or defense (electric eels and skates). Shocks of several hundred volts and many amperes have been recorded for the electric ray, *Torpedo*, with a maximum power output of 6000 watts (16, 25, 30).

All cells continuously synthesize new cell material to replace that which is destroyed during metabolism. For this work they require a continuous supply of energy and nutrient. In growing cells such syntheses are especially prominent and can be demonstrated by tagging some of the raw materials used. The rate of incorporation of the raw material, experimentally, is indicated by the speed with which the cells become marked with C^{14} supplied in glucose, for example. The same method shows that even tissues of mature animals "turn over" their cellular proteins and other constituents—some, like the liver, fairly rapidly; others, like connective tissues, very slowly.

Many cells form special secretions. The material secreted is synthesized in the cells of the gland which produces the secretion. This type of work, while restricted to certain cells, is widespread in plants and animals. Microbes also secrete enzymes and often a mucilagenous substance found around the colony.

It is important to note that in almost all cases mentioned, ATP serves as the immediate source of energy for the work to be done, being degraded to ADP and inorganic phosphate in the process. The ADP can again pick up a high-energy phosphate from metabolic reactions or from CP to regenerate ATP. This normally happens rapidly in those tissues in which considerable activity is occurring, as is shown experimentally by the rapid incorporation of labeled phosphorous (P^{32}). The exact manner in which this energy is utilized to perform the kind of work needed is not entirely understood.

The nerve excitability process and its propagation seemingly requires little energy, as indicated by the difficulty experienced in measuring heat evolved during passage of the nervous impulse (15, 17). Furthermore, the breakdown and recovery reactions in nerve are so fast that biochemical techniques are unable to resolve the chemical changes rapidly enough to determine their sequence. However, when nerves are stimulated continuously they evolve measurable heat, and in the process inorganic phosphate, ammonia, and other products are accumulated. Nerves stimulated repeatedly in the absence of oxygen use up their glycogen supplies. Thus, when much glycogen is present, as in crab nerve, discharges continue longer anaerobically than when little glycogen is present, as in frog nerve. Probably because of its low energy consumption, nerve is practically incapable of fatigue. Normally it discharges only 100 times per second and it recovers within a few thousandths of a second, ready again for immediate action. But in the laboratory similar nerves have been found capable of discharging up to 1000 times per second for long periods of time. Only when oxygen is lacking does such a nerve preparation finally fatigue. It is therefore probable that the immediate source of energy for the nervous impulse is the ATP and CP stored in the nerve. Aerobically, these can be resynthesized in time to enable the nerve to function effectively for long periods of time, if not indefinitely, by the same types of reactions as occur in all cells.

The process by which the electric organs of electric eels do work is apparently just an exaggeration of the reactions which occur in normal nerve transmission and depends upon the way in which the individual cellular units, considered as minute batteries (each capable of producing about 70 millivolts), are united. Union of discharging units in series gives high voltage, and union of several such series units in parallel makes possible large amperages such as those recorded in the electric ray, *Torpedo* (16, 30).

Muscle contraction has been studied most extensively and a wealth of data is available on its energy-work relationship (12, 13, 27). If a muscle is stimulated successively again and again, it continues to contract for a long time before fatigue sets in. In the absence of oxygen the muscle fatigues much sooner than in its presence. If now, in addition to lack of oxygen, iodoacetic acid is used to poison the anaerobic reactions, contraction ceases much sooner than in the absence of the poison. When contraction stops under these circumstances, analysis shows that the phosphagen reserves have been decomposed and inorganic phosphate appears in their stead. The muscle, having neither aerobic nor anaerobic pathways, is unable to synthesize any more high-energy phosphate bonds and, consequently, muscle contraction ceases. It is clear that muscle is ordinarily ready to react by contraction almost immediately after stimulation, but is dependent upon the energy from ATP for contraction. Since ATP could be synthesized from CP it is obvious that the ultimate limit of $\sim$P at any one time is the sum of that present in ATP and in CP. Ordinarily during reactions of the Krebs cycle, muscle resynthesizes $\sim$P so rapidly that there is seldom a lack of it. Also, considerable glycogen is present in muscle serving as a reserve in times of need, since glycogen, on decomposition, supplies glucose phosphate which can be decomposed to produce more $\sim$P. Muscle in extreme activity goes into oxygen debt; that is, it liberates energy from glucose anaerobically. Recovery from oxygen debt is possible only after the period of extreme effort is ended.

If ATP is involved in active transport, one might expect that adding it to cells poisoned with a metabolic inhibitor should reverse the action of the inhibitor. This has now been shown in a number of instances—for example, in the giant axon of the squid (5). High-energy phosphates consequently figure in most of the theoretical schemes proposed for the mechanism of active transport, although they need not be the only energy source for such work.

ATP appears to be required for bioluminescence in firefly extracts, but the precise way in which it is involved in the cells of the luminous organ has not been established. In luminous bacteria on the other hand, a luciferin precursor is known to be reduced by dehydrogenases of the cell, but necessity for ATP has not yet been demonstrated.

Where ATP has been shown to play a striking role is in the synthesis of various compounds by the cell. Almost invariably phosphorylated compounds are required for synthesis, as well as the presence of enzymes specific for each reaction. Even the linkage of the monosaccharides, glucose and fructose, to form the disaccharide, sucrose, requires the presence of glucose phosphate (not glucose) and fructose in addition to an appropriate enzyme—for example, an enzyme from a bacterium, *Pseudomonas saccharophila*. Starch is also formed *in vitro* only from glucose-1-phosphate, not glucose, and only in the presence of an appropriate phosphorylase, such as one from the potato. The formation of polypeptides, and presumably proteins, is possible only with phosphorylated amino acids which are linked together in the presence of appropriate enzymes (1).

One of the most exciting syntheses is that of deoxyribonucleic acid (DNA), the genetic material of the gene (see Fig. 2.12). DNA is usually composed of four nucleotides: deoxyadenylic acid, deoxyguanylic acid, deoxycytidylic acid, and thymidylic acid. It has been shown that only when these are available as the triphosphates, and an appropriate enzyme is present (extracted from the bacterium *Escherichia coli*), will DNA specifically resembling the sample supplied as a model (template) be synthesized (18). Similar studies have been made with ribonucleic acid (RNA), which is prominent in the nucleolus and the cytoplasm.

In summary, then, it appears that the work done by an organism other than the green plant depends upon the capacity of the organism to liberate potential energy from chemical stores obtained in food. The chemical potential energy may be used to produce light or electricity, to do mechanical work, or to synthesize other compounds required by the organism. Some of the food ingested is stored by the organism for future use, most commonly as glycogen and fat. A smaller store exists as ATP and CP. These high-energy phosphate compounds,

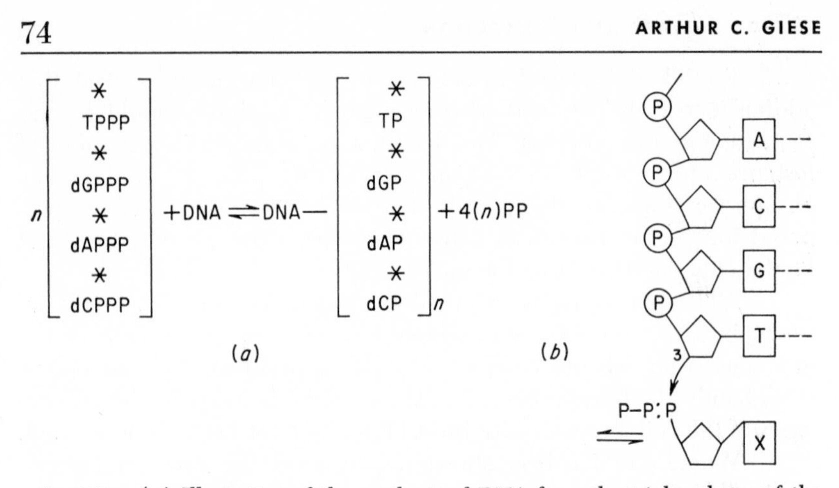

Fig. 2.12. (*a*) Illustration of the synthesis of DNA from the triphosphates of the nucleotides according to Kornberg (18). TPPP refers to thymidine triphosphate, dGPPP to guanidine triphosphate, dAPPP to adenosine triphosphate, and dCPPP to cytidine triphosphate. In the presence of an enzyme extracted from the colon bacillus the triphosphates are united in such a manner as to duplicate the model (template) DNA supplied. The high-energy phosphates are degraded in the process and inorganic phosphate appears as a product of the reaction. The asterisk indicates a phosphate in which the phosphorus is labeled as a marker to give information on the mechanism of the reaction. (*b*) Reaction of one of the four deoxynucleotide triphosphates, *X*, with the ends of a DNA chain illustrating the method by which the DNA chain is lengthened step by step with the energy derived from the degradation of the triphosphate. (Redrawn from A. Kornberg, *The Harvey Lectures* 53, Academic Press, 1959. With permission.)

however, are the most ready stores of energy, immediate liberation of which makes possible the urgent work of the organism.

It is perhaps self-evident that no energy cycle comparable to the cycles of matter (carbon cycle, nitrogen cycle, etc.) is known to exist in the living world. Practically all the energy available to living things has come from the sun. Vast amounts of photic energy strike the surface of the earth daily. Some of the photic energy from the sun is converted by green plants into chemical energy and stored in various nutrients, and from these—directly or indirectly—all animal life gets its food. The potential energy in the food is liberated by the plants and by animals and microorganisms, enabling them to perform all the fundamental activities of life. In the course of performance of work the high-grade energy of the food is ultimately degraded and converted into heat, and as such escapes into the atmosphere. Degradation of energy, then, occurs in living systems just as it does in the inanimate world and in accordance with the laws of thermodynamics.

It has been argued by some that the living organism is never in equilibrium with its environment but rather that it is a system maintaining a steady state; therefore, since the laws of thermodynamics apply only to a system in equilibrium, it cannot be thought that these laws should apply to the living organism. While it is true that the laws of thermodynamics do not apply to the individual reactions in a cell (since while the cell is alive, these do not reach equilibrium in the thermodynamic sense), they do apply to the entire organism and its environment, as a system (4). The increase in orderliness of a growing and developing organism is always at the expense of potential energy coming from the environment. The overall trend in the system consisting of organism and environment is always the degradation of energy. Such reactions are therefore irreversible as predicted by the laws of thermodynamics.

REFERENCES

1. ANFINSEN, C. B., 1959, *The Molecular Basis of Evolution.* New York: John Wiley.
2. ATKINSON, M. R., AND R. K. MORTON, "Free energy and the biosynthesis of phosphates," in *Comparative Biochemistry* (M. Florkin and H. Mason, eds.) *2:*1–95, 1960.
3. BALDWIN, E., 1957, *Dynamic Aspects of Biochemistry,* 3d ed. Cambridge: Cambridge University Press.
4. BLUM, H. F., 1955, *Time's Arrow and Evolution,* 2d ed. Princeton, N. J.: Princeton University Press.
5. CALDWELL, P. C., AND R. D. KEYNES. "The utilization of phosphate-bond energy for sodium extrusion from giant axons," *J. Physiol.* (London), *137:*12P–13P, 1957.
6. FRIEDEN, E., "The enzyme-subtrate complex." *Sci. Am., 201:*119–125, Aug. 1959.
7. GABRIEL, M. L., AND S. FOGEL, 1955, *Great Experiments in Biology.* Englewood Cliffs, N.J.: Prentice-Hall.
8. GIESE, A. C., 1962, *Cell Physiology,* 2d. ed. Philadelphia: Saunders.
9. GREEN, D. E., "Biological oxidation." *Sci. Am., 199:*56–62, July 1958.
10. GREEN, D. E., "The synthesis of fat." *Sci. Am., 202:*46–51, Feb. 1960.
11. HARVEY, E. N., 1952, *Bioluminescence.* New York: Academic Press.
12. HAYASHI, T., AND G. A. W. BOEHM, "Artificial muscle." *Sci. Am., 187:* 18–21, Dec. 1952.
13. HUXLEY, H. E., "The contraction of muscle." *Sci. Am., 199:*67–82, Nov. 1958.
14. KAMEN, M. D., "A universal molecule in living matter." *Sci. Am., 199:*77–82, Aug. 1958.
15. KATZ, B., "The nerve impulse." *Sci. Am., 187:*55–64, Aug. 1952.

16. KEYNES, R. D., "The generation of electricity by fishes." *Endeavour, 15:*215–222, Oct.1956.

17. KEYNES, R. D., "The nerve impulse and the squid." *Sci. Am., 199:*83–90, Dec. 1958.

18. KORNBERG, A., "Enzymatic synthesis of DNA." Harvey Lectures, 1957–58: 83–112, 1957.

19. KREBS, H. A., "Control of metabolic processes." *Endeavour, 63:*125–132, July 1957.

20. LAIDLER, K. J., 1954, *Introduction to the Chemistry of Enzymes.* New York, McGraw-Hill.

21. LEHNINGER, A. L., "Energy transformation in the cell." *Sci. Am., 202:*102–114, May 1960.

22. MCELROY, W. D., AND B. L. STREHLER, "Bioluminescence." *Bact. Rev., 18:*177–194, 1954.

23. PEARSON, O. P., "The metabolism of hummingbirds." *Sci. Am., 190:*69–72, Jan. 1953.

24. PEARSON, O. P., "Shrews." *Sci. Am., 191:*66–70, Aug. 1954.

25. PROSSER, C. L., AND F. A. BROWN, JR., 1961, *Comparative Animal Physiology,* 2d ed. Philadelphia: Saunders. Pp. 455–459.

26. ROSE, A. H., "Yeasts." *Sci. Am., 202:*136–146, Feb. 1960.

27. RUCH, T. C., AND J. F. FULTON, 1960, *Medical Physiology and Biophysics.* Philadelphia: Saunders. Pp. 971–976.

28. SCHOENHEIMER, R., 1942, *The Dynamic State of Body Constituents.* Cambridge, Mass.: Harvard University Press.

29. SIEKEVITZ, P., "Powerhouse of the cell." *Sci. Am., 197:*131–140, July 1957.

30. STEINBACH, H. B., "Animal electricity." *Sci. Am., 182:*40–43, Feb. 1950.

31. STUMPF, P. K., "ATP." *Sci. Am., 188:*85–92, April 1953.

32. THEORELL, H., "Nature and mode of action of oxidation enzymes." *Science, 124:*467–472, 1956.

33. UMBRETT, W. W., R. H. BURRIS, AND J. F. STAUFFER, 1957, *Manometric Techniques and Tissue Metabolism,* 2d ed. Minneapolis, Minn.: Burgess.

34. UPJOHN CO., 1960, *The Cell. A Scope Monograph on Cytology,* 2d ed. Kalamazoo, Mich.: The Upjohn Company. (Available on request.)

35. ZAMECNIK, P. C., "The microsome." *Sci. Am., 198:*118–124, Mar. 1958.

CHAPTER 3

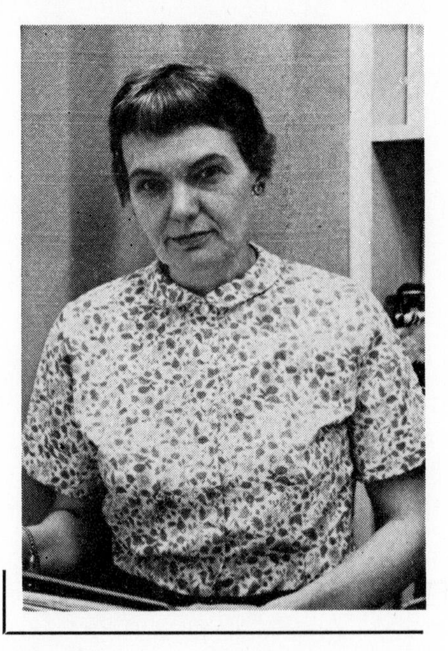

RUTH V. DIPPELL

Research Associate (with Dr. T. M. Sonneborn)
Department of Zoology
Indiana University

Ruth V. Dippell was born at Hintington, Indiana, in 1920. She received the Ph.D. degree from Indiana University in 1949. She was the recipient of an American Association of University Women Fellowship and a Sigma Delta Epsilon Research Award. In 1946 she shared with T. M. Sonneborn the American Association for the Advancement of Science prize.

Dr. Dippell's general field of interest is cellular heredity and cytology; her special field is Paramecium genetics, cytology, and ultrastructure in relation to problems of nucleocytoplasmic interaction.

Among her recent scientific publications are the following: "Some cytological aspects of aging in variety 4 of *Paramecium aurelia,*" *J. Protozool.*, 1955, 2 (Suppl.); "Structure of the *Paramecium aurelia* macronucleus as revealed by electron microscopy," *Proc. Ind. Acad. Sci.*, 1957, 60:60; "The fine structures of Kappa in Killer stock 51 of *Paramecium aurelia,*" *J. Biophys. Biochem. Cytol.*, 1958, 4(1):125; "The modes of replication of cortical organization in *Paramecium aurelia,* syngen 4," *Genetics,* 1961, 46(8):899.

Ultrastructure and function

CHAPTER 3

RUTH V. DIPPELL

Indiana University

When we look into the microscope and see, for the first time, a totally unfamiliar cellular component, our first questions are likely to be: "What is it?" and "What does it do?"

For over 150 years, biochemists and cell biologists have been challenged by precisely these same questions: "What is the structural organization of the various cell constituents?" and "What role does each play in the economy of the cell?" In addition, it was necessary to ask a third, and perhaps the most important, question: "How are structure and function related?" For even the earliest morphological and biochemical information indicated that the complex chemical reactions involved in carrying out the various cell functions could scarcely take place with such speed and effectiveness unless associated with some sort of structural organization. One aspect of this interdependence can readily be observed at the cellular level where alterations in the biological activity of a cell are accompanied by corresponding changes in the structure of that cell.

In a multicellular organism, for example, the functional versatility originally possessed by a cell sooner or later becomes sacrificed for individual specialization. Most cells initially capable of executing a variety of biological activities become restricted, through a cooperative division of labor, to the performance of but one or a few tasks. When such specialization of function occurs, it is invariably accompanied by a corresponding structural specialization. Thus, the extensive working surface resulting from the flat, sheetlike design of squamous epithelial cells uniquely adapts these cells to their function of filtration and exchange of gases and materials in the organism. Similarly, the elongated, fiberlike construction of the muscle cell enhances muscular contraction, since a long cell is capable of much greater contraction than a short one. A plant's sedentary existence is reflected in its more or less rigid architecture and, in contrast, the amoeba's flowing movements in locomotion and in feeding mirror the unique structural organization of its protoplasm.

Put into general terms, *the performance of each function depends upon a particular structure adapted, through evolution, to specifically implement that function.* This interrelationship has come to be regarded as a basic principle of biology, extending not only to all forms of life but to all levels of organization. Its mode of expression is unique to each level but, in turn, reflects that of a preceding, lower level. In order to understand and interpret, then, the life processes operating within this hierarchy, it is necessary to explain ultimately how aggregations of molecules can become integrated into the fascinating, structured, and metabolically active material we call living matter. As one descends the organizational ladder to levels below that of the cell, however, the interrelations between structure and function become increasingly more difficult to establish.

Earlier progress was undoubtedly handicapped by a lack of communication between biochemistry and cytology. Until the past two or three decades, biologists restricted themselves largely to the use of fixed and stained materials in their studies of cell morphology. Consequently, they obtained a more or less static image of a dynamic object. Biochemists, on the other hand, were intent on analyzing the composition and biological activity of cell constituents isolated by maceration and differential centrifugation, and they frequently failed to interpret their results in terms of the intact morphology of the cell. Despite the cooperative efforts which later resulted from a unification of these two fields, however, the problem remained as perplexing as before.

It seemed implausible that such important cytoplasmic components as mitochondria, golgi bodies, centrioles, and even the cytoplasmic "ground substance" could carry out their elaborate biochemical activities in the absence of structural organization. Certainly, this was not true for the nucleus of the cell. Yet, a most intensive microscopic search of both living and fixed material revealed little, if any, internal differentiation within these various organelles. It was not surprising, then, that cytologists in the half-century between 1880–1930 should become resigned to accepting this principle as an article of faith and should turn their attention to those aspects of cell biology more amenable to direct observation and manipulation. Out of this period, for example, came the great classic embryological studies on cell lineage, on the role played by chromosomes in heredity, and on analysis of the nuclear events accompanying fertilization, development, growth, and reproduction.

Contribution of electron microscopy. Within the past three decades, however, a major shift in emphasis in biology has redirected attention toward subcellular organization by attempting to explain relations between structure and function in terms of the organization and interaction of macromolecules. Investigators in this new area of molecular biology would like to know, first of all, how heterogeneous aggregations of macromolecules become assembled into the orderly architectural patterns associated with visible structure; and, secondly, how these supramolecular patterns in turn are related to biological activity. The latter approach, relying on indirect experimental methods, proved almost from the beginning to be singularly fruitful. Attempts to relate macromolecular organization directly to visible structure, however, continued to meet with failure: optical instrumentation could not provide the necessary resolving power.

You will recall that an object is clearly defined in the optical microscope only if its diameter equals or exceeds one-half the wavelength of visible light. (The average length is calculated at about 7500Å.) Since the shortest wavelength (violet) in this range is approximately 4000Å, it follows that the smallest body capable of being resolved must possess a diameter of at least 2000Å or 0.2 micron. This inverse proportionality established between wavelength and resolution thus places an absolute physical limit to the maximal resolving capacity of the optical microscope.

In the late 1930's, however, experimentation in a field then unrelated to biology afforded a possible means of circumventing this impasse—namely, by suggesting that electrons, with their very short wavelengths (1/100,000 that of visible light) might conceivably be controlled and focused, within a vacuum, by magnetic lenses in a manner comparable to the focusing of visible rays by the glass lenses of the optical microscope (Fig. 3.1). A resolution approaching 0.075Å would thus be theoretically obtainable! (In practice, however, a variety of op-

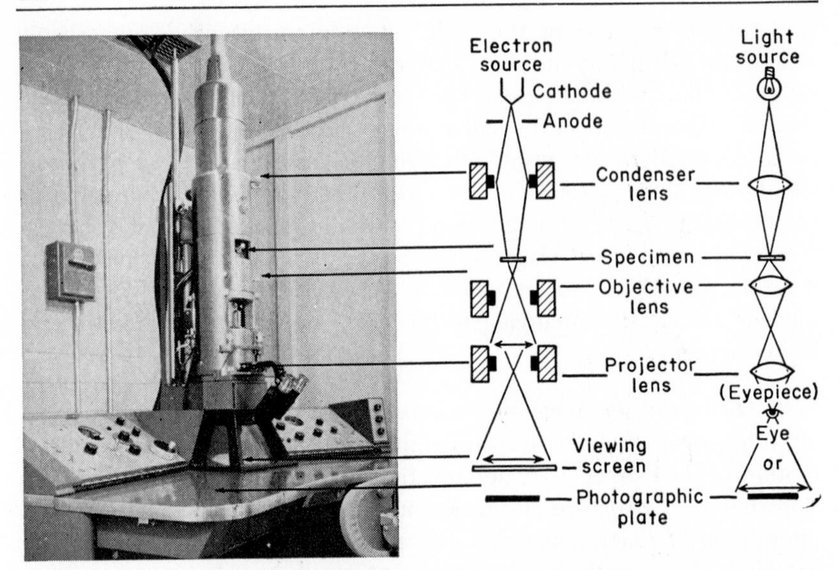

Fig. 3.1. *Left:* A recent model of an American-made electron microscope, the RCA–EMU3C. *Right:* A schematic comparison of the essential lens components of the optical microscope and the electron microscope. The entire complicated system of the latter operates in a high vacuum, since electrons travel further under these conditions. Focusing is achieved by varying the strength of the current in the magnetic lens rather than by moving the lens. When the electron stream hits a specimen, electrons penetrate the less dense portions of the material, but they are absorbed or deflected by the more dense structures. The pattern thus created becomes visible as the specimen image when the electrons reach the viewing screen and excite its fluorescent coating.

erational factors prevents this from being achieved.) This possibility was quickly seized upon and exploited, first by Knoll and Ruska in 1932 and later (1936) by von Borries and Ruska in Germany, and Prebus and Hillier in the United States. Construction of a series of magnetic electron microscopes followed rapidly in the next five years, and almost overnight in comparison with the slow progress of optical microscopy, the practical limit of visibility was extended more than two-hundred-fold, revealing a vast and seemingly unlimited array of subcellular structures.

As was to be expected, this substantial increase in magnification imposed certain technical restrictions, the most serious of which were those concerned with specimen thickness and size of the field to be examined. Present electron microscopes are capable of resolving structural details within a range of from 6 to 1000Å, yet satisfactory images are usually obtained only when the material is less than 500Å (1/20 of a micron) thick. At least 700 longitudinal sections are thus required to

only intimately associated with the membrane but, like the pattern in a piece of cloth, was actually woven in as part of the structural fabric.

Membrane structure and function related. In a beautiful series of experiments from 1956 to the present, both Lehninger and Green and co-workers used sonic vibration to disrupt and fragment mitochondria into successively smaller pieces. These were separated into various fractions, observed in the electron microscope, and analyzed for their biological activity. The capacity to carry out the complete Krebs cycle was found to be lost as soon as the general form of the mitochondrion was destroyed and matrix material was permitted to leak out. The coupling of the oxidative process to the synthesis of ATP remained, however, as long as double membranes, such as those formed by the apposition of crista walls or of inner and outer membranes, persisted. When sonation split this double structure into its component single-membrane fragments, however, the latter retained only the capacity for electron transport activity. Additional data have suggested that a single molecular assembly represents the ultimate functional unit and that multiples of this unit are spaced along the entire inner mitochondrial membrane.

Continued improvement in resolution and methods of specimen preparation have led several investigators—among them F. S. Sjöstrand in Sweden—to conclude that membrane ultrastructure may prove to be even more complex than is currently thought. Indeed, the new observations of Green and Fernández-Morán reveal for the first time the presence of minute granules, approximately 80Å in size, spaced along and attached to the inner mitochondrial membrane. Each granule apparently represents a single electron transport unit in which the carrier enzyme molecules are fixed in position with their electron acceptor sites having sufficient freedom of movement to permit "pick-up and delivery" of electrons from one to the other without loss of energy. The granules or units are believed to be bonded to the membrane proper through structural protein molecules. Thus our most recent concept of mitochondrial membrane organization, that of a tridimensional molecular meshwork patterned by the interweaving of phospholipids, structural proteins, and enzyme molecules, already requires further revision. It is abundantly clear from the mitochondrial story, however, that *the structural unit and the functional unit are one and the same thing, appearing as two facets of a single architectural design.*

Unraveling the molecular details of the energy transfer mechanism and determining the precise chemical composition and orientation of the various macromolecular devices are the next big steps to be taken in cell research. Here again, it is interesting to note that earlier studies have anticipated some of the current biophysical and ultrastruc-

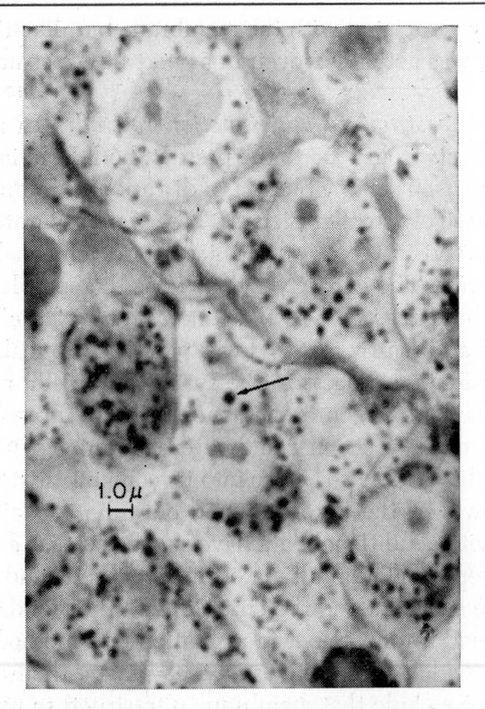

a

Fig. 3.2. (*a, above; b, c, d, facing.*) *a:* Photomicrograph of mitochondria in the chick pituitary, highly magnified in the optical microscope. (Courtesy F. Payne.) *b:* Electron micrograph of a thin section through a mitochondrion in a guinea pig pancreatic cell. At *X,* the inner of the double membrane complex infolds to form fingerlike projections, the cristae (*C*). (Courtesy G. Palade.) *c:* Identification of the mitochondrial components, based on electron microscope studies of Palade *et al. d:* A schematic representation of the basic molecular components of a double membrane complex. Each mitochondrial membrane element apparently is composed of at least a single layer of diverse protein molecules (large circles) associated with a bimolecular layer of lipid molecules (small circles). The protein molecules probably include those concerned with structural as well as enzymatic and electron-transport function.

tural information. Thus, the general composition of the mitochondrial membrane was indicated as early as 1936 by investigations of Danielli who postulated, on the basis of conductivity and polarization-optic data, that the cell membrane was actually a "sandwich" comprised basically of two single layers of protein molecules enclosing a double layer of oriented lipid material. Since cell membranes of many other forms appeared to have the same general composition, it was suggested that the membrane systems associated with various organelles inside the cell also might display the same characteristics.

Mitochondrial membrane elements were at this time unsuspected, but, following their discovery and chemical analysis, it could

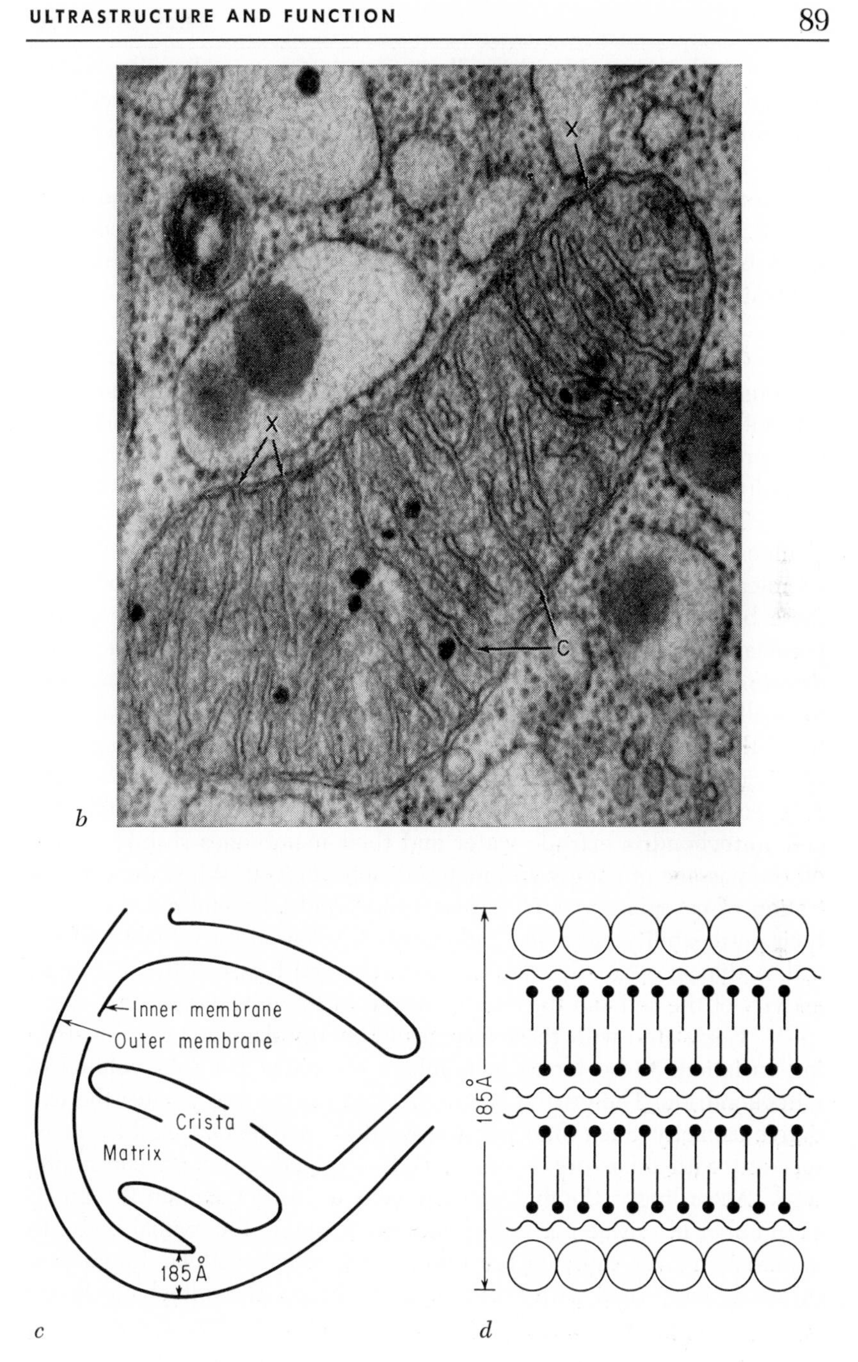
X
X
C
b
Inner membrane
Outer membrane
Crista
Matrix
185 Å
c
185 Å
d

Fig. 3.2.

be shown that they, like the cell membrane, contained, among other substances, lipids and proteins in a ratio of one protein molecule to two lipid molecules (Fig. 3.2d). In the electron microscope, both the cell and mitochondrial membrane systems appeared to be composed of two dense layers of material sandwiching a thicker, less dense layer (Fig. 3.2b). The dimensions of the components of the two systems differed, but strong support was nevertheless provided for the correctness of Danielli's triple-layered model proposed sixteen years earlier.

Correlating mitochondrial behavior and intracellular activity. Although we are not concerned here with the grosser aspects of organelle morphology and function, we can now nevertheless interpret with profit mitochondrial behavior in terms of this newer biochemical and ultrastructural information.

There is already considerable evidence to show that the constant changes in motion and form of mitochondria are reflections of the lively chemical activity associated with an interchange of materials between these bodies and their cytoplasmic environment. Any increase in the permeability of the mitochondrial membrane leads, for example, to its drastic expansion (a property of the molecular protein component) and to swelling of the mitochondrion. Large volumes of new substrate material thus become available as fuel for the respiratory processes. According to Lehninger, such membrane changes appear to be related to ATP concentration. When the latter is present in high amount in the cell, mitochondria extrude water and their membranes shrink, closing off the passage of energy and materials into the cell. When the concentration of cytoplasmic ATP is low, mitochondrial membranes expand, their permeability increases, and energy is released for refueling of the cell. A dynamic "steady state" is thus achieved between the metabolic activity of the cell and the energy output of the mitochondrion.

Correlated with these changes in energy demands are the striking variations to be found in numbers of cristae per unit volume of mitochondrion. The greater the number of cristae, the greater the oxidative capacity. Such mitochondria would hence be expected to be associated with other organelles or cells engaged in energy-consuming work. Accordingly, the flight-muscle cells of insects contain the greatest number of cristae per mitochondrion of any in the animal body. In mammalian liver cells, on the other hand, where cellular function is primarily concerned with synthesis and storage, the mitochondria are correspondingly rich in enzymatic devices that catalyze the synthesis of proteins, phospholipids, and the like, and correspondingly poor in oxidative enzyme capacity. In line with this function, relatively few cristae are present in liver mitochondria.

The unique localization of mitochondria in certain areas of the cell can now also be interpreted in terms of their function. Thus in *Paramecium* these bodies, confined mainly to the ectoplasmic layer of the cell, can establish intimate associations with the bases of thousands of cilia whose intense activity must require a substantial and continuous supply of utilizable energy.

Finally, the curious association between mitochondria and lipid bodies becomes intelligible from the new biochemical and ultrastructural data. In the exocrine cells of the pancreas of fasting animals, where lipid bodies rapidly accumulate in the cytoplasm, Palade and Siekevitz have shown that mitochondria literally wrap themselves about the lipid inclusions, their outer membranes in intimate contact with the membrane of the lipid body. Under these conditions, lipid material has been observed within the outer membrane of the mitochondria. With refeeding of the animal, the mitochondria assume their original position in the cytoplasm and the lipid droplets disappear. Since mitochondria are known to oxidize fatty acids, their association with lipid bodies suggests that oxidation of reserve fat material is taking place in the cell—an emergency measure by which the cell acquires energy when its normal supply becomes depleted through fasting. It is of historical interest to note that under these conditions mitochondria were believed, on the basis of optical microscope observations, to be transforming themselves into lipid bodies: a further example of how the integration of biochemistry and electron microscopy has caused us to modify our conceptions of structure and function based on optical microscope data.

Another type of biochemical machine. The salient feature of the mitochondrial work is the unequivocal demonstration that functional properties (those of energy conversion) cannot be separated from structural organization (the mitochondrial membrane). If this relationship were to extend to other cell components, we might then expect to find that all cellular functions concerned with the conversion, transfer, and storage of energy might be associated with multilayered lamellar, or membrane, systems. Our concept of the cell as a chemical factory in which complex reactions take place in a random and unordered fashion would thus have to be substantially modified. It is of interest, therefore, to look into the structural basis of the mechanisms by which other cellular biochemical machines operate.

Aside from the mitochondria, the most extensively analyzed system is that associated with the *chloroplast* of the green plant cell. By a process known as *photosynthesis*, this body converts the kinetic energy of sunlight into chemical energy for direct utilization or for storage by

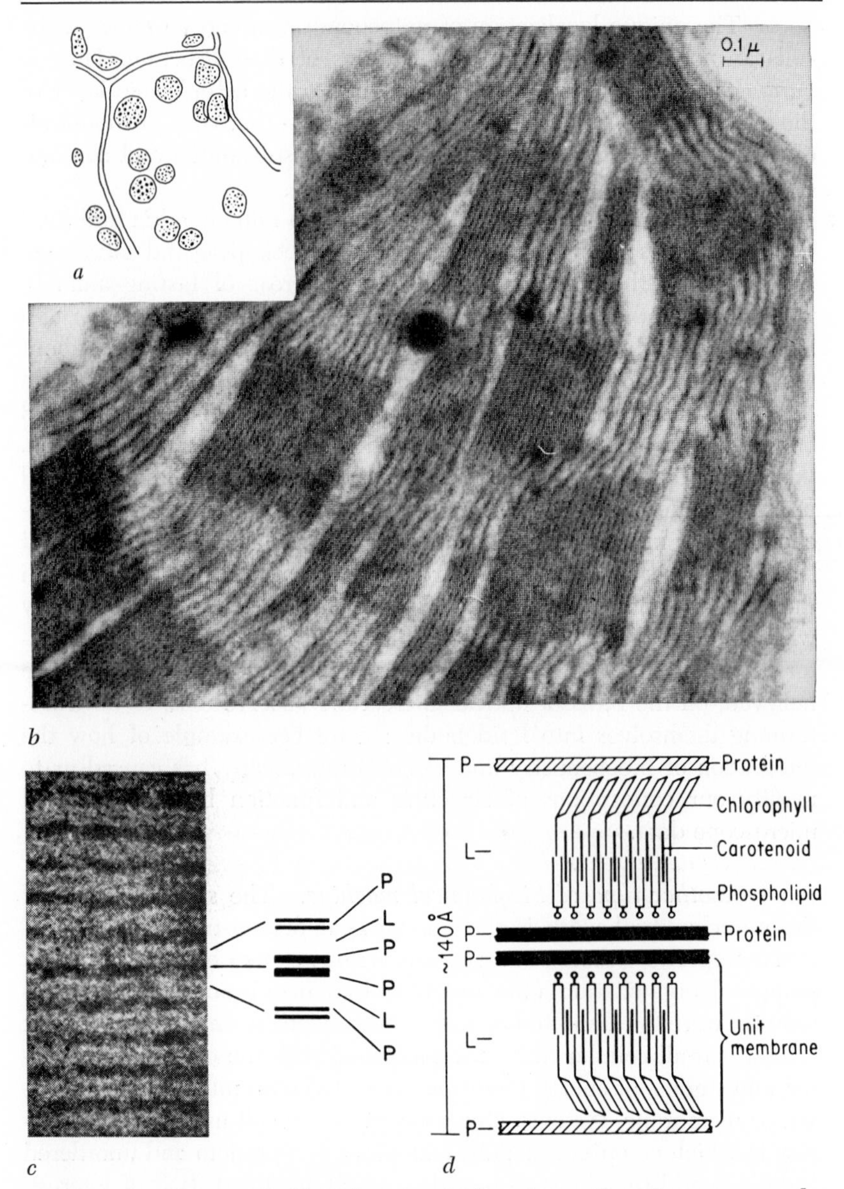

Fig. 3.3. *a:* A diagram of chloroplasts in a higher plant cell as they appear under high magnification in the optical microscope. The grana are resolved only as minute, homogenous dots within each chloroplast. *b:* An electron micrograph of a thin section through a corn plant chloroplast. This magnification reveals that "grana" (the dense, rectangular areas) are structurally complex, comprised of stacks of oriented membrane units containing the biochemical machinery for photosynthesis. The lamellae of the less complex "stroma" interconnects the grana elements. (Courtesy A. J. Hodge.) *c:* Electron micrograph of a portion of a granum, revealing

the cell (see Chapter 1 in this book). In broadest terms, the chlorophyll pigment in the chloroplast absorbs "packets" of solar energy (photons). This energy passes in the form of energy-rich electrons through a series of enzymatically controlled reactions leading, as in mitochondrial respiration, to its incorporation into ATP. In turn, some of the incorporated energy is utilized in a second process, the reduction of atmospheric carbon dioxide into simple carbohydrate (glucose) molecules from which are formed the more complex building blocks of the cell. It is the latter which, when broken down, also serve as the preformed fuel supply for mitochondrial respiration. Thus, while both the mitochondrion and chloroplast ultimately deposit their energy in the same place, the ATP molecule, each derives that energy from a different source.

Chloroplast ultrastructure. Again, as in mitochondria, the reaction sequences associated with the photosynthetic processes appear, by indirect methods, to possess a high degree of order and to be precisely arranged within the chloroplast. The basis of the order, however, cannot be seen in the optical microscope. This level of resolution shows, instead, that in higher plants, adult chloroplasts are characterized by the presence of minute dotlike bodies, called grana, which contain chlorophyll and lie embedded in a uniform (stroma) material (Fig. 3.3a). With the improved resolution of the electron microscope, the stroma appears finely granular, corresponding to the soluble matrix of the mitochondrion. When, on the other hand, grana are sectioned, they show a complex internal organization, each granum being composed of a variable number of membrane elements stacked one on top of the other to form an orderly, usually cylindrical, array that resembles a pile of coins (Fig. 3.3b). These membrane elements are, in part, structurally continuous with simpler intergrana, or stroma, elements that course through the stroma material to form connections with other grana in the chloroplast.

At relatively low magnifications (less than 100,000×) the grana membrane elements appear to form a repeating pattern of alternating light and dark, or dense, layers (Fig. 3.3b). At high magnifications (above 300,000×), however, this pattern can be shown to be more com-

---

an additional structural complexity—that is, lines of intermediate density spaced between the major dense lines. Each of these two types of line is now believed to be double and to represent layers of protein (P), the less dense interspaces containing lipid (L) and other components. A triple-layered, P–L–P structure forms the unit membrane, and two such membranes comprise the basic functional (lamellar unit of the granum. (Electron micrograph courtesy A. J. Hodge.) *d:* The principal molecular components of the functional unit.

plicated. Each dense layer appears to be double, or rather, to be composed of two closely apposed layers; and an additional, apparently double, layer of intermediate density now makes its appearance in the light area between two dense lines (Fig. 3.3c). This pattern, when correlated with information derived from physical-chemical analyses, indicates that a chloroplast granum of a higher plant is made up of repeating, basic membrane units, each unit being a triple-layered, protein-lipid-protein (or P–L–P) sandwich containing, in chloroplasts, chlorophyll and other molecules. At high magnifications, therefore, a single layer of intermediate density is believed to correspond to one protein component (in addition to some lipid), the "light" layer to an additional lipid component, and a single dense layer to the other lipoprotein component.

Such a triple-layered, P–L–P membrane element (Fig. 3.3d) has been defined by Robertson as a "*unit membrane,*" and many membrane systems of plants and animals are now believed to represent single, double, or multiple arrays of this unit. (On this basis, the so-called "double-membrane system" of the mitochondrion would be, instead, an expanded unit membrane whose inner surface infolds to form the mitochondrial cristae.) The two protein layers of a unit membrane usually appear to be of about equal thickness and density in the electron microscope, but when stacked, one of the two (corresponding to a line of intermediate density) exhibits an asymmetry reflected in decreased density and thickness.

While a unit membrane appears to be the basic structural element in a chloroplast granum, the *functional* unit is a *pair* of these unit membranes united at their ends to form a flattened "closed circuit" double-membrane structure (P–L–PP–L–P). Such a pair is called a *lamellar unit.* Variable numbers of these lamellar units stack to form a chloroplast granum of higher plant. The precise nature of their arrangement in the complex organization of the granum still is not known with certainty. In lower forms of plants (the green algae, for example) they may appear singly or in small stacks of two, three, or four lamellae (p. 95).

In chloroplasts, carotenoid and chlorophyll (and presumably other molecules) are precisely positioned between the lipid and protein components of the membrane units. The chlorophyll is arranged in a monolayer, and its orientation with respect to the lamellar surface and its manner of close packing with other molecules apparently makes for a most efficient photon-trapping and energy-conducting arrangement, the details of which are now being explored by such investigators as Melvin Calvin at the University of California and Alan Hodge at M.I.T. (Fig. 3.3d).

Correlating chloroplast ultrastructure and photosynthesis. Regardless of the details, the integration of structure and function in chloroplasts is indicated by the fact that chlorophyll synthesis appears to parallel lamellar formation. Any genetic or environmental factors (physical or chemical agents) which block the development of pigment synthesis, destroy the integrity of the lamellar structure. In higher plants, electron microscopy has shown that the young chloroplast, in an early stage of its development from a proplastid granule, internally "buds" off vesicles from its limiting membrane. These vesicles dissociate from the membrane wall and cluster within the interior of the developing chloroplast to form a "center" or prolamellar body. Under conditions of normal illumination, the vesicles somehow flatten, extend, and fuse to form lamellar structures which then become arranged in parallel arrays typical of those characterizing the adult grana. If light intensities are low, however, prolamellar centers may develop but typical lamellae are seldom, if ever, formed. Under these conditions, photosynthetic activity is minimal or generally lacking. The significant biochemical and formative events going on within the complex, lattice-like center, however, have only recently begun to be explored. Our current concepts regarding lamellar formation and the development of photosynthetic activity may, therefore, be substantially altered in the light of future work.

The stacking pattern found in the chloroplasts of higher plants is not essential for efficient photosynthesis, since in many lower forms, like the green algae, grana usually are absent, and the lamellar units lie distributed throughout the finely granular matrix. Here, however, the units frequently are greatly elongated, often forming extensive membrane systems in the cell, suggestive of grana lamellae placed end to end and fused. It is the presence of the lamellar unit that is essential to chlorophyll synthesis and hence to photosynthetic activity; the way it is arranged in the cell is of secondary importance. Clearly, then, as in mitochondria, the structural and functional aspects of the plant chloroplasts are inseparable.

From photosynthesis to photoreception. Still a third and different model of a biochemical machine is found in the *photoreceptor cells* of the retina of the eye. As in all photosensitive systems, a pigment is required for absorption of light energy. The visual pigment, rhodopsin, which is present in the outer segments of the rods and cones of the vertebrate retina (Fig. 3.4a), performs this function. How the absorption of light, mediated by this pigment, generates nerve impulses that are then transmitted to the brain by the optic nerve, remains largely a mystery.

Indirect evidence from chemical and polarization-optic studies shows that the rod and cone outer segments contain transversely oriented, alternating layers of lipid and protein material. That these alternating layers should have the form of submicroscopic membranes might be predicted from the preceding observations and from the operational similarity between this system and those discussed earlier.

The prediction was confirmed by the ultrastructure studies of Sjöstrand. Depending on the organism, from tens to hundreds of compactly stacked "triple-layered disks" were observed to fill the outer segments of the rods and cones (Fig. 3.4b). Each disk strikingly resembled a mitochondrial crista in its general (lipoprotein) composition and arrangement of layers. The recent work of Fernández-Morán has revealed, however, the presence of a layer of intermediate density interspaced in the middle of the "light" (lipid) layer. This suggests a more complex ultrastructure than had previously been suspected and gives the photoreceptor "disks" a closer resemblance to a chloroplast lamellar unit.

Closely associated with this photoreceptor system are large numbers of mitochondria, occupying the immediately adjacent, inner segment of the cell. The opposite end of the outer segment is capped by a monolayer of pigment epithelial cells which extend down in fingerlike fashion, surrounding the outer segment. Scattered throughout the cytoplasm of the pigment epithelial layer are curious structures called myeloid bodies. These were shown by K. R. Porter at Harvard University to be composed of angular stacks of paired membranes, resembling in thickness those which comprise the outer segments. They apparently are derived from another major cellular membrane system, the endoplasmic reticulum (p. 100).

The structural and functional interrelations between the various other components associated with the outer segment are now being investigated. The pigment epithelial layer is known to transmit to outer cells of the rod and cone numerous metabolites essential in vision. Intimate contact with the pigment epithelium is, in fact, required for rhodopsin synthesis—as is shown by the inability of excised frog retina to manufacture this pigment until restored to physical contact with pigment epithelial cells. The photoreceptor "disks" of the outer segment are known to contain large amounts of rhodopsin and so to resemble, in this respect, chlorophyll-containing lamellar units. Considered together with certain other observations, it appears likely that metabolic products and materials involved in production of the visual pigment are transferred directly to the photoreceptor units from projections of the pigment epithelium, through their intimate contact with the outer segment. Rhodopsin may then function, along with the other mem-

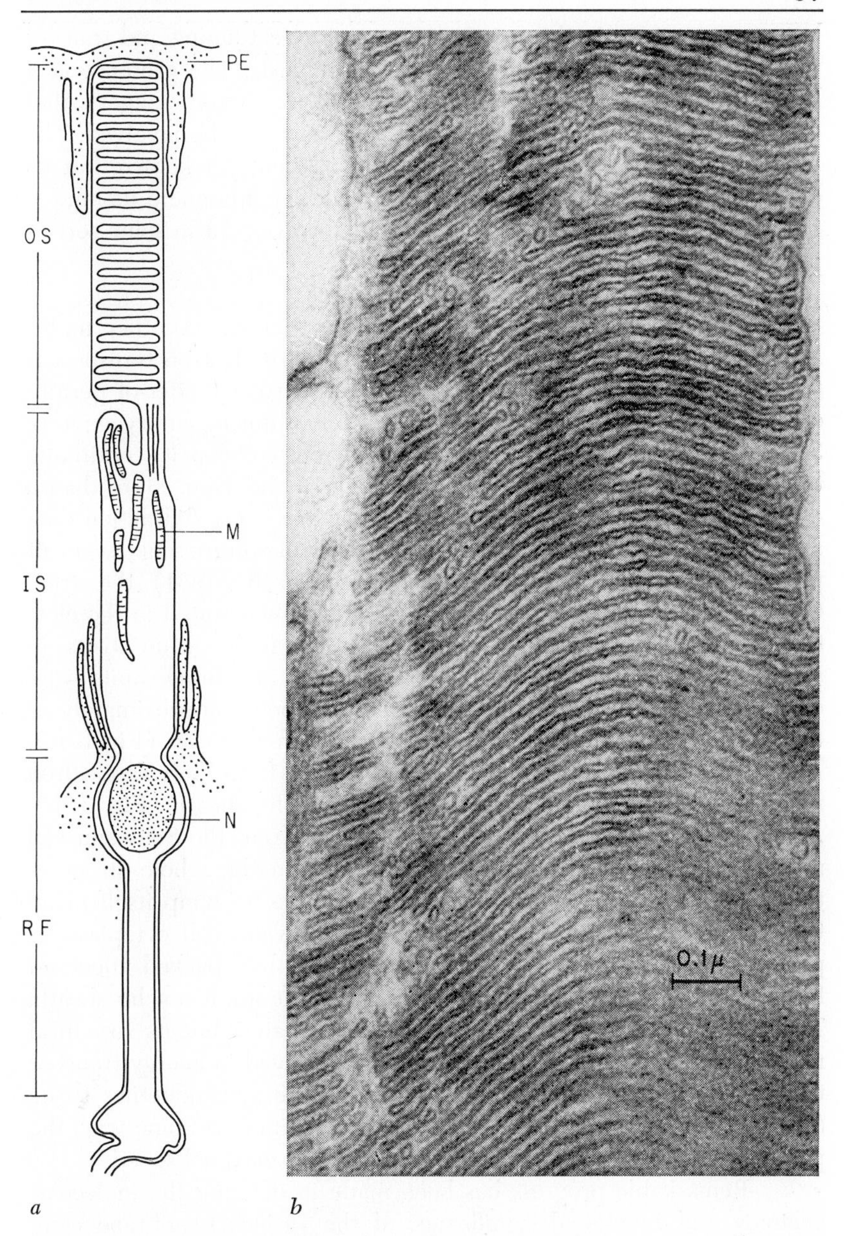

Fig. 3.4. *a:* A schematic representation of a vertebrate retinal rod. PE, pigment epithelium; OS, outer segment; IS, inner segment; RF, rod fiber; N, rod nucleus; M, mitochondria. *b:* An electron micrograph of a longitudinal section through the outer segment of a retinal rod cell from the perch eye, showing the stacked, photoreceptor disks. (Courtesy F. Sjöstrand.)

brane components, in the creation of an energy-extracting and transfer system not unlike that found in plant chloroplasts. The presence of a large population of mitochondria adjacent to the system suggests that mechanisms requiring the presence of ATP may also be involved. The functional significance of the myeloid body is not yet known, but its derivation from smooth-surfaced endoplasmic reticulum and its unique pattern of membrane stacking suggests its involvement in some sort of photoreceptive activity.

The Myelin sheath: a third lamellar system. Another multilayered lamellar system probably associated with electron transport is that of the *myelin sheath* which surrounds the axis cylinder of peripheral nerve cells (Fig. 3.5a). As the axon develops during embryogenesis, Schwann cells follow it along and completely envelop it, continuing to wrap themselves spirally many times about the axon. More than a quarter of a century ago, polarization-optic and x-ray diffraction data showed the myelin sheath to be comprised of alternating layers of protein and oriented lipid molecules. Subsequently (1954), the structural basis for this multilayered pattern was domonstrated in the electron microscope by Finean and Fernández-Morán. Multilayers of spirally arranged and closely packed "double" membrane units were observed to encase the axon, each such unit being approximately as thick as a photoreceptor "disk" or chloroplast lamellar unit (Fig. 3.5c).

This curious pattern became intelligible from Geren's electron microscope studies of the formation of the myelin sheath (Fig. 3.5b). After the Schwann cell tightly surrounds the axon, the Schwann cell membrane occupying the outermost position in the whole structure then begins to infold, continuing, by this process, to wrap itself many times around the axon. Concurrently, the Schwann cell cytoplasm is pressed from between the membrane layers thus packed together, forming the multilayered structure typical of the adult myelin sheath. The function of this body is now being investigated, but its structural resemblance to other multilayered systems involved in energy transfer, together with its intimate association with energy-conducting tissue (the nerve cell), suggest that it may act to facilitate, in some way, the passage of energy waves along the nerve fiber at maximal speed.

Remarkable progress has been made in defining the molecular anatomy and functional significance of the various membrane complexes described. The most significant and fundamental fact to be appreciated, however, is the discovery that cells apparently require an elaborate, and hitherto unsuspected, common structural framework of lipoprotein composition for the implementation of these varied functions. The protein constituent confers an ability to expand and contract

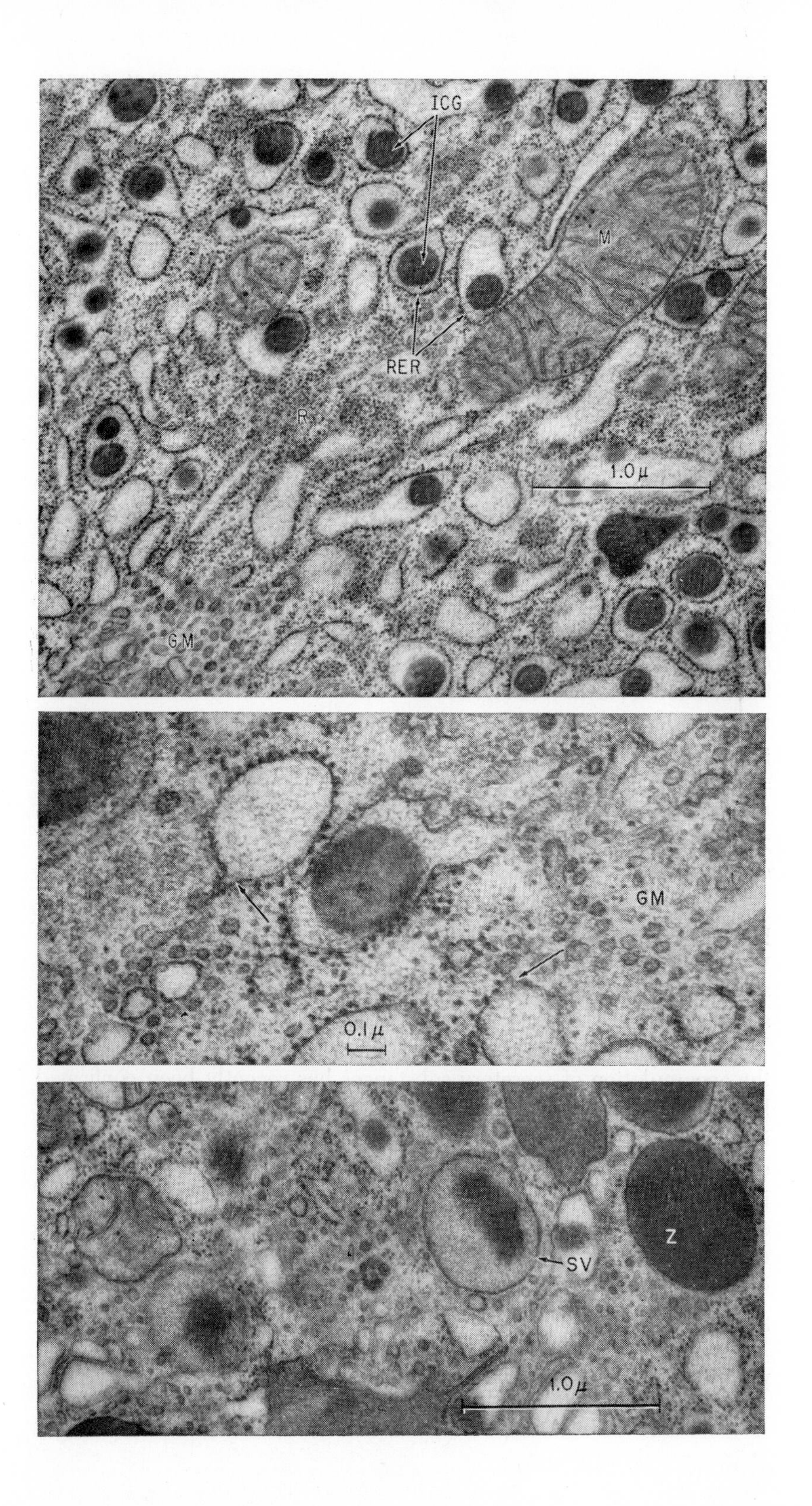
ICG
M
RER
R
1.0 μ
GM
GM
0.1 μ
Z
SV
1.0 μ

becomes separated from this granule and is transferred or segregated to the internal vesicular spaces enclosed by the membranes of the reticulum. It can then be transported, within these cisternae, to other parts of the cell.

The synthesis and transport of zymogen in the pancreatic cells constitutes one of the best-analyzed examples of endoplasmic reticular function. Through integrated biochemical and electron microscope studies, Siekevitz and Palade have shown that the rough-surfaced endoplasmic reticulum of guinea pig pancreatic exocrine cells is concerned with the large-scale synthesis of digestive enzymes. Produced by the ribosomes of the membrane, these proteins are first observed as dense granules within the cavities of the rough-surfaced reticulum occupying the basal region of the cell. Appearing small at first, the granules or prozymogen bodies rapidly increase their size and enzymatic content within the distending cisternae. Concurrently, the rough-surfaced reticulum containing these bodies appears to concentrate near the opposite, apical end of the cell where large "piles" of smooth-surfaced tubules and cisternae, identified as the Golgi complex, connect with them (Fig. 3.7). All gradations are now found between empty or partially filled, smooth-surfaced Golgi vesicles and adult zymogen bodies closely bounded by a smooth-surfaced membrane. Direct transfer of the zymogen material from the rough endoplasmic reticulum to the smooth-surfaced membrane elements of the Golgi complex is thus indicated, the membrane of the latter forming the limiting membrane of the zymogen body which then establishes contact with the cell boundary. Fusion of the cell and zymogen body membranes then occurs, and an opening is created through which the zymogen contents are emptied into the pancreatic lumen. This discharge of digestive enzymes thus takes place without a break in membrane continuity, an important move to forestall escape of these enzymes into the cytoplasm and consequent destruction of the cell that created them.

The involvement of the Golgi element as an important agent in the accumulation of secretory substances has recently been confirmed by Caro, who used a labeled (radioactive) amino acid, introducing it into the animal and following its pathway in the pancreatic exocrine cells in relation to protein synthesis. Fifteen to twenty minutes after injection, the label is concentrated in the Golgi zone near the apical end of the cell. Subsequent observations clearly show that the newly synthesized protein is channeled through this complex on the way from its site of synthesis in the ribosomes to its storage depot in the adult zymogen granule.

The nuclear and cell membranes, like the rough-surfaced endoplasmic reticulum, contain attached RNP particles, and there is good

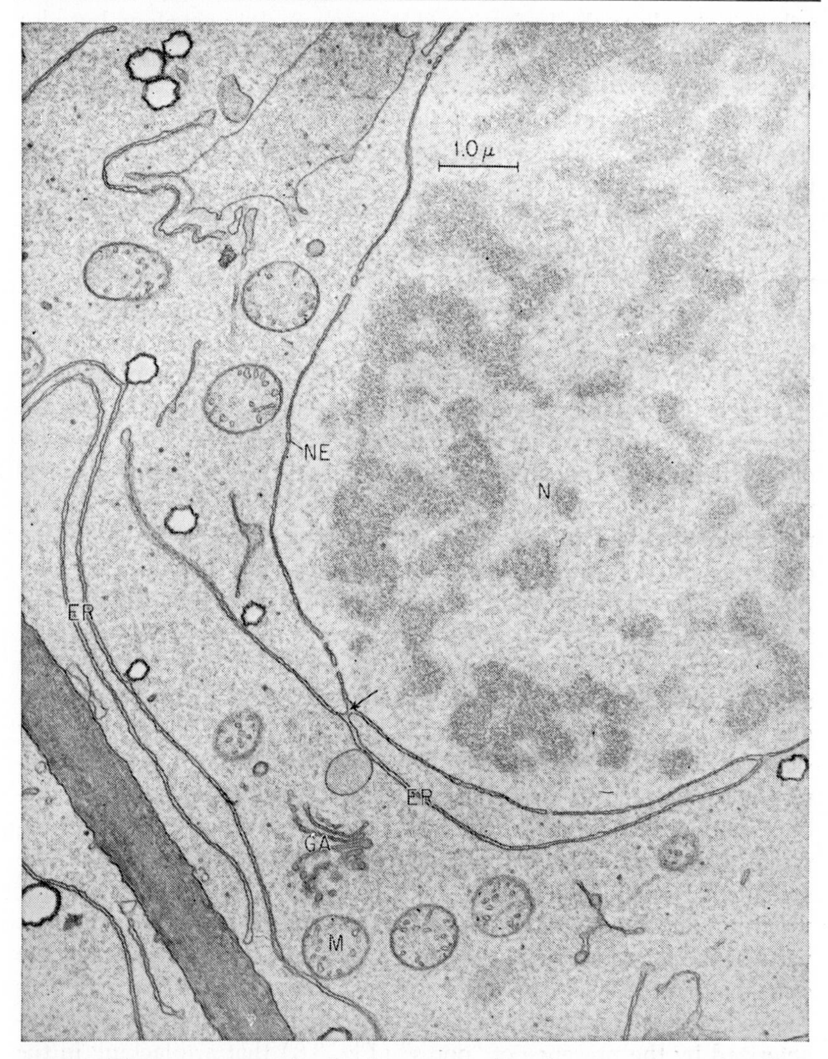

Fig. 3.8. Electron micrograph of a thin section through a corn plant root cell. At arrow, endoplasmic reticulum (ER) appears as an extension of the nuclear envelope (NE). RNP particles associated with the endoplasmic reticulum are not revealed when cells are fixed in $KMnO_4$. N, nucleus; GA, Golgi apparatus; M, mitochondria. (Courtesy G. Whaley.)

evidence of connections among these three components. In interphase nuclei, it is not uncommon to find long extensions of the nuclear envelope into the cytoplasm where they may dissociate, and even fragment, into structures indistinguishable from the cytoplasmic reticulum (Fig. 3.8). The latter, on the other hand, appears during mitosis to contribute not only to the formation of the new nuclear envelope but also to the production of a new cell membrane and to the formation of the plant-cell plate.

Agranular or smooth endoplasmic reticulum is related mainly to the transportation and exportation of enzymes and materials. Thus, in the liver, it functions in transporting glucose to the cell surface; in the pancreas, zymogen is its export product. In muscle fibers, however, the elements of the reticulum are organized into an elaborate network that not only orients and extends parallel to the length of the myofibrils but is continuous transversely across the fibrils, reaching interiorly to the deepest ones (Fig. 3.6b). From its organization and biochemical properties, it would appear that this sarcoplasmic reticulum may function as a signal-transmitting system, carrying excitatory impulses into the innermost fibrils and thereby providing an explanation for the mystery of how these fibrils are able to contract simultaneously with the outermost ones, many microns away. In this connection, the endoplasmic reticulum observed to extend through intercellular bridges between cells may also act as a signal transmitter, supplying the necessary continuity for the high degree of coordination existing among differentiating cells.

Currently, the most commonly accepted hypothesis is to regard all of these endoplasmic reticular structures as various aspects of a single, unified system extending throughout the cell. This view is not shared by all biologists, however. Thus Sjöstrand believes that the morphological differences distinguishing these components also reflect distinct functional differences. He would therefore recognize in the cytoplasm a number of, at least structurally, diverse components of the system that would not be morphologically interconnected. Certainly, structural and functional differences are found even within the various parts of the rough-surfaced system. For example, different parts of the same cell membrane can differ enzymatically from other parts, as shown in the microvilli of liver cells. And the nuclear envelope is characterized by the presence of "pores" (Fig. 3.8) that are lacking in the cytoplasmic (yet presumably interconnected!) parts of the same system. Regardless of the morphological relationships, however, this differentiation among the various membrane components of the cell cannot help but lead to speculation concerning the origin of the specificity of these differences. How is it that a membrane can come to differ chemically along its length? What ultimately dictates this specificity—chromosomal DNA? And what determines the "positioning" of specificity along a membrane or its restriction to a particular array?

Certainly, whatever the biochemical or structural modifications required to accommodate specific functions, it is clear that the vast and elaborate cellular membrane systems, totally unsuspected before the discovery of the electron microscope, now must be regarded as vital components of the living cell. Containing many different enzymes capable of catalyzing a wide variety of reactions, these membranes not only serve as sites for synthesis and storage of energy and materials but they contribute directly, during cellular differentiation and reproduction, to the structural organization of cell parts.

REFERENCES

BESSIS, M., 1960, *The Ultrastructure of Cells.* Sandoz Monographs.

BRACHET, J., "The living cell," *Sci. Am.*, September 1961.

BRACHET, J., AND A. E. MIRSKY, 1960, *The Cell,* Vol. II: *Cells and Their Component Parts,* New York: Academic Press.

HOAGLAND, M., "Nucleic acids and proteins," *Sci. Am.*, December 1959.

HUXLEY, H. E., "The contraction of muscle," *Sci Am.*, November 1958.

LEHNINGER, A. L., "How cells transform energy," *Sci. Am.*, September 1961.

SIEKEVITZ, P., "Powerhouse of the cell," *Sci. Am.*, July 1957.

Research Associate Director

SEYMOUR H. HUTNER

Haskins Laboratories, New York

Seymour H. Hutner was born in 1911 in New York City. He obtained a B.S. degree in 1931 from the City College of New York. His interest in protists began in those Depression years, when, as he puts it, lacking funds for commercial amusements but having the use of his brother's microscope, he made many trips by rowboat with some of his classmates to the salt marshes of Jamaica Bay and to some adjacent fresh-water ponds near where the present administration building of Idlewild Airport now stands to collect organisms for study. His graduate work was at Cornell (1932 to 1937, except for a year in the Department of Physics at the Massachusetts Institute of Technology). At Cornell his interests were broad and he pursued studies in both the traditional fields of biology and in the emerging field of biochemistry. His doctoral thesis was on the nutrition of streptococci. Sumner, one of his professors at Cornell, had crystallized catalase and wondered whether it contained genuine heme. Since certain trypanosomid flagellates require heme, Dr. Hutner suggested microbiological assays for the heme in catalase; this became his minor thesis.

Since 1940 he has been at the Haskins Laboratories. A charter member of the Society of Protozoologists, he has been on the editorial board of its Journal of Protozoology since its founding in 1954, and vice president of the Society for 1960–61. His 100 or so research papers have dealt with many different protists in problems of nutrition, evolutionary relationships, microbiological assays, and the application of microbial tools to the problems of higher animals. In addition to these technical papers he was coeditor (with A. Lwoff) of *Biochemistry and Physiology and Protozoa*, Volume II, Academic Press.

Nutrition of protists

CHAPTER 4

S. H. HUTNER

Haskins Laboratories
New York

The Scope of Protist Nutrition

Like the introduction to the classical recipe for rabbit pie: "Catch a rabbit," many a microbe-dependent biochemical or genetic enterprise has trouble getting past step 1: "Catch a protist" (colloquially, "bug").* We shall therefore begin by describing some ways in which knowledge of the nutrition of protists is applied to their isolation and, conversely, how knowledge about isolation opens the way to nutritional investigations; and, finally, how this knowledge contributes to biochemistry and evolutionary theory.

Many universal metabolic pathways are most accessible in protists. The term *fundamental,* tossed about lavishly in applications for research grants, does have one accepted connotation: a fundamental compound is found in all creatures, even viruses. From the recipes for cultivating protists one can get a fair idea of what is, and what is not,

* *Microbe* is imprecise: it stresses a superficial attribute, size; emphasis belongs on *organization. Protist* properly emphasizes *uni-* or *a*-cellularity. Protists are the organisms *not* built on the cellular, compartmentalized plan that characterizes the "higher" plants and animals.

fundamental. Thus these recipes over and over again call for one or more of the following nutrients besides the usual minerals and bulk sources of carbon and energy:

1) The purines and pyrimidines of nucleic acids.

2) The common amino acids of proteins.

3) B vitamins: thiamine, nicotinic acid, riboflavin, pantothenic acid, vitamin B_6 (pyridoxine and related compounds), folic acid and relatives, vitamin B_{12}, and biotin.

4) Simple fatty materials—for example, saturated and unsaturated fatty acids, cholesterol and, rather rarely, vitamin K.

Some protists require compounds which man makes for himself and so they are not vitamins in the usual sense. These include hematin (the pigmented portion of hemoglobin and related heme enzymes such as catalase), and lipoic (thioctic) acid—a compound close to thiamine in function and as widely distributed. Because *vitamin* originally meant organic compounds needed in traces by man and higher animals, the expression *growth factor* is widely used for protists. It is hard to anticipate what will be a vitamin for a particular organism. Man, for example, unlike most protozoans and some, perhaps all, insects, makes his own purines and pyrimidines, yet their constant presence in food would seem an irresistible temptation toward biochemical parasitism in the form of dependence on prefabricated purines and pyrimidines. Nevertheless, the vertebrates have not abandoned purine and pyrimidine synthesis. This is not for lack of ability to absorb external purine or pyrimidine, because isotope studies have shown that the intake of dietary purine and pyrimidine does tend to supplant ("spare") synthesis to some extent.

Since protists have evolved in their own right—that is, they are not merely foreshadowings of the cellular plants and animals—some require growth factors not found in multicellular organisms. Two of these are the *terregens* factors or ferrichromes, and diaminopimelic acid, an intermediate in the bacterial synthesis of lysine which follows a pathway not found elsewhere. We shall speak of these growth factors later in connection with soil microbes.

The Winogradsky Column as a Totem Pole; Ecological Vacuums and Photosynthetic Protists

Driven by natural selection, organisms have exploited every possible energy-yielding reaction. There are, however, limits to the possible. The limits are as follows: the reactants must be in adequate concentration in the environment; the energies of activation must not exceed the capabilities of living matter; and the conditions (temperature, pH, reactant concentration) must not disrupt the indispensable chemical bonds of protoplasm. As used here, *protoplasm* is shorthand for "living matter"; protoplasm does not exist apart from the organism, for the organism is the unit of life.

Within limitations, therefore, it seems no exaggeration to say that there is a protist filling every available biochemical job. A wide assortment of protists can flourish in what would seem monotonous, unfavorable environments. Analysis of the Winogradsky column, that protistological totem pole, brings out the fact nicely. Dr. Wolf Vishniac, an experienced hand with Winogradsky columns, has kindly given the following instructions and quoted comments:

> Take a 1-liter hydrometer cylinder and a bucketful of marine mud. The mud should be black and anaerobic; mix a small amount of mud with some shredded paper to make a paste. Place it at the bottom of the cylinder. Mix a spoonful of $CaCO_3$ with a spoonful of $CaSO_4$, and some mud. Put this mixture on top of the shredded paper. These two layers should occupy about the bottom 2–4 cm of the cylinder. There should be no bubbles left. Fill the remainder of the cylinder with mud to within 1 cm of the top. It should be clear of trapped bubbles and there should be a shallow layer of water left on top of the mud. Cover the cylinder with an inverted beaker and expose to a goose-neck lamp from one side. Don't use fluorescent light and don't illuminate from both sides.

Fig. 4.1 shows what happens in 2 or 3 weeks.

The upper zone may contain blue-green algae, green algae, various phytoflagellates, diatoms, and photosynthetic flagellates. Elucidation of these events by Dutch microbiologists—an epochal achievement of comparative biochemistry—was crucial to an understanding of photosynthesis (see Chapter 1 in this book). If on a totem pole the newer generations are added at the top, then the Winogradsky column is an evolutionary totem pole, with our anaerobic ancestors at the bottom, culminating at the top in an aerobic association which may hold clues to how our ancestors emerged into a newly oxygenated atmosphere, with O_2 opening to them powerful new energy sources.

The *green* photosynthetic sulfur bacteria (*Chlorobium*) at the bottom carry out anaerobic reactions:

$$(1)\quad CO_2 + 2H_2S \xrightarrow{\text{light}} (CH_2O) + 2S + H_2O$$

$$(2)\quad 3CO_2 + 2S + 5H_2O \xrightarrow{\text{light}} 3(CH_2O) + 2H_2SO_4$$

Another species of *Chlorobium,* easier to handle, can use thiosulfate in addition to H_2S:

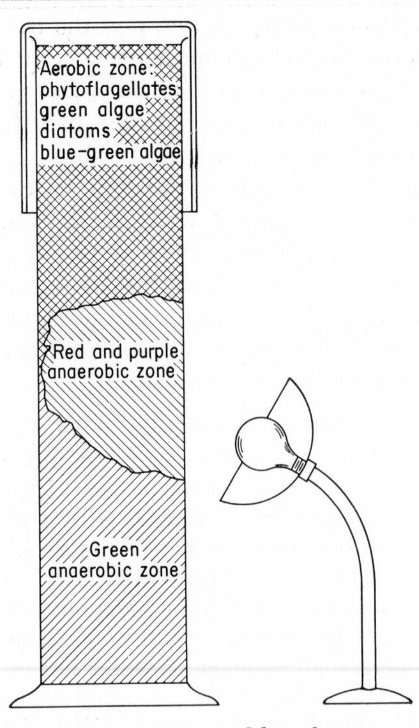

Fig. 4.1. Winogradsky column.

$$2CO_2 + Na_2S_2O_3 + 3H_2O \xrightarrow{\text{light}} 2(CH_2O) + Na_2SO_4 + H_2SO_4$$

Both can use H_2 as the reducing agent (electron donor):

$$H_2 + CO_2 \xrightarrow{\text{light}} (CH_2O) + H_2O$$

The *red* photosynthetic bacteria (*Chromatium*) located above *Chlorobium* can use organic compounds such as malic acid as hydrogen donors in photosynthesis.

Most nonsulfur "purple" bacteria (*Athiorhodaceae*) (many are yellow, brown-pink, or red; others have a magenta tinge) can live aerobically. Strains that can live aerobically can live in the dark, behaving like ordinary aerobic bacteria. To live anaerobically they need light. But despite this utilization of gaseous oxygen by purple bacteria, neither they nor the other photosynthetic bacteria give off oxygen during photosynthesis.

To one introduced to bacteriology from the medical side, isolation of these photosynthetic bacteria in pure culture calls for unfamiliar operations. The bacteria are first "enriched" in suitable liquid media in illuminated glass-stoppered bottles (a blob from a suitable area on a Winogradsky column is a good inoculum, or mud directly), then transferred to the same media made semisolid with a little agar (0.2–0.3 percent). If the agar is well shaken and suitably illuminated, discrete colonies will develop in the deeper layers where O_2 does not penetrate (O_2 is lethal for all but Athiorhodaceae). The agar column is then ejected into a petri dish, and the colonies picked off with a needle. Transfer to fresh semisolid medium, if there is consistent growth, will usually yield pure cultures. Most of these bacteria grow poorly on agar surfaces but do nicely as deep stabs in agar.

Most Athiorhodaceae, while best isolated anaerobically, grow on agar slants and so can be handled by the usual methods for aerobes.

These laboratory column-and-bottle exercises parallel large-scale events such as sulfur formation in desert lakes or formation of foul black mud (due to FeS) at the bottom of many bodies of fresh and marine waters; the Black Sea is especially noted for its deep, deadly H_2S-rich layer, and for its frequent surface blooms of pink and red photosynthetic bacteria. Methane bubbles breaking the surface of black-mud ponds provide another parallel to events in a Winogradsky column. One can usually find a good assortment of purple bacteria on the underside of lily pads in black-mud ponds. Since the main absorption of chlorophyll in purples is in the infrared and green, they use wavelengths that are poorly absorbed by the green leaf. They may thus be said to "scavenge" light unused by green plants.

Some blue-green algae are rather H_2S-tolerant; they are commonly found just above the purples. Whether they can use H_2S in photosynthesis is a moot point. Some protists live in nature under conditions hard to duplicate in the laboratory. A striking example is *Thiovulum,* a hypermotile giant spherical bacterium. It lives at the upper limit of the H_2S zone. Since it contains sulfur globules, presumably it lives by the oxidation of H_2S and sulfur, much as does the filamentous *Beggiatoa.*

The writer recalls viewing a seawater tank at Woods Hole with a dead fish at the bottom and over it a sharp, dense, white zone. The white layer consisted of *Thiovulum* zooming up and down like corn in a popper, as if they were diving down into the poisonous H_2S zone to snatch H_2S molecules, then fleeing up to the O_2 zone for processing of the H_2S. Putting it less anthropomorphically, the narrowness of the *Thiovulum* zone suggested that the bacteria cannot tolerate high concentrations of either H_2S and O_2, preferring something in between. Since H_2S and O_2 cannot long coexist, the H_2S–O_2 system is a thermodynamic squeeze.

Quite likely the original photosynthesizers were anaerobic, perhaps like the green and red bacteria at the bottom of the column. Free oxygen entered the atmosphere when algae learned to render harmless the oxidized component coming from the photolysis of water by splitting off oxygen gas from it. In the purple bacteria this oxidized component is reduced by means of external hydrogen donors, among them simple organic compounds of the *metabolic pool* (see below in discussion of enrichment cultures). The familiar photosynthetic equation for conventional plants would then be derived in the following manner:

$$CO_2 + 2H_2X \xrightarrow{\text{light}} (CH_2O) + 2X + H_2O$$

If X is oxygen instead of sulfur (for some bacteria, no X at all may be needed: H_2 will serve as reducer for green and red bacteria), one writes:

$$CO_2 + 2H_2O \xrightarrow{\text{light}} (CH_2O) + O_2 + H_2O$$

Subtracting an H_2O from each side, the familiar equation emerges:

$$CO_2 + H_2O \xrightarrow{\text{light}} (CH_2O) + O_2$$

The first O_2 producers could well have been blue-green algae, followed perhaps by red algae, and flagellates. The phylogenetic tree—or rather, shrub (Fig. 4.2)—diagrams possible relationships between anaerobes and aerobes. This does not mean that the present-day anaerobes are all archaic. The evolution of anaerobes into pathogens of warm-blooded animals is one set of examples of how far some have come from their presumably free-living ancestors.

Oxygenation of the atmosphere probably doomed most of the original anaerobic microflora. Anaerobic photosynthesizers might have been enabled to survive by the evolution of SO_4 reducers; photosynthetic bacteria are always intermingled with SO_4 reducers. Anaerobic photosynthetic bacteria may, then, be the most primitive surviving form of life on earth, and the aerobic chemosynthetic bacteria, oxidizing such materials as Fe^{2+}, H_2, NH_3, S, and thiosulfate, would be latecomers, as would also SO_4 and NO_3 reducers. Another inference is that aerobes developed reducing systems and antioxidants to protect essential metabolites that were functional only in the reduced state. We shall see that certain nutritional requirements of aerobes are in keeping with this idea.

Classical Bacteriological Peptone Media

Fortunately for the rise of bacteriology and mycology, most nonviral protistan pathogens of man and domestic animals grow in air on

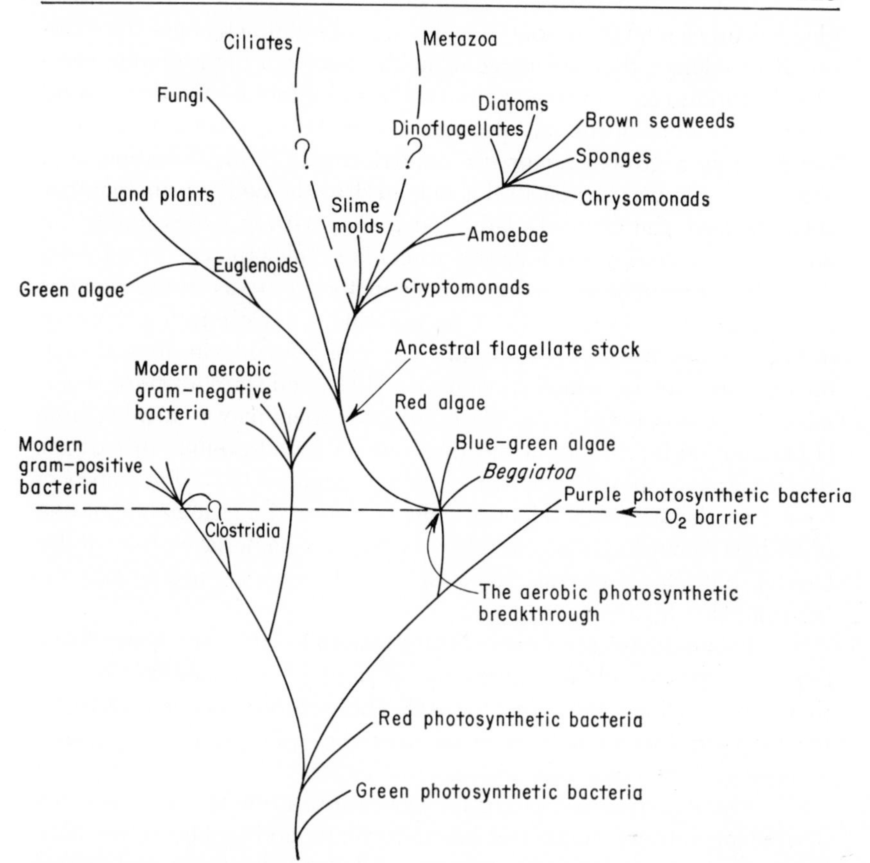

Fig. 4.2. Phylogenetic tree. The dotted horizontal line separates aerobes from anaerobes.

the surface of solid media, forming spots from which pure cultures can be picked off. The era of isolations of pathogens, starting with Koch's isolation of the turbercle bacillus on heat-coagulated bovine serum, is sometimes referred to as the golden age of bacteriology: it ended about 1910.

The ecology of the common pus-forming *Staphylococcus aureus* explains why this bacterium is easy to isolate on agar plates. Its commonest habitat is the skin and mucous membranes. The skin, sweating and drying, is like a salt marsh under a summer sun, prone to form salt rimes. Not surprisingly, some media for primary isolation of staphylococci contain 7.5 percent NaCl. Furthermore, S. *aureus* grows well on enzymatic digests of crude natural materials—for example, blood fibrin, and milk and soybean proteins ("peptones")—and its essential nutrients withstand sterilization by steam. Media in the time-honored cotton-plugged tubes tend to dry out, but this would not much affect staphylococci considering their tolerance of media having a high osmotic pressure. S. *aureus* requires some amino acids and a few B vitamins, among them nicotinic acid, the anti-pellagra factor. When nicotinic acid was identified as a growth factor for staphylococci, its identification as a human vitamin was hastened; this helped drive home the principle that not only were the Colonel's lady and Judy O'Grady sisters under the skin, but so also were their staphylococci kin under the cell membrane.

The pneumococci living deeper in the body, as in the mucous membranes of the lung, are far more exacting. They are rather sensitive to O_2, perhaps because they form hydrogen peroxide in air and lack the enzyme catalase which decomposes H_2O_2, and so in air burn themselves up. Blood is rich in catalase (older readers may remember how H_2O_2 solution bubbles on a bleeding cut), which accounts in part for the efficacy of blood agar for growing pneumococci. Pneumococci have, then, become dependent to some extent on the functioning of one of its host's enzymes. Certain other pathogenic bacteria with a similar habitat, but not closely related, show a similar dependence on catalase in artificial cultivation.

Pneumococci are metabolically anaerobes in other ways. They require sugar and obtain energy by splitting sugar anaerobically; but they cannot oxidize the split products. This extravagance is underwritten by their human host, who oxidizes the split products of sugar, thereby getting much more energy from sugar.

Many protists important for agriculture grow well in solid media: nitrogen fixers, lactic acid bacteria, yeasts and molds, all the antibiotic-producing bacteria and fungi, and many bacterial and fungal plant pathogens. The nutritional requirements of nearly all protists isolable by simple techniques have been worked out.

Some habitués of mucous membranes have much more complicated nutritional requirements, presumably reflecting their more intimate access to the cellular fluids of the host. Thus some strains of *Borrelia vincentii*, a generally harmless spirochete-like anaerobic bacterium, grow best with the highly thermolabile coenzyme forms of vitamins—for example, thiamine pyrophosphate, pyridoxal phosphate, diphosphopyridine nucleotide (DPN, one of the coenzyme forms of nicotinic acid), CoA (the coenzyme form of pantothenic acid), glucose-1-phosphate, and adenosine pyrophosphate (ATP). Such a requirement for energy-rich unstable materials (compare them with their usual, stable, nonenzymatic form in Fig. 4.3) accounts for *Borrelia*'s needing unheated materials like those in ascitic fluid (fluid from the abdominal cavity; patients with dropsy are valuable sources of ingredients for some of the Macbethish brews used for pathogens). The syphilis spirochete has not been grown in artificial media; it presumably wants very labile growth factors.

Intimacy with vital enzymatic systems of the host could lead to dependence on unstable, high-molecular (hence poorly diffusible) nutrients—of the kind conveniently supplied by living matter. No virus has yet been grown on nonliving media, which by implication, would suggest that they have traveled far down the road of biochemical dependency, requiring nutrients so unstable as to be beyond present biochemical knowledge. Indeed recent studies of an animal that lives in and on red cells, the malaria parasite (an animal, because it ingests red cells, microbite by microbite, as revealed by electronmicroscope studies), has requirements resembling *Borrelia*'s, but presumably more complicated because its sustained growth on nonliving media has not been achieved; provision of phosphorylated compounds merely lengthens the time it can be kept alive removed from intact cells.

Evidently, had organisms like *Borrelia* or the malaria parasite been investigated earlier, important metabolic intermediates would have been discovered sooner. Reciprocally, progress in biochemistry, especially enzymology, should mean better recipes for growing protists. In some schools the union that has come about between microbiology and biochemistry is legitimized by their fusion into a single department. A microbiologist has been defined as a biochemist who has been appointed head of a department of bacteriology. This is not so *outré* as it may sound today: Kluyver, who called himself a microbiologist and developed the concept of the "unity of biochemistry," of which some examples have been offered here, was a chemical engineer, with small experience in biochemistry and microbiology at the time of his appointment to the chair of microbiology at Delft; with his innocence of formal training in biology he might have had trouble being admitted to certain American graduate departments of biology without having to work off lengthy course requirements. Fortunately, at Delft, he came in as department head. His pupil, van Niel, was originally a civil engineer. Recall, too, that Pasteur called himself a chemist. The application of chemistry is what transforms concocting soups for protists from an art to science; the biological question is, is the soup worth devising?

Enrichment Cultures and Degradations

There *must* be protists to dispose of every metabolite. For example, suppose the steroid hormone cortisone was invulnerable to degradation. Its accumulation through geological time might result in eventually finding ourselves sliding through cortisone-greased muds. Many

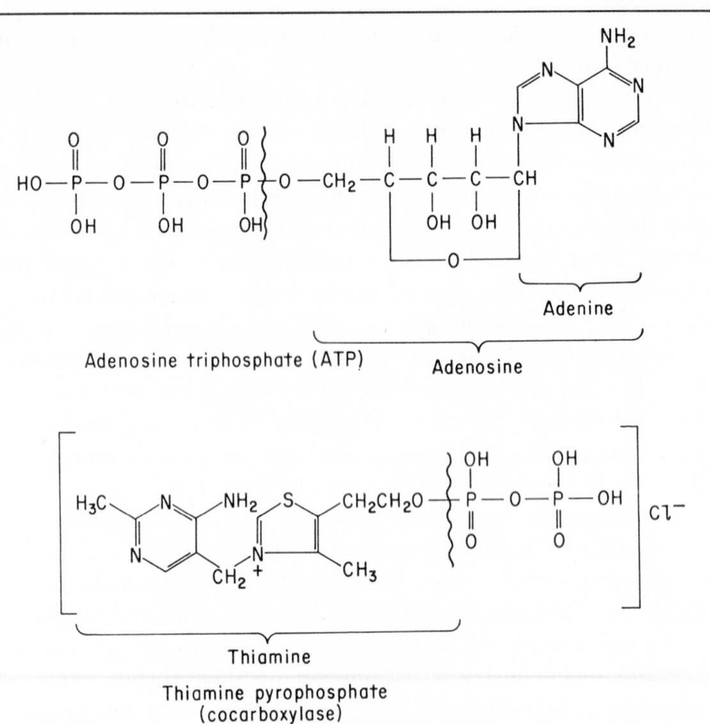

Fig. 4.3. (*Above and facing*). Adenosine triphosphate (ATP) and coenzyme forms of vitamins. ATP is, more strictly, adenosine pyrophosphate. (From *The Merck Index,* 7th ed. Courtesy Merck and Co., Inc.)

steroid-attacking protists have been described, and thanks to the discovery of a fungal attack on progesterone that introduced an oxygen atom at the critical carbon 11—and stopped there—the cost of cortisone was drastically lowered.

If one sets up enrichment cultures with a hitherto unstudied metabolite, and then isolates the bacteria living off the metabolite—that is, using it as sole source of carbon and energy and sometimes nitrogen—the chances are good that new "species" will be found.

To visualize the biochemical opportunities in this sort of investigation, consider the pigmented portion of hemoglobin: hematin or heme (Fig. 4.4.). All aerobic cells, and the photosynthetic bacteria, have heme enzymes—catalase is one. Heme, then, is fundamental. Nevertheless nothing is known about heme degradation by protists. Does degradation follow the same sequence as in a bruise such as a black eye? The familiar sequence of colors—blue, purple, green, and yellow—represent stages in the rupturing of the hematin molecule in the blood clot to form bile pigments, which are degraded further to unknown

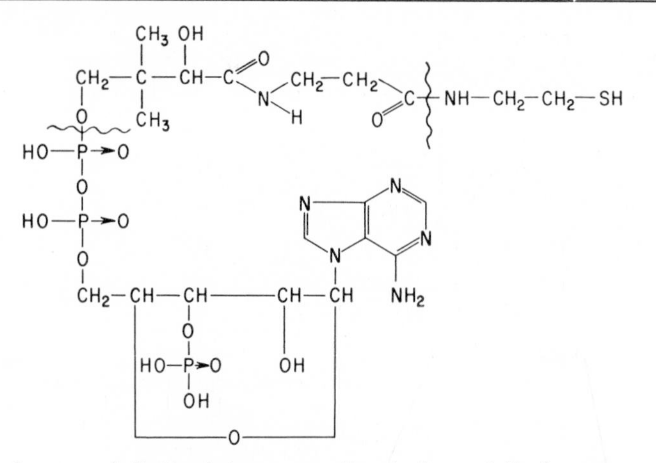

Coenzyme A. Portion between wavy lines is the pantothenic group

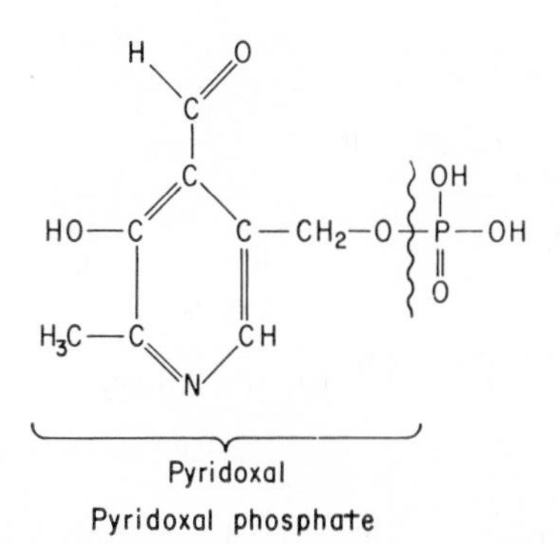

Pyridoxal phosphate

colorless fragments. Chances are, some heme-degrading bacteria will, by present criteria, be new species. If one used as enrichment substrates all the compounds mentioned in a one-volume textbook of biochemistry, and used uniform 1-gram inocula from the same soil sample, it could well require the equivalent of two or three Manhattan telephone directories to enumerate all the "species" in a 1-gram crumb of soil. Several additional volumes would probably be needed if other kinds of inocula were used—say intertidal muds, freshwater muds, or marine muds from the continental shelf.

The implications of this situation for understanding ecology and providing protistan tools for investigating metabolism are only beginning to be grasped. The work to be done, and worth doing, is awesome. A central question is, what kinds of culture media are generally best for isolating biochemical specialists from soil and natural waters? We shall see this is no mean problem.

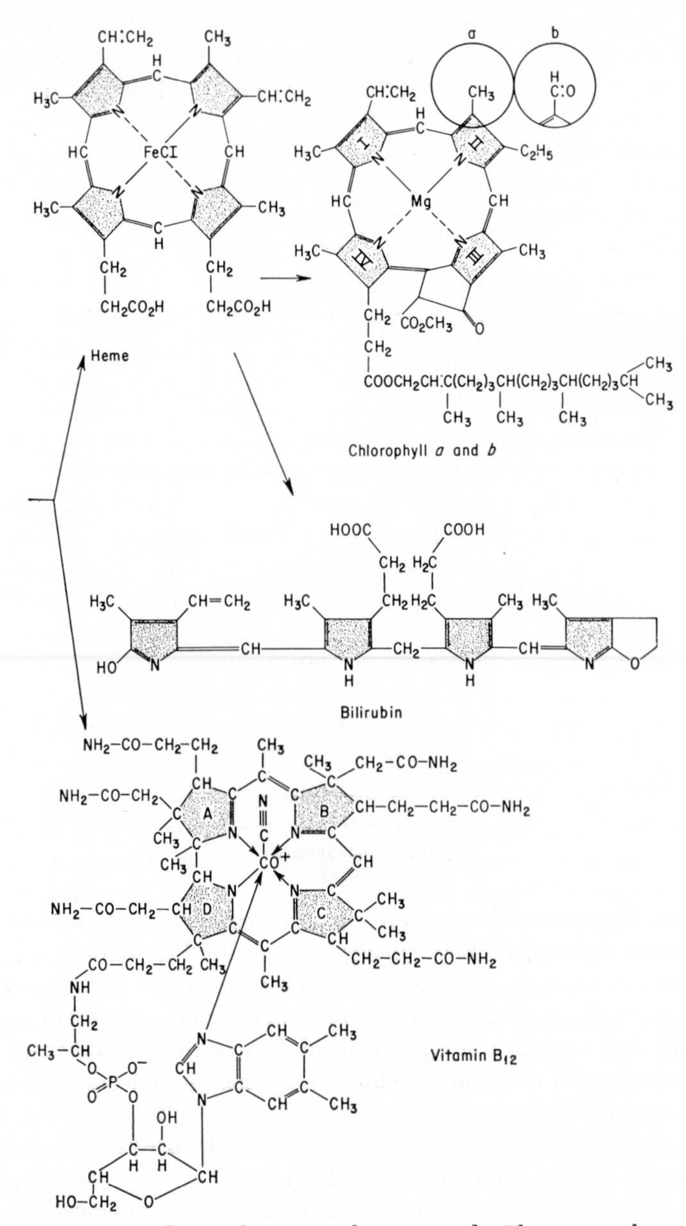

Fig. 4.4. Fundamental tetrapyrrole compounds. The arrows show biosynthetic relationships. The shading of the rings indicates their basic similarity. (From *The Merck Index*, 7th ed. Courtesy Merck and Co., Inc.)

By enrichment technique, it should be possible to trace *every* metabolite, step by step, back to the bits and pieces which are the currency of metabolism and which, collectively, comprise the *metabolic pool.* Prominent in this pool or stockpile are acetate, lactate, malate, succinate, propionate, glycerol, pyruvate, β-hydroxybutyrate, glycine, glutamate, aspartate, and formate. These, along with energy-rich compounds such as glucose, are generally used as substrates for microbe and man.

Intermediates in degradation may serve as the points of departure for new syntheses. Thus, while the bile acids are ordinarily thought of merely as degradation products, in blue-green and red algae and in some cryptomonad flagellates, they are photosynthetic pigments. Similarly, kynurenine in the mammal is a catabolite (degradation product) of tryptophan; in insects, kynurenine is the starting point for synthesis of a series of eye pigments. The odds would seem good, then, for these "degradation" products in man to have fundamental, if wholly unknown, functions. Degradations are worth studying for their own sake: they may reveal new group reactions. The folic acid-catalyzed transfer formimino groups were discovered in this way, and so, too, was the function of vitamin B_{12} in catalyzing certain interconversions of branched-chain and straight-chain aliphatic acids.

The structures of hematin, bile pigments, vitamin B_{12} and chlorophyll seem too intricate for any one protist to "mineralize" them completely—that is, to degrade them to CO_2, NH_3, and H_2O. Instead, one would expect protists to chip away at such molecules, some cracking the rings open, others detaching side groups such as the phytyl hydrocarbon chain of chlorophyll, the dimethylbenzimidazole and ribose of B_{12}, and so on. Then another set of protists might carry out the main degradations of the opened-ring compounds. Soil microflora constitute just such a cooperative wrecking crew.

How does one set about isolating the microbes that bring about piecemeal degradation of a compound as complex as hematin, where the microbes act in tandem, successively smaller fragments passing from protist to protist like a relay in which the runners nibble away at the baton?

Let us set up enrichment cultures with hematin; to the writer's knowledge, this enrichment has not yet been done. In a flask (Fig. 4.5), one puts about 100 ml of liquid media containing about 0.05 percent hemin (hematin chloride) as sole source of energy, carbon, and nitrogen; and the usual salts. One adds a gram or so of screened soil, and incubates the flask on a shaker. In a few days or a week the fluid in the flask should become cloudy. One then transfers a loopful to a fresh flask and repeats the incubation on a shaker. Some loopfuls of flask 2 are then streaked on hemin agar containing about 0.05 percent yeast or liver extract to supply growth factors. If colonies appear, they are picked onto slants of hemin agar. The cultures are then tested for their hemin-attacking specificity by comparing growth on the slants with and without hemin.

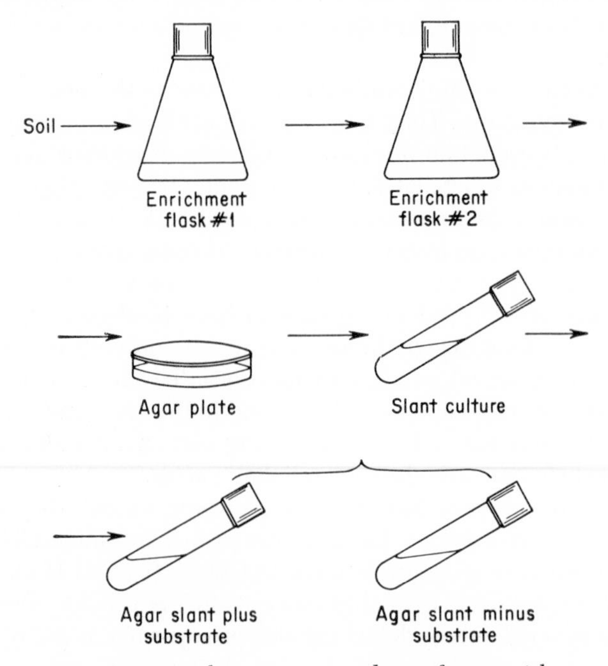

Fig. 4.5. Steps in obtaining pure cultures from enrichment cultures.

If things go as expected, one out of five isolates or fewer will turn out to be hemin utilizers. The others probably are secondaries, living off the cell-wall materials and excretions of the hemin utilizers; these organisms in turn give rise to a tertiary population, and so on. An enrichment culture, like a Winogradsky column (which is an enrichment culture with light and O_2 versus $H_2S + H_2$ as the main variables), can thus proliferate into a complex collection of microenvironments. We shall see that this can happen rapidly even if one begins with a single substrate.

The most informative degradations are those going only part way, with accumulation of intermediates. Scavengers of that kind are detectable through respirometric measurements: if the oxygen uptake in the presence of the substrate is less than that theoretically required for complete oxidation (with a correction for the proportion of substrate assimilated as a source of carbon and fuel), then presumably a more or less oxidized fragment (here coming from the heme molecule) must be piling up. One then isolates this product from mass cultures, and uses it in turn as a substrate for new enrichments. The use of isotopically labeled substrate permits rapid fractionation of intermediates: one follows the labeling. Eventually one arrives at fragments only a step away from complete oxidation.

Stanier and colleagues have shown that the *dissimilation* (that is, breakdown, as distinguished from *assimilation*) of tryptophan by bacteria may take at least three different routes. At least one of these three parallels a mammalian route—the one leading to kynurenine. If a simple substrate like tryptophan can be dissimilated via at least three pathways, each with distinctive intermediates which may again branch out, imagine how many kinds of bacteria may flourish on the products of heme alone.

If one were to set up similar enrichments with B_{12} and chlorophyll, one would expect that the scavenging protists would not be altogether different from the assortment of heme degraders; some might be specialized for cracking open methine-linked pyrole rings, the feature common to all these molecules. One could sort out these scavengers by the chemical bonds they sever. One of the important criteria for determining species—that is, a means of making order out of the microjungles that are soil or mud—would be its ability to attack this or that linkage. A manual of scavengers would then parallel a manual on the linkages that form the subject matter of organic chemistry.

One more complication: some of these degradations might reveal linkages new to organic chemistry, as has happened from time to time with other natural products, notably antibiotics. This appeals greatly to organic chemists who have become blasé about conventional organic chemistry. Many great chemists have been attracted to biochemistry by nature's versatility as a chemist.

Growth Factors and the Succession of Forms in Nature; the Pinch-of-Yeast Effect

In earlier work on the "mineralization process," sometimes no protists could be isolated from enrichments with substrates that one would have expected to be easily attacked. It was gradually noted that one had better chances of isolating scavengers for a given substrate if a little yeast extract or peptone was added to the isolating medium—enough to supply the growth factor but not so much as to contribute appreciable unwanted substrate.

Van Niel's original directions for isolating purple bacteria included an especially provocative pinch-of-yeast-extract recipe, for in those days one did not think of photosynthetic organisms as requiring growth factors. The active ingredients proved to be *p*-aminobenzoic acid, biotin, thiamine, and nicotinic acid, alone or in combinations that faithfully reflected distinctions among species erected on other grounds. Soon after, with this encouragement, a common green flagellate of ponds, *Euglena gracilis,* was shown to need vitamin B_{12}, the anti-pernicious anemia vitamin; *Euglena* had previously been known to require thiamine.

Following this gambit as far as the phytoplankton—the micrograss—at the base of the food pyramid of fresh-water bodies and the ocean, revealed that more than half the species examined required vitamins: B_{12}, thiamine, and biotin, in order of descending frequency. Since the two filamentous red algae in pure culture need B_{12} (quite likely the seaweed *Porphyra* grown by the Japanese for food will prove to be another), probably many multicellular red algae need it. Among the vitamin-dependent phytoplankton organisms are the centric diatoms; many pinnate diatoms; most dinoflagellates, chrysomonads, and cryptomonads; all euglenoids; and some deep-water blue-green algae.

The growth of *Euglena,* up to a point, is linearly proportionate to B_{12} concentration. Hence, if *Euglena* is put into a medium complete for everything except B_{12}, its growth will depend on the source of B_{12}. If blood, suitably diluted, is added to such a medium, the amount of *Euglena* growth will tell how much B_{12} is in the sample, and so whether the patient has pernicious anemia. The accuracy and sensitivity of the method (it easily detects one part B_{12} in a trillion) is such that hospitals the world over have installed banks of lamps for growing *Euglena.*

Ecologically, however, the interesting material is the ocean: how much B_{12} has it, and where, when, and whence? Does B_{12} ever limit plankton (and so fisheries) production? The Provasoli-Pintner principle reasonably argues: If a growth factor is needed by a protist in the laboratory, the factor or its physiological equivalent is present in the natural environment. How this applies to B_{12} in the North Sea is being examined by means of the *Euglena* method. An amazing train of consequences has followed the designing of a soup for growing *Euglena,* protected against B_{12} coming in inadvertently from bacteria growing in distilled water (fertilized by the leachings from the glass container, with energy coming from dust particles; for example, steel filings will support the growth of H_2-oxidizing bacteria). B_{12} in the ocean is either washed in from soil or produced by blue-green and green algae at the shore and bacteria in the muds. The land plants and related green algae are totally devoid of B_{12}; strict vegetarians develop the equivalent of pernicious anemia (B_{12} once absorbed by *Euglena* is converted into forms which are completely inert for all known assay organisms, including man). Why the world's main fisheries are near the shores of the continents now becomes a little more understandable.

Winogradsky columns have, then, another set of interrelationships: the purple bacteria must be obtaining their growth factors from other protists. Conceivably, the prevalence and succession of species in waters may depend on a subtle set of scavengers—those using vitamins not as vitamins but as substrates. Such scavengers might at times act like valves controlling the distribution of large populations. Observations suggest that in many ecological niches, vitamin requirers compete with vitamin-independent forms. When the vitamin is in the environment, the vitamin requirer would seem to have the advantage since it should be free to divert to other purposes the building blocks and synthetic enzymes otherwise expended in making the vitamin.

How is one to isolate a representative sampling of soil, freshwater, and marine bacteria? The older isolation media were carried over from medical microbiology and contained peptones and the like, rich in amino acids and other fragments of proteins and cell material. One worker bravely generalized that marine bacteria were predominantly proteolytic—a not astonishing conclusion in view of the selective factor embodied in the method itself: because such isolation media are rich in readily attackable substrates, they select for a restricted assortment of fast-growing opportunists, specialized for attacking low-molecular materials. As an industrial example, actinomycetes to be screened for antibiotic production are isolated from soil on high-sugar media.

The Canadian bacteriologist A. G. Lochhead a few years ago showed how to solve the problem for soil bacteria. As substrate he boiled up soil in water, filtered the product, and added this soil extract to the usual salts. On prolonged incubation agar plates of this medium inoculated with soil yielded numerous small colonies. These turned out to be predominantly diphtheroids in the obscure genus *Arthrobacter*. These bacteria had been known to be abundant in soil, and had occasionally been isolated from enrichment cultures with resistant substrates; but proof of their predominance in soil was new.

These colonies on soil-extract agar were then transferred for maintenance and faster growth to soil-extract agar enriched with yeast extract; the bacteria were then classified according to their growth-factor requirements. The following table shows the quite unexpectedly high incidence of isolates requiring growth factors.

Another remarkable discovery was that a small but constant proportion of the soil bacteria (less than 1 percent) needed a second factor which, like B_{12}, was absent in yeast extract but present in soil or liver extracts. This growth factor, "terregens factor," proved to be a family of polypeptides, perhaps generally containing the unusual hydroxamic acid group, and binding iron with extraordinary tenacity. This growth factor had previously been recognized as required for a mushroom and produced in high concentration by smut fungi. The availability of soil bacteria which can be used as assay organisms for terregens factor means that a whole new chapter of biochemistry is accessible. Whether its distribution in nature parallels that of B_{12} raises the question of what is responsible for "terregens" activity in liver extracts or other metazoan materials.

TABLE 4.1

Incidence in a Field Soil of Bacteria Requiring Specific Vitamins

Vitamin required (alone or with others)	Vitamin-requiring bacteria	
	Percent of total isolates	Approx. no. (millions per g)
Thiamine	19.4	10.2
Biotin	16.4	8.6
Vitamin B_{12}	7.2	3.8
Pantothenic acid	4.6	2.4
Folic acid	3.0	1.6
Nicotinic acid	2.0	1.1
Riboflavin	0.6	0.3
One or more factors	27.1	14.1

Of the strains needing vitamins, 64 percent needed more than one factor.

From Lochhead, A. G. and Burton, M. D., 1957. "Qualitative studies of soil microorganisms. XIV. Specific vitamin requirements of the predominant bacterial flora," *Can. J. Microbiol.*, 3, 35–42.

The fact that soil underfoot may have 3,800,000 B_{12}-requiring bacteria per gram points up the futility of setting limits to pure versus applied research: had the soil microflora been investigated sooner for its own sake, B_{12} might have been discovered years earlier, saving many lives. Virtually all B_{12} on the market is produced microbiologically, not from liver. Certain antibiotic-producing actinomycetes are also high B_{12} producers; and cobalt added to the culture medium greatly enhances B_{12} production. Use of antibiotics to remove bacteria has speeded isolation of some of the protozoa widely used as assay organisms for B_{12}, notably *Ochromonas malhamensis* which seems to have precisely the human type of B_{12} requirement. Use of this plant-animal flagellate (it ingests particles as well as being photosynthetic) has in turn aided the industrial production of B_{12}—an illustration of the old Russian proverb that "one hand washes the other."

A growth factor, or vitamin, has a value beyond the familiar dietary one conveyed in the statement: "A vitamin is something bought in a drug store that should have been bought in a grocery"; vitamins are also chemotherapeutic targets. Thus some of the antimalaria and antileukemia drugs are essentially fraudulent folic acids: they imitate folic acid closely enough to deceive the folic-dependent malaria organism and, for a while, certain kinds of leukemia cells. A new development in making anti-B_{12}'s is to modify some of the side chains of the intact B_{12} molecule. B_{12} itself is the starting point for these syntheses, since the B_{12} molecule is too complicated to synthesize. If the new anti-B_{12}'s prove clinically useful, they must be made as inexpensive as possible, which will depend therefore on cutting B_{12} production costs further.

Our present knowledge of protist nutrition offers leads that could result in producing cheaper B_{12}: (1) There has been no systematic study of B_{12} production in the presence not only of cobalt but of comparatively cheap portions of the B_{12} molecule such as 5,6-dimethylbenzimidazole (or its precursor, guanosine), plus methionine (the source of some of the angular methyl groups), plus aminopropanol; (2) The base of selection of B_{12} producers has been narrow: marine organisms have hardly at all been screened for B_{12} production. The Phosphorescent Bay in Puerto Rico has enormous populations of dinoflagellates. Judging from the behavior of other marine dinoflagellates, the luminescent species will prove to be B_{12} requirers. The Burkholders have shown that the bordering mangrove muds are rich enough in B_{12} to amply satisfy any dinoflagellate requirements for B_{12}. Presumably these muds harbor high B_{12} producers.

All this confronts us with the problem of how to isolate a representative assortment of marine bacteria that will include high B_{12} producers. The immediate problem is finding the marine counterparts of soil extract. Actinomycetes are responsible for the odor of fresh earth; marine muds do not have earthy odors, which at once shows a major difference between the marine and soil microflora. Whether soil extract would permit isolation of a representative assortment of marine bacteria is not known. Nor is any specific method known, for example, for enriching for phosphorescent bacteria, prominent members of the marine microflora. Picking luminous spots off a moist 5-day-caught flounder seems as good a method as any. A marine mud extract by itself would probably not work because, unlike soil, marine muds have their solubles continually leached out by sea water. An extract of a marine mud from just above the high-tide mark, blended with soil extract, might do. The qualifier "representative" is slanted—how does one judge that? One aims at a culture medium which yields the highest bacterial count and which does not exclude known members of the population.

So, amid the various projects in biological oceanography that will permit more intensive farming of the sea, are gaps in fundamental knowledge that have to be filled. One such is that no pelagic (open-ocean) phytoplankton organisms have been grown in pure culture; thus far, some subtle nutrient or nutritional balance has eluded investigators.

Scavenger bacteria are beginning to be appreciated as research tools. A case history: γ-aminobutyric acid is in high concentration in brain tissue and may be important in nerve activity. Efforts to assign a definite function to it were badly handicapped by lack of a specific technique of measurement. This problem was solved by W. B. Jakoby. He isolated a soil bacterium from an aminobutyrate enrichment, and extracted from the bacterium a specific enzyme system that could be used to estimate microquantities of γ-aminobutyric acid, by coupling changes in the aminobutyric acid with spectrophotometrically observable changes in the coenzyme.

Herbivores and Carnivores; the Herbivorous Ciliate *Tetrahymena pyriformis*

The food pyramids of meadow and jungle are familiar: herbage supports mice, rabbits, deer, and cattle; these in turn support a few eagles, wolves, wildcats, lions, tigers, etc. In natural waters the order is much the same: phytoplankton is preyed on by crustaceans, and crustaceans by fish, squid or whales, and these by sharks, barracuda, pickerel, and killer whales.

In the microbial jungles that are soils, muds, and waters, these pyramids are varied and—as intimated in the foregoing discussion of soil bacteria—largely unexplored biochemically. The predators, too, are fantastically diverse, as inspection of decoctions of rich, moist soils, pond weeds, wet mosses, or seaweeds will show: giant amoebae and slime molds like self-propelled sheets of flypaper trapping all manner of motile creatures and devouring everything in their path like a raiding column of army ants; the sea anemone-like vorticellas and stentors; the sedentary spiderlike suctorians; the moray eellike *Spathidium* that is all mouth; *Didinium,* adept at sucking like a weasel the juices from paramecia; the elephantine *Dileptus* waving a trunk above its gaping mouth; and the euglenoid *Peranema* with its monstrous flagellum flickering ahead like a snake's tongue as it glides along—the list could be extended for many pages.

Few carnivores have yet been grown in pure culture, but advances in defining the nutritional requirements of related herbivora—that is, feeders on bacteria or algae—show that the requirements of even obligate carnivores, as distinguished from omnivores, can be worked out by applying well-understood principles. This is not meant to imply that defining the needs of the ciliate carnivores will be any the less arduous.

A chemical-by-chemical commentary on a defined medium for the common ciliate *Tetrahymena pyriformis* will do to sketch the jumping-off point, so to speak, for tackling the nutrition of carnivores. Many workers contributed to the knowledge that is reflected in the description of this medium. Despite the complexity of this medium, the problem was technically easy: the usual tetrahymenas, including the one for which the medium was designed, grow well in autoclaved peptone supplemented with a little glucose; no water-insoluble or heat-unstable nutrients are needed, so that rather crude fractionation techniques sufficed to identify the active components in crudes such as peptones.

***Defined Medium for* Tetrahymena pyriformis**
variety 1, mating type II
(wt per 100 ml final medium)

$MgSO_4 \cdot 7H_2O$	0.08 g
K_3 citrate $\cdot H_2O$	0.04 g
$Fe(NH_4)_2(SO_4)_2 \cdot 6H_2O$	8.4 mg
$MnSO_4 \cdot H_2O$	3.0 mg
$ZnSO_4 \cdot 7H_2O$	2.6 mg
$(NH_4)_6MoO_{24} \cdot 4H_2O$	0.11 mg
$CuSO_4 \cdot 5H_2O$	0.24 mg
$CoSO_4 \cdot 7H_2O$	0.29 mg
H_3BO_3	0.068 mg
$Na_3VO_4 \cdot 16H_2O$	0.55 mg
NaI	5.7 μg
$Na_2Se_2O_3$	5.2 μg
L-arginine (free base)	0.18 g
L-glutamic acid	0.1 g
Glycine	0.08 g
L-Histidine HCl $\cdot H_2O$	0.15 g
L-Isoleucine	19.0 mg
L-Leucine	15.0 mg
L-Lysine HCl	15.0 mg
DL-Methionine	10.0 mg
DL-Phenylalanine	27.0 mg
DL-Serine	0.1 g
L-Threonine	20.0 mg

Defined Medium for Tetrahymena pyriformis *(cont.)*

DL-Tryptophan	20.0 mg
DL-Valine	25.0 mg
Guanylic acid	16.0 mg
Uracil	6.0 mg
Nicotinic acid	0.4 mg
Ca pantothenate	0.1 mg
Thiamine HCl	0.1 mg
Na_2 riboflavin PO_4	0.1 mg
Pyridoxamine · 2HCl	0.06 mg
Folic acid	0.02 mg
Dl-Thioctic acid	5.0 μg
Biotin	0.4 μg
Na_2 glycerophosphate · $5H_2O$	0.02 g
glucose	0.1 g
pH 6.5–6.8	

Notes on the *Tetrahymena* medium

$MgSO_4 \cdot 7H_2O$ and the sulfur requirement. $MgSO_4 \cdot 7H_2O$ is stable at ordinary humidities. Recipes which call for anhydrous $MgSO_4$ sometimes force one to guess whether this is an oversight or whether the salt is to be used under desert conditions. Mammals can incorporate sulfate directly into cartilage, but the bulk of the sulfur requirement in mammals and *Tetrahymena* alike is met by methionine, an absolute requirement for both. Cystine spares methionine in higher animals, probably also in *Tetrahymena.* Cystine is almost insoluble; it must be dissolved separately in strong acid or alkali. The diethyl ester is much more soluble, and has been used in synthetic liquid diets for rats. Preliminary results with several protozoa besides *Tetrahymena* show this ester to be a good cystine source. The small amount of ethanol released by hydrolysis is more favorable than not: ethanol is a fundamental metabolite, especially relished by *Euglena gracilis* and certain other phytoflagellates. In the future, when the sulfur requirement has been met in some such complicated, more natural way, it may be desirable to eliminate the excess sulfate by supplying magnesium as carbonate. But $MgCO_3$ may render the medium too alkaline: if the pH of the medium before adjustment is 6.0 or above, there may be difficulty in getting the ingredients to dissolve. In that event extra acid must be added elsewhere.

K_3 citrate · H_2O. This salt serves both as source of potassium and metal buffer. Citrate is a chelating agent, forming complex ions with a variety of metals; the metals form rings, caught in the claws

failure of viruses to grow on nonliving media. There is a further difficulty, which can be expressed as: "You can lead a phagotroph (particle-ingester) to a particle, but can you make it ingest?" The incitants to ingestion—appetizers, so to speak—are very poorly known.

Concluding remarks

Some biologists think that as a field of investigation nutrition is played out: that the rich ore has been mined, leaving only tailings to be worked over. We see, on the contrary, that nutritionists have dealt with isolated outcrops: the mother lode, the metabolic heart of the organism, has hardly been touched. It is as though we had discovered lead, and used it for pipes and roofing, oblivious of its parent uranium, with all the power potential it represented. The main nutritional requirements of man and of most hardy organisms have been worked out, but how these nutrients act is poorly known. The coenzyme form of B_{12} was only recently discovered; it had been overlooked because it was extremely light sensitive. Perhaps there are organisms that require this native form of B_{12}; transformation of B_{12} by *Euglena* (and by other green plants) into unstable forms that break up into unassayable fragments could account for the apparent absence of B_{12} in green plants. There must be many more nutritional unknowns awaiting discovery.

Another favorite study project for students is growing of *Chlorella* for food or for regenerating the atmosphere in closed systems such as spaceships. Here again ignorance of protist nutrition is inhibiting, for though *Chlorella* is a contamination-resistant green plant and so is suitable for large-scale nonaseptic work, in closed systems photosynthetic efficiency or quality of food are more important. Its protein, like that of other nonleguminous green plants, is poor in quality; its lack of B_{12} has been noted. It does not use major regions in the spectrum photosynthetically. Some such system as *Ochromonas danica* plus a purple bacterium, perhaps with *Euglena*, too (the latter for high O_2-output), would seem superior to a simple *Chlorella* system. We have seen that advances in knowledge of protist nutrition make possible assembly and analysis of these systems.

Nutritional studies disclose metabolic mechanisms otherwise poorly accessible or utterly hidden: they point toward the core of life. Sometimes, on the other hand, protistan nutrition is a servant, acting to provide markers for genetic studies (see Chapters 6 and 7 in this book).

Amid the ardors and drudgery of protistological cookery one has intimations of ancient forkings in the evolutionary road and of master catalysts and controls. When these by their abstractness momentarily pall, one can go out into the field to seek beguiling protists to domesticate. The big game has retreated before roads, farms, and cities, but the protists hold on, in some places flourishing furiously, as in sewage-disposal plants. Let us make the most of these opportunities.

REFERENCES

———— The United States Treasury, for income tax computation, allows writeoff of a technical library in five years. With this obsolescence in mind, the serious reader should not depend on any one textbook and should also cultivate the habit of browsing through current journals. Journals predominantly in English with many important, well-written articles on the nutrition of protists are:

Journal of General Microbiology
Journal of Bacteriology
Bacteriological Reviews
Journal of Protozoology
Canadian Journal of Microbiology
Annual Review of Microbiology
Antonie van Leeuwenhoek

Some of these journals offer special student rates.

The various journals of biochemistry carry much material on protist nutrition.

This browsing should be backed up by solid, up-to-date texts on organic chemistry and biochemistry. An excellent general book on microbiology is: L. E. Hawker, *et al.*, 1960, *An Introduction to the Biology of Microorganisms,* New York: St. Martin's Press.

A good introduction to chemical bacteriology is: C. Lamanna and M. F. Mallette, 1959, *Basic Bacteriology,* 2d ed. Baltimore, Md.: Williams & Wilkins.

A stimulating little book is: A. J. Kluyver and C. B. van Niel, 1958, *The Microbe's Contribution to Biology,* Cambridge, Msss.: Harvard University Press.

Volumes now in press (Vols. III, IV, and V) of *The Bacteria,* edited by I. C. Gunsalus and R. Y. Stanier, New York: Academic Press, will provide a comprehensive and authoritative knowledge of bacterial nutrition. Vol. IV will be devoted to growth.

For *fungi,* an excellent general book is: V. W. Cochrane, 1958, *Physiology of Fungi,* New York: Wiley; London: Chapman & Hall.

Yeasts are treated excellently in a multiauthor volume edited by J. W. Cook, 1958, *Chemistry and Biology of Yeasts.* New York: Academic Press. It is remarkably up-to-date and comprehensive in its biochemistry.

Algae will be dealt with in a symposium now in press, edited by R. A. Lewin (Academic Press).

There is no up-to-date treatment of the nutrition of *protozoa* except for the multiauthor, fast-aging *Biochemistry and Physiology of Protozoa* (Vol. I, 1951; Vol. II, 1955), Academic Press. This has treatments not too outdated of phytoflagellates, ciliates, and parasitic flagellates.

A masterly exposition of the B_{12} story, tracing the astounding confluence of many different lines of investigation, is given by Lester Smith, 1960, *Vitamin* B_{12}. London: Methuen; New York: Wiley.

Other monographs in the Methuen series on "biochemical subjects" are highly recommended, as for instance, the introduction to chemotherapy by A. Albert, 1960, *Selective Toxicity*, 2d ed.

It is not a bad idea to see at firsthand the variety of protists disporting in nature. A comprehensive, up-to-date (but expensive) reference work is: W. T. Edmondson, 1959, *Fresh-water Biology*. New York: Wiley.

There are two excellent guides to fresh-water *algae:*

G. M. Smith, 1950, *The Fresh-water Algae of the United States*, 2d ed. New York: McGraw-Hill.

G. W. Prescott, 1954, *How to Know the Fresh-water Algae*. Dubuque, Iowa: W. C. Brown Co.

Another useful volume in this "How to Know" series is: T. J. Jahn, 1949, *How to Know the Protozoa*.

ALBERT SIEGEL

Professor of Biochemistry
University of Arizona

Albert Siegel was born in New York City in 1924. He attended Cornell University in 1941–43 and in 1946–47. The intervening years were spent in the Army as an artilleryman. His graduate education was received at the California Institute of Technology where he was awarded the Ph.D. degree in 1951. From 1951 to 1959 he was a member of the Botany Department of U.C.L.A. where his work was concerned with the genetics and intracellular multiplication of tobacco-mosaic virus. He joined the staff at the University of Arizona in 1959 and there he has continued work on many of the research problems he initiated in California.

Professor Siegel is the author of numerous technical papers, among which are "The early events of infection with tobacco-mosaic virus nucleic acid," *Virology,* 1957, 3:554 (with S. G. Wildman and W. Ginoza); "Mutual exclusion among strains of tobacco-mosaic virus," *Virology,* 1959, 8:470; "Some aspects of the structure and behavior of tobacco-mosaic virus," *Ann. Rev. Plant Physiol.,* 1960, 11:277 (with S. G. Wildman).

CHAPTER 5

Viruses: Reproduction and heredity

ALBERT SIEGEL

University of Arizona

Viruses hold a peculiar fascination for biologists, not only because they are disease-producing entities, but also because the virus-host system presents a unique experimental tool for the study of fundamental biological problems related to heredity. Although relatively simple in structure, viruses do contain genes, the hereditary determiners present in all organisms. When a cell becomes infected with a virus particle, the genes contained in the particle enter the cell. It thus becomes possible to study the mechanisms by which genes newly introduced into a cell make their influence felt. Viruses are obligate parasites; that is, they can increase in number only inside a living cell. Outside a living cell, the virus particles are quite inert and lack most of the attributes possessed by living cells, such as metabolism and the capacity for reproduction. A virus can, therefore, be considered as a small package of genes which, when introduced into a cell, alters the cellular metabolism to suit its own ends—the production of more virus.

This chapter will outline some of the presently known facts relating to virus reproduction and heredity, and will also indicate the methods by which some of these facts have been obtained. By no means has all there is to know about viruses been discovered. There are large gaps in our knowledge, areas yet to be charted by present and future generations of scientists.

The catalogue of different virus types is long; yet it is quite likely that many viruses still await discovery and description. The reason for this is not difficult to assess. With few important exceptions, only those viruses which are of marked importance to mankind, either from a public health or economic viewpoint, have been studied. From the public health viewpoint, we are concerned with all of the viruses that cause disease in man. The viruses which have economic importance are those that cause severe losses in the plant and animal crops upon which we depend for survival.

Although viruses in general are a serious pest to mankind, there are a few instances in which viruses have been adapted to the benefit of mankind. In Australia, for instance, a fair degree of success has been achieved in reducing the voracious rabbit population by deliberately initiating an epidemic of a mortal virus-induced disease. In parts of the United States, a virus is being used in a similar manner to kill insects which feed on alfalfa.

As was mentioned earlier, there are some exceptions to the rule that scientists study only those viruses of importance to mankind. These exceptions involve virus-host systems which are investigated primarily because they lend themselves to study in the laboratory. So much has been learned about these accessible viruses that they now provide model systems against which virus-host systems that are more difficult to study may be compared. One laboratory system consists of a group of viruses that attack bacteria. These bacterial viruses, often called bacteriophages, are relatively easy to manipulate in the laboratory. Much that has been learned about the events that occur within an infected bacterium has been found to be applicable to events going on in other types of virus-infected cells. One virus that has received more than its normal share of attention is the tobacco mosaic virus, a virus that attacks members of the plant kingdom. This virus can be obtained in large quantities in a pure form and has proved particularly useful in studying the structural aspects of viruses.

Viruses can be classified in a number of ways. One method of classification is based on the type of host the virus attacks. Accordingly, there are four major groups of viruses: animal, plant, bacterial, and insect. The animal viruses which have been studied are mainly those that attack mammals and birds. The plant viruses find as their host the higher flowering plants. The insect viruses have been set aside in a group by themselves because they appear to be quite different from the other animal viruses. Of the bacterial viruses, some are known to attack many different groups of bacteria. This classification

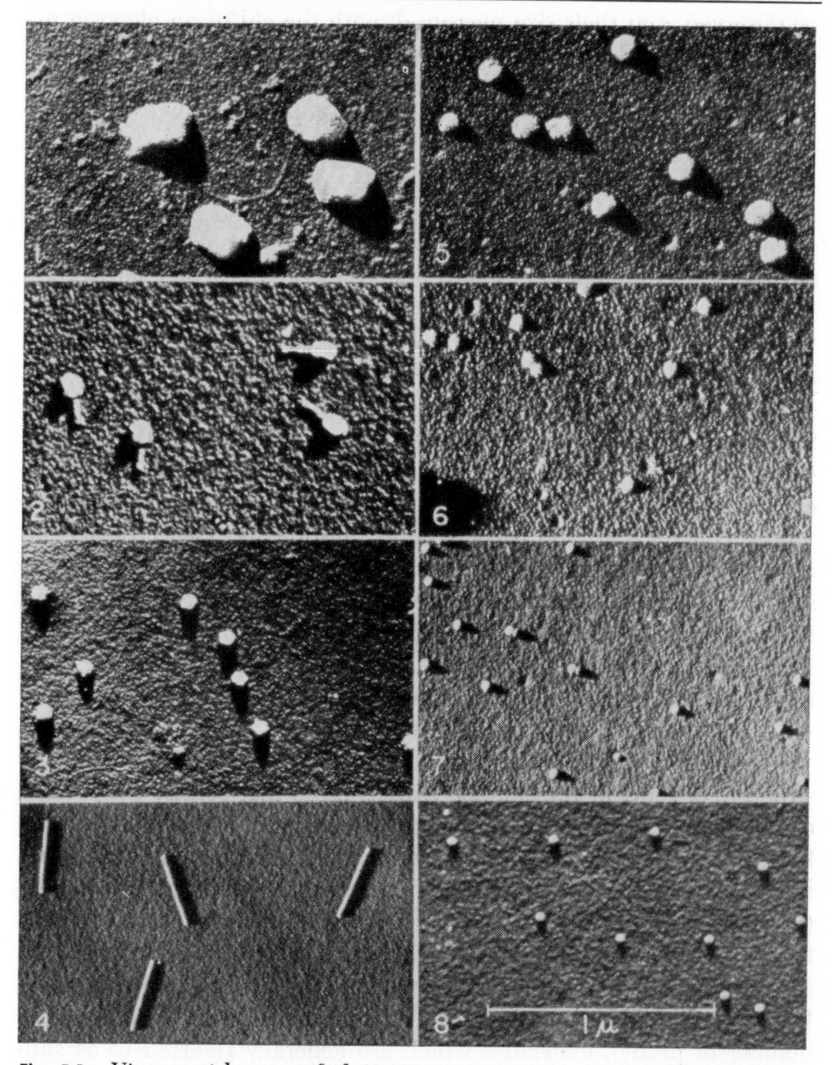

Fig. 5.1. Virus particles magnified 42,000 times as seen with the aid of the electron microscope. *1:* Vaccinia; *2:* T_2 phage; *3:* T_4 phage; *4:* Tobacco mosaic; *5:* Influenza; *6:* Papilloma; *7:* Bushy stunt; *8:* Polio. (From W. M. Stanley, and E. G. Valens, *Viruses and the Nature of Life,* Dutton, 1961. With permission. Photograph courtesy of Dr. Robley C. Williams.)

by host type, although convenient, actually does not account for all of the virus-host associations. For example, there is a group of viruses, nominally placed in the plant virus class, which also multiply in the insect that transmits the virus from one plant to another.

Viruses are extremely small and have several shapes. They can be observed, and their size measured, with the aid of an electron microscope. The polio virus is spherical and has a diameter of 27 millimicrons (a millimicron is equal to 1/10,000,000 of a centimeter). Tobacco mosaic virus is cigarette shaped and is 300 millimicrons long with a diameter of 15 millimicrons. The vaccinia virus particle is brick shaped with dimensions 280 × 220 × 220 millimicrons. The bacterial viruses are tadpole shaped; a typical bacteriophage has a head the shape of an elongated hexagon, 95 × 65 millimicrons, and a cylindrical tail 100 × 25 millimicrons. These few examples show that viruses are of many sizes and shapes. Within the representative group just mentioned the difference in volume between the largest and the smallest is two thousandfold.

Although viruses differ in size and shape, they do have several features in common. One of these is a basic similarity in their chemistry. All of the viruses are composed of at least two classes of biological compounds, called nucleic acids and proteins. In addition, some viruses contain lipid and carbohydrate constituents. Two types of nucleic acids in nature are called ribonucleic acid and deoxyribonucleic acid. (It is convenient to abbreviate these two classes of compounds as RNA and DNA, respectively, and this will henceforth be done.) All living cells contain both types of nucleic acids. Viruses, however, contain either one or the other, not both; this feature alone serves to set the viruses apart as a group from all other living cells and organisms.

Great strides have been made in recent years in determining the structure of some of the simpler viruses, those that consist only of nucleic acid and protein. These advances have largely been made possible by the development and refinement of several biophysical tools and techniques, among which may be mentioned the electron microscope, the analytical ultracentrifuge, x-ray diffraction analysis, and light-scattering analysis. With the use of these and other devices it has been discovered that the simple RNA-containing viruses consist of a single long strand of RNA, surrounded in some manner by a relatively large number of protein molecules which are generally referred to as subunits. The tobacco mosaic virus is composed of 2130 identical protein subunits which are packed in helical array (like a screw) to form a hollow cylinder. Each turn of the helix contains 16⅓ protein subunits. The single, giant, threadlike nucleic acid molecule is wound around the inside of the hollow cylinder also in the form of a helix or spring. The nucleic acid follows the pitch and is attached to the helix formed by the protein subunits. The protein subunits of other simple RNA viruses, such as polio and turnip yellow mosaic virus, are arranged in the form of a hollow sphere or polyhedron with the nucleic acid occupying the center.

Fig. 5.2. In this drawing of the tobacco mosaic virus, the internal chain helix is RNA and the external bodies are the protein subunits or individual peptide chains. The entire rod contains 2200 protein units in 130 turns of the helix and has a relative length of about 20 times that shown here. The protein subunit has a molecular weight of 18,000. (From H. Fraenkel-Conrat and W. M. Stanley, "Implications of recent studies of a simple virus," *Chemical and Engineering News,* May 15, 1961. With permission.)

The protein that is a part of the virus particle is like the proteins found in living cells. It is a large molecule composed of smaller building blocks. The building blocks are called amino acids and they all have in common the chemical structure

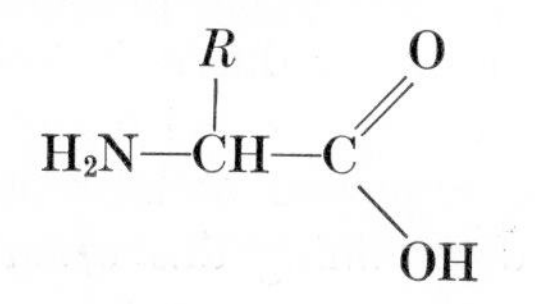

There are some twenty different naturally occurring amino acids that differ from each other only in the side chain R. Each protein has a different, and characteristic, complement of amino acids joined together through peptide linkages as follows:

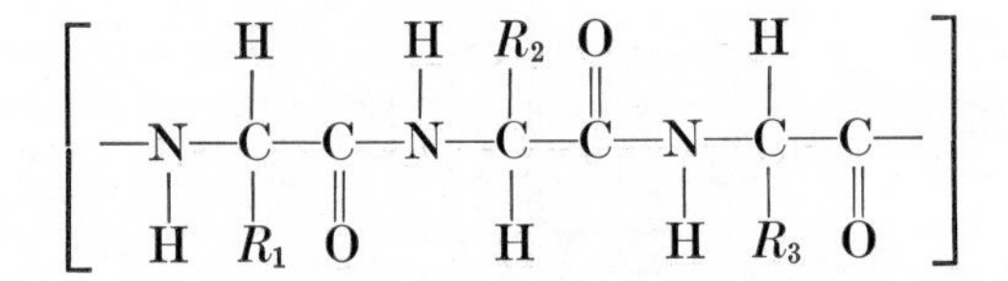

The specific properties of proteins result from the sequence of amino acids in the polypeptide chain. The polypeptide chain is generally folded in such a manner as to assume a spherical or ellipsoidal shape. A great deal of effort has been devoted in recent years to the determination of the amino acid sequence of several viral proteins. The sequence of the 158 amino acids in the tobacco mosaic virus subunit has just recently been determined.

A description of the structure and composition of nucleic acids is given in Chapter 7 of this book. Since some of the discussion in this chapter will be devoted to the function of the viral nucleic acid, a brief summary of its main features will be given here. The nucleic acids are giant molecules also composed of building blocks, as are the proteins. The basic units of these polymers are quite different, however, from amino acids, and are called nucleotides. The nucleotide is itself made up of three components, a nitrogenous base, a sugar, and a phosphate group. In chemical constitution DNA and RNA differ in that the sugar of DNA is deoxyribose ($C_5H_{10}O_4$), whereas the sugar component of RNA is ribose ($C_5H_{10}O_5$). Another difference resides in the nitrogenous bases: both nucleic acids have the three bases adenine, guanine, and cytosine in common, but whereas DNA has as its fourth base thymine, the fourth base of RNA is uracil. The nucleic acids are composed of these nucleotides joined together by linkages between the sugar and phosphate groups. Finally, independent of these chemical differences, an important structural difference exists between the two nucleic acids. The nucleotides of RNA are organized into a single, long, threadlike strand. DNA, on the other hand, is composed of two threadlike strands which are related to each other in a manner described more fully elsewhere in this book.

It is believed that the specific properties of nucleic acids reside in the sequence of the four different types of nucleotides along the nucleic acid strand. Although biologists and biochemists would very much like to know the sequence of nucleotides in a nucleic acid strand, techniques for determining this order are not yet available.

The chemistry of nucleic acids is, however, an active field of investigation at the present time.

Having considered the chemistry and structure of the virus in general terms, we will now discuss the sequence of events which occurs when a virus particle comes into contact with a susceptible cell. A system that has been particularly well studied is the infection of the bacterium, *Escherichia coli,* by any one of a series of well-defined bacterial viruses. A test tube containing a culture of vigorously growing bacteria will appear cloudy. If enough virus particles of an appropriate strain are added to the test tube, little will happen that can be observed superficially for a period of 20 minutes. At the end of this interval, known as the latent period, the tube will rapidly clear, indicating that essentially every bacterial cell in the culture has burst. Further analysis reveals that every bacterium has released into the medium about 100 newly synthesized virus particles.

A common method of detecting bacterial virus particles is to mix a dilute suspension of virus particles with an excess of bacteria and to spread this mixture on the surface of a transparent solid nutrient medium. The bacteria will grow over the surface of the medium and form a thin semitransparent film except where there is a virus particle. Here a clear area will result because the virus particle has infected a bacterium at that place, releasing virus particles which infected more bacteria, etc. The clear area, commonly called a plaque, results then from the disintegration of infected bacteria. The number of infective virus particles contained in the volume of liquid mixed initially with the excess of bacteria will be represented by the number of plaques appearing on the surface of the nutrient medium. Similar techniques are used for assaying plant viruses on leaves of plants where certain virus-host combinations lead to the appearance of dead spots. The study of animal viruses at the cellular level received great stimulus when techniques were developed for plaque type assays using either tissue culture cells or certain thin tissues of chicken embryos.

Many virus particles are synthesized in the bacterial cell in a relatively short period of time. The new virus particles, however, do not leak out of the cell but, rather, are released suddenly from the disintegrating cell at the end of the latent period. It will be our purpose now to explore some of the events that occur in the infected bacterium during the course of the latent period.

The first thing that happens when the virus is mixed with bacteria is that the virus particles become attached to the bacteria by the tips of their tails. This phenomenon can be readily seen in the electron microscope. The tip of the virus tail appears to have a specific affinity for receptor sites on the surface of the bacterium.

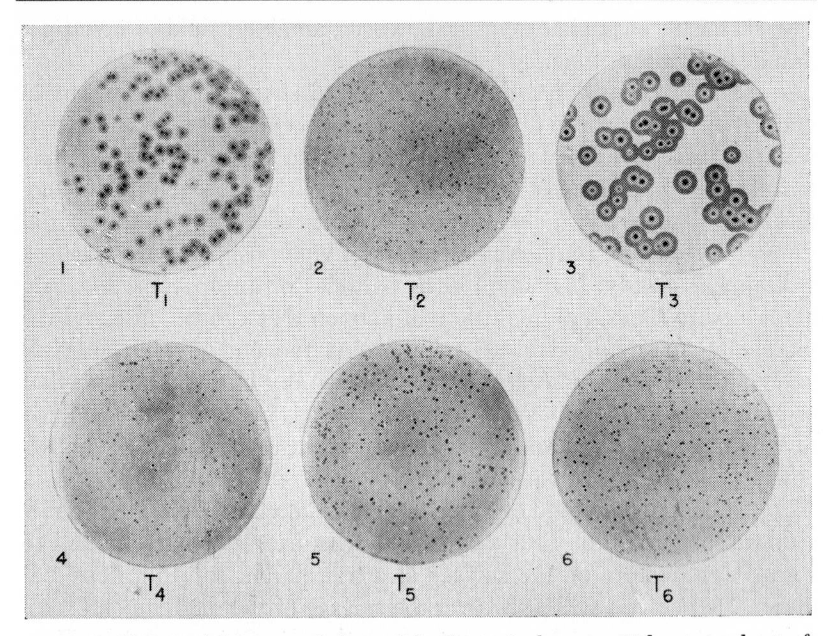

Fig. 5.3. Plaques (clear areas) formed by bacteriophage particles in a sheet of bacteria growing on a solid nutrient medium in a petri dish. Plaques shown were produced by six different viruses attacking a common host, the bacterium *Escherichia coli.* (From S. E. Luria, *General Virology,* Wiley, 1953. With permission.)

Soon after attachment of the virus to the bacterial surface, a most remarkable phenomenon occurs. *The virus particle comes apart.* The nucleic acid contained within the proteinaceous saclike membrane of the virus head passes through the tail and into the bacterium. The empty head and tail remain attached to the bacterial surface. Only the DNA of the virus which enters the bacterium plays a role in the further course of the infection. The empty sac may be removed from the surface of the bacterium by mild treatment and the bacterium will still burst at the end of the latent period and release new virus particles into the medium.

The principle that infecting virus particles come apart at or soon after infection has become quite general in the field of virology. This principle was first discovered by Hershey and Chase in 1952. The experimental method employed by these workers, which we shall now describe, is illustrative of the many ingenious techniques that have been employed in investigations of viral life cycles.

These workers harvested bacterial virus particles from a suspension in which the host bacteria had grown in a nutritive medium containing P^{32} and S^{35}—radioactive isotopes of phosphorus and sulfur. As

nucleic acid and also the specific protein that surrounds the nucleic acid. It will become clear during further discussion that the viral nucleic acids also possess the property of mutation.

Let us now return to an examination of the further sequence of events in the bacteriophage-infected bacterium. When do the newly synthesized virus particles appear within the cell? This problem can be answered by disrupting the cell at different times after it has come into contact with an infectious unit and examining the released contents. When this is done it is found that there are no virus particles within the cell during the first half of the latent period: this interval has been termed the "eclipse period." During the second half of the latent period there is a steady and linear increase in the number of particles present in the cell until the time when the bacterium bursts and releases its content of virus particles into the external medium.

The eclipse period was quite remarkable and mysterious when it was first defined, for not only was the cell devoid of newly synthesized virus particles during this period, but in addition, no trace of the original infecting virus particle could be found. Understanding of this peculiar phenomenon came later with the discovery that we have already reported: the virus particle comes apart early in the infectious process. The fact that the infecting virus particle dissociates into its component parts is indeed the reason that the infecting virus particle cannot be detected during the eclipse period. The eclipse period is not unique for bacteriophage infection. It has been found to occur in all virus infections examined in detail and appears to be a standard feature of viral infection.

The eclipse period by no means represents a quiescent period during which nothing concerned with virus synthesis occurs. Biochemical studies have shown that synthesis of viral nucleic acid starts very soon after the initiation of infection and that the synthesis of viral protein starts soon thereafter. From this type of information, together with other types of evidence, it becomes clear that the mode of viral replication is fundamentally different from the multiplication of living cells. Starting soon after division, cells generally grow in size and in content and then divide by a fission process to form two daughter cells. Viruses, on the other hand, have their different components produced independently, presumably at different sites within the cell. The appearance of new infectious virus represents a maturation process in which the separately synthesized components are assembled into complete virus particles. This general principle has been amply demonstrated for a number of virus-host systems.

One technique for isolating the synthetic mechanisms for the different viral components is to treat a cell at an appropriate time with the antibiotic chloramphenicol. This antibiotic has the property of shutting off cellular protein synthesis while at the same time permitting cellular nucleic acid synthesis to continue. It has been demonstrated that the infected bacterial cell, while under the influence of chloramphenicol, will synthesize viral nucleic acid to relatively high concentrations within the cell, but neither viral protein nor complete virus particles will be formed. Upon removal of the cell from the presence of chloramphenicol, it proceeds to synthesize the viral protein components and, in addition, complete infectious virus particles. These virus particles, moreover, contain nucleic acid which was synthesized during the time when protein synthesis was inhibited by the antibiotic. The result of this type of experiment clearly indicates the independence of the synthesis of the different viral components within the cell.

The general principle that the two main components of virus undergo independent synthesis within the host cell has been demonstrated in other host-virus systems. In the case of tobacco mosaic virus growing in a tobacco leaf cell, for instance, the synthesis of the viral RNA precedes the synthesis of the viral protein subunits. The presence of free viral subunits within the cell can also be detected and it has been demonstrated that these free viral subunits are later incorporated into the intact virus particles.

We may summarize our current knowledge of the gross aspects of the infection of a bacterium with a virulent bacteriophage particle as follows. The bacteriophage attaches to the bacterial surface by its tail and then releases its nucleic acid into the bacterial cytoplasm. An independent synthesis of the viral components occurs within the cell followed by an assembly of these components into complete virus particles. After a well-defined period the bacterial cell bursts and releases the newly formed virus particles into the external medium. The middle part of this sequence appears to be general for all types of virus infections. That is, a virus infection is pretty well defined by the following phenomena: a) the coming apart of the virus, b) the key role played by nucleic acid, c) the independent synthesis of the viral components, and d) the maturation of the virus consisting of assembly of the independently synthesized components.

The very first and last parts of the infection, however, occur differently in the many host-virus systems. Little is known about the mode of entry of some viruses into their host cells. It is known that the influenza group of viruses contains an enzyme that attacks one of the components of the host-cell membrane and it is reasonable to suppose that this mechanism serves to aid the virus in its entrance into the cell. More is known about what happens to different types of cells after they produce mature virus particles. Many types of cells are able to subsist for relatively long periods of time even though they contain large quantities of mature virus particles. These virus particles within the infected cell are frequently organized into variously shaped inclusion bodies, some of which are crystalline in nature. Many types of infected animal cells slowly release virus particles into the medium as they undergo pathological changes as a result of infection, while, nevertheless, still retaining a high concentration of virus within the cell. The explosive

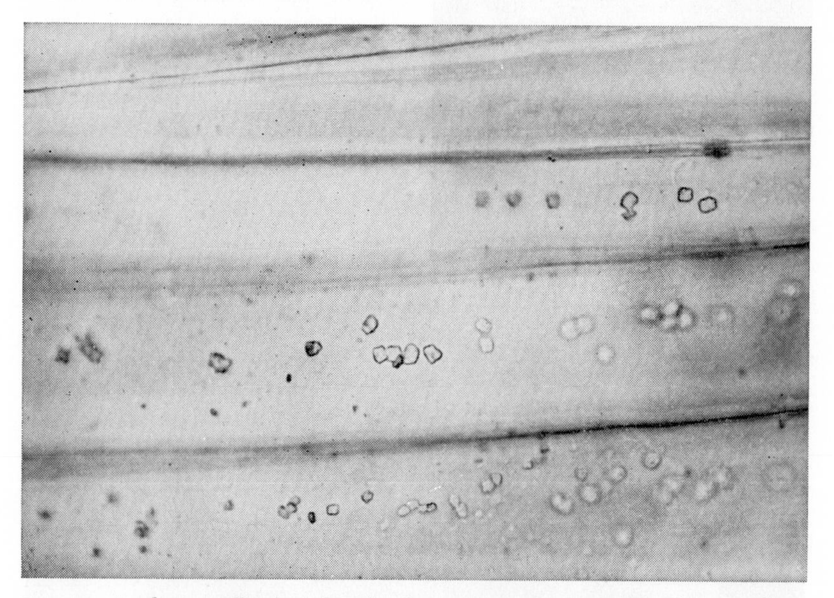

Fig. 5.6. A tobacco cell infected with tobacco ringspot virus. Note the crystalline inclusion bodies which are composed of packed virus particles. (From F. C. Bawden, *Plant Viruses and Virus Diseases,* 3d ed., Ronald, 1957. With permission.)

release of mature virus particles exhibited by bacteria appears to be characteristic of this group of hosts.

The type of life cycle described above is typical of many virus-host combinations. An interesting modification of this life cycle occurs when a certain type of bacteriophage, termed temperate, infects certain types of bacteria. In this instance the genetic material of the temperate virus attaches itself to the bacterial chromosome in a manner which is not yet understood. The bacterium shows no immediate sign of infection and continues to grow and divide as if nothing had happened. There is no synthesis of virus components and no mature virus particles appear. Such a bacterium is termed lysogenic and, even though it is not synthesizing virus, it does have the capacity to synthesize virus under appropriate conditions without contact with another external virus particle. In a growing culture of lysogenic bacteria there are always

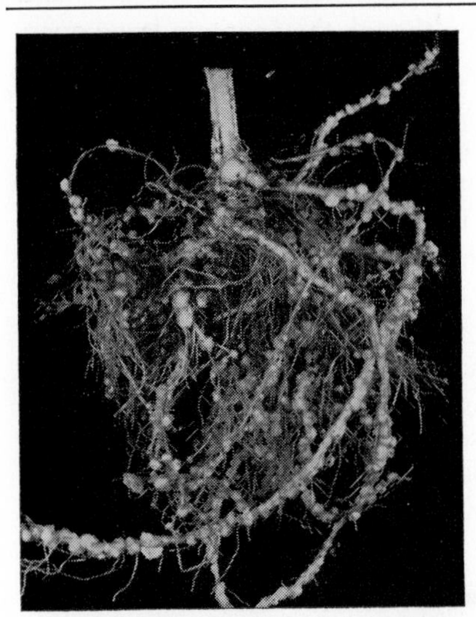

Fig. 5.7. Examples of abnormal growth caused by virus infection. *Left:* Tumors produced by wound tumor virus on the roots of sweet clover. *Below:* Papillomas produced by artificial inoculation of papilloma virus in a wild cottontail rabbit. (From S. E. Luria, *General Virology*, Wiley, 1953. With permission.)

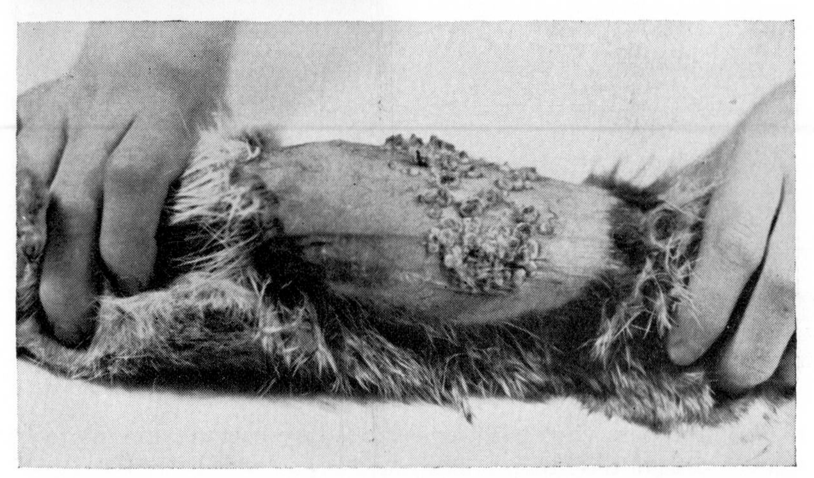

some free virus particles present. These virus particles make their appearance because occasionally one of the lysogenic bacteria will show a sudden change; it will spontaneously start making viral components and these components will be assembled into mature virus particles. The cell will then lyse or disintegrate and release these virus particles into the external medium. The factors which cause an occasional lysogenic bacterium to suddenly start making virus are poorly understood. Scientists have discovered, however, several agents which will trigger all of the bacteria to start making virus. One of the most effective of such triggering agents is ultraviolet light. Many cultures of lysogenic bacteria, when treated with a small dose of ultraviolet light resemble a culture of bacteria that has just been added to an excess of virulent virus particles. That is, upon treatment with ultraviolet light, the lysogenic bacteria will all suddenly start making virus components and will burst with release of complete virus particles after a characteristic latent period.

The temperate bacteriophage are a valuable tool for the study of bacterial genetics because of a peculiar phenomenon associated with their life cycle. When the temperate virus is released from a lysogenic bacterium it will frequently carry with it a small piece of the bacterial chromosome. When this virus particle infects another bacterium the piece of bacterial chromosome is carried into the infected bacterium and will frequently replace a piece of the host's chromosome. If the bacterial genetic information carried by the temperate bacteriophage is different from that contained by the new host bacterium, then one or another of the characteristics of the host bacterium is likely to be altered. A more complete description of this method of genetic exchange that occurs among certain types of bacteria is given in Chapter 6 of this book.

Although temperate viruses are defined and are definitely established as a class of bacterial viruses, it has been postulated that there are also temperate viruses that have animal cells as their host. Speculations have been made by eminent scientists that actually some forms of cancer may consist of lysogenically infected cells. There is no scientific proof that this is so but a great deal of effort is currently being devoted to the cancer problem with the model of the lysogenic bacterium as a guidepost.

That some forms of cancer do trace their cause to a virus infection has definitely been established. Several types of tumors in chickens, rabbits, mice, and plants occur as a result of virus infection. How general this phenomenon may be and whether it is applicable to the human cancer problem is a subject of active investigation at the present time. A fact of interest is that a certain type of virus infection of mice which leads to the formation of cancer can be initiated with the nucleic acid obtained from the virus. This has proved to be the first instance of an infectious DNA; all of the previously discovered infectious nucleic acids were RNA's.

We have discussed earlier the evidence for the genetic nature of the viral nucleic acids and it was shown that the viral nucleic acids have the genetic properties of autocatalysis and heterocatalysis. It remains now to discuss the fact that viruses also possess the property of mutation, the third property of genetic material. If a tobacco plant is infected with tobacco mosaic virus, the leaves of the plant will exhibit the typical dark green, light green mosaic characteristic of the disease produced by this virus. In addition, occasional yellow spots will appear on the leaves and if virus is extracted from these yellow spots, virus particles will be isolated which induce a disease with symptoms different from that of the original starting virus. Literally hundreds of such variants have been isolated either from yellow spots or by other techniques. It is presumed that these new variants have arisen by mutation.

Many mutant or variant strains of bacterial and animal viruses have also been isolated. In fact, advantage is taken of the mutability of

Fig. 5.8. Leaves of tobacco. *Left:* uninfected; *center:* infected with tobacco mosaic virus; *right:* infected with tobacco mosaic virus and containing a bright yellow spot of a yellow mosaic mutant. (From S. E. Luria, *General Virology,* Wiley, 1953. With permission.)

virus in the preparation of vaccines. It is a common procedure to select a spontaneously occurring variant of a disease-producing virus that has low virulence; that is, it causes a subclinical disease. The variant, however, retains the ability to arouse the body's defense mechanisms not only against the strain of low virulence but also against the disease-producing strain.

The phenomenon of mutation has been best studied in the bacteriophage system where methods are available for rigid analysis of the location of the gene damage associated with the mutation. Among some of the more common mutant types that investigators have worked with are those affecting the size of the clear area, or plaque, appearing in a sheet of bacteria as a result of virus infection and those in which the host range of the virus has been increased so that the virus is now capable of attacking some cell types which are resistant to the parent virus.

In addition to the appearance of spontaneous mutants, agents have been discovered which will markedly raise the frequency of mutation. Agents that are capable of mutating the genes of higher organisms have been known for some time, but only recently have agents been found which will induce mutation in viruses. These agents are of interest because they are mostly of the type which directly modify the viral nucleic acid in known ways. An example of a viral mutagenic agent whose action is well known is nitrous acid, a chemical that has the property of altering the nucleotide components of the nucleic acid

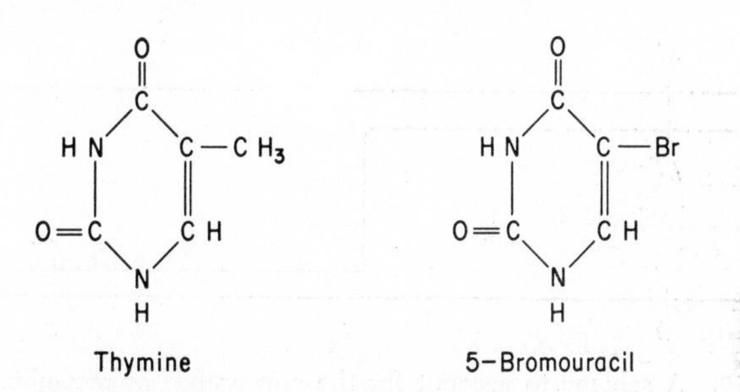

Fig. 5.9. An example of a base analogue. Thymine is one of the four naturally occurring bases present in DNA. The compound on the right, 5-bromouracil, is synthesized in the laboratory and is similar to thymine except that a bromine atom replaces the CH_3 group of thymine. 5-bromouracil is an analogue of thymine and when fed to organisms will frequently be incorporated into newly synthesized DNA in place of thymine.

without, at the same time, breaking the sugar-phosphate linkages which hold the nucleic acid together. This agent induces extremely high levels of mutation. Other agents that are effective mutagens are the base analogues. These compounds resemble the natural nitrogenous bases found in nucleic acids, but are slightly different in composition. When fed to a host cell that is actively synthesizing virus, these analogues are incorporated into the viral nucleic acid. This incorporation of unnatural nitrogen bases frequently results in mutation although the precise mechanism by which the mutants appear is not yet fully understood.

Still another method by which new virus variants appear is by exchange of genetic characteristics between two or more existent strains. This phenomenon, called recombination, has been found to occur among some of the animal viruses, particularly influenza and vaccinia. It has not as yet been found to occur among plant viruses and it has been best studied, again, among the bacterial viruses. If a bacterium is infected with two virus particles differing in two characteristics from each other, then, frequently, four types of virus will be found among the progeny virus issuing from the bacterium at the end of the infection.

Recombination experiments with virus as well as with higher organisms make use of a shorthand method of notation for ease of describing the procedure and results. The different characteristics of the organisms are denoted by letters. For instance, in an example to be described here, we will deal with two characteristics of the virus, host

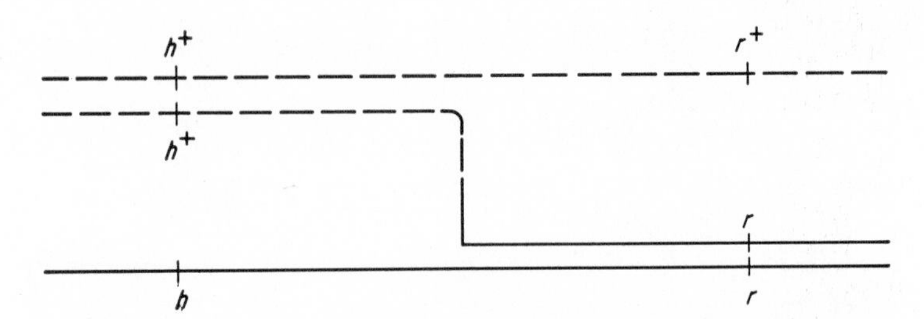

Fig. 5.10. A scheme to account for the appearance of recombinants in a mixed bacterial virus infection. The upper dashed line represents the chromosome of the h^+r^+ parent; the lower solid line represents the chromosome of the hr parent. The middle line represents a newly synthesized chromosome, half of which has been synthesized like the top chromosome and half like the bottom one. It contains the genes h^+ and r and is, therefore, a recombinant. The further apart the two genes under observation are on the chromosome the greater will be the probability for a switch to take place when a new chromosome is synthesized and the higher will be the observed frequency of recombination.

range and plaque size, which are abbreviated h and r, respectively. The standard or "wild type" form of a character that the virus possesses when it is first isolated from nature is denoted with a superscript $^+$, whereas the mutant form lacks such a designation. Thus, a virus strain with standard host range and standard plaque size is designated h^+r^+ and a virus strain with an extended host range and large plaque size is designated hr. If a bacterial culture is infected with a mixture of h^+r^+ and hr particles, then there will be four types among the newly synthesized virus particles found in the culture after the bacteria have burst. There will be particles just like the parents of the cross, h^+r^+ and hr. In addition, two new types appear that recombine the characteristics of the parent particles, h^+r and hr^+.

The amount of the four types of particles produced in such a cross can easily be determined. The proportion of new types among the progeny virus is a measure of the frequency of recombination that has occurred between the genes responsible for the two characteristics.

It has been known for some time that the genes responsible for the characteristics of higher organisms are linearly arranged on chromosomes. This has also been found to be true for the genes contained in the bacterial virus particles that have been examined. In the case of the bacterial viruses, the chromosomes appear to be DNA molecules, whereas as in the higher organisms, the chromosome has a more complex structure. The linear order of the genes on the chromosome in higher organisms as well as viruses is inferred from the results of recombination studies. If the genes responsible for two certain characteristics of the organism are on separate chromosomes, then they will exhibit random reassortment of these two characteristics in the progeny. If the genes are on the same chromosome, however, recombinants will still appear, but the frequency of the recombinants will be a function of the distance between the two genes on the chromosome.

If the two genes are close together on the chromosome, there will be little chance for interchange and the frequency of recombinants will be low. If they are far apart on the chromosome, then the chance for recombination will be high and will tend to approach a random reassortment. If the frequency of recombination between a large number of genes is determined, it will be seen that the different genes can be ordered in linear sequences like blocks on a string. This is true whether the organism is a fruit fly, a human, or a bacterial virus.

In summary, genes are arranged linearily on chromosomes. Genes which are close together on the same chromosome will exhibit a very low frequency of recombination. Genes which are further apart on the chromosome, however, will exhibit a higher frequency of recombination and genes which are located on different chromosomes are transmitted to progeny independently of one another.

One advantage which the virus system offers for recombination studies is that large numbers of progeny can be examined with relative ease. This feature of the experimental system permits the recognition and measurement of very low frequencies of recombination with the concomitant ability to map the genetic characteristics of the viral nucleic acid with extreme finesse. Not only has it been possible to determine the linear order of the different genes in the bacteriophage genetic material, but it also has been possible to study in considerable detail the fine structure of individual genes.

The modern concept of the gene is that it is a segment of genetic material that is responsible for a particular function. This function is usually expressed through the control of the synthesis of a single enzyme protein. If the gene is damaged or altered, then the function of the gene will be eliminated or altered. We may imagine that if the gene has an appreciable linear dimension, then it possibly could be altered or damaged at many places. If now a bacterium were infected by two bacteriophage particles, each of which was damaged in the same gene but in different positions, then, possibly, progeny virus could be produced which would have the gene present in the undamaged, or wild type state, as a result of recombination of the undamaged parts of the two genes present in the parent virus particles. This situation has actually been found to occur in bacteriophage, and analysis of the situation reveals that the parts of the gene which can be damaged independently of each other occur in a strict linear sequence just as do the genes. The number of positions that can be independently damaged has been determined in two bacteriophage genes called *rIIA* and *rIIB*, by collecting a large number of mutants which showed damage in these genes, and by positioning these damages by determining the amount of recombination occurring between the different mutants. Such a fine structure mapping is shown in Fig. 5.11.

We have already said that the genetic information of the bacteriophage is contained in its nucleic acid which is of the DNA type. Chemical analysis has established that the particular bacteriophage species that contains the *rIIA* gene responsible for a single viral characteristic has 100,000 nucleotide pairs in its DNA. (It should be recalled that DNA is a two-stranded structure. The term "nucleotide pair" refers to the two nucleotides, one from each strand, which are coupled to each other.) From recombination studies it can be estimated that the *rIIA* gene is composed roughly of 500 sequential nucleotide pairs or approximately 0.5 percent of the total genetic material of the virus particle. The fine-structure analysis of this gene reveals that any damage or alteration to very few—probably only one—of the nucleotide pairs of which the gene is composed will lead to a change of the physiological function of the gene and thus to a mutation.

The ability to locate gene damage with extraordinary precision in the bacteriophage system has permitted the comparison of the action of a number of mutagenic agents. It has been found that mutagenic agents do not act with equal efficiency on all of the sites of a gene that can be mutated. They will induce mutation at particular sites much more frequently than they will at other sites. Furthermore, the different mutagenic agents behave in a unique manner; they each will alter certain of the sites with high efficiency while leaving other sites unaltered. The rationale for this differential behavior of mutagenic agents is not completely understood but is being actively explored at the present time.

We can readily appreciate from the foregoing that viruses represent a powerful tool for the analysis of gene structure. A far-reaching goal of such analysis is to learn the manner in which a gene specifies

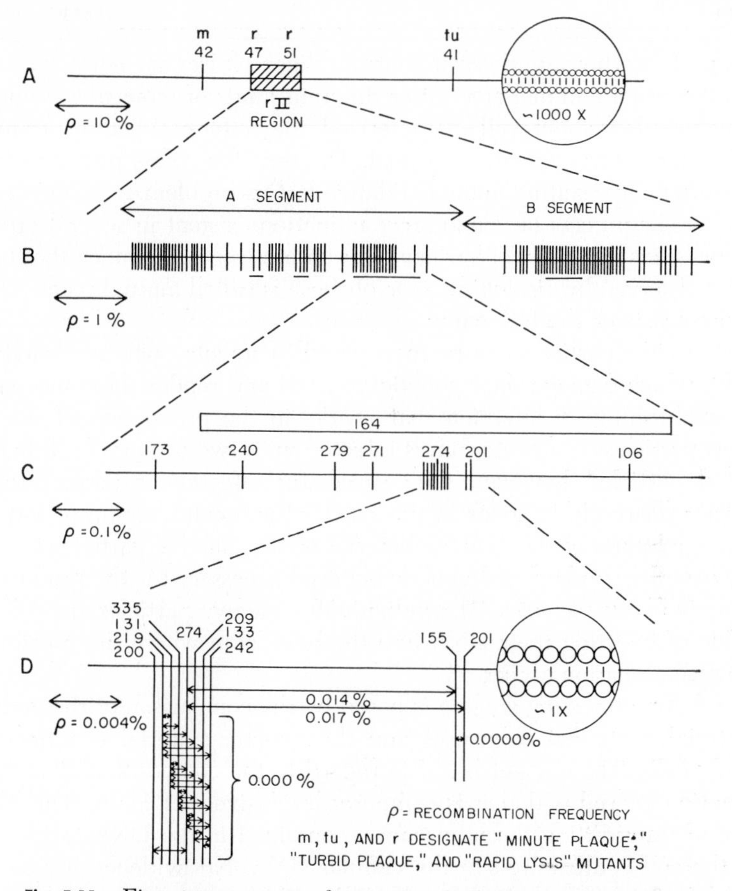

Fig. 5.11. Fine structure map of a section of a bacterial virus chromosome. *A:* The position of four genes are shown on the bacterial virus chromosome (the *rII* region contains two genes which are close to each other). The distance between two genes with 10 percent recombination is shown by the double headed arrow on the left. The inset on the right shows a segment of DNA molecule magnified 1000 times. *B:* The *rII* region shown on (A) is expanded tenfold. The vertical lines indicate the position of independent mutants which have been discovered within the *A* and *B* genes. The short horizontal lines beneath the vertical lines indicate mutants in which a section of the chromosome has been lost. *C:* A tenfold expansion of a section of (B). The numbers refer to the individual mutants. *D:* A twenty five-fold expansion of a section of (C). Since the recombination frequency of the eight mutants clustered on the left is zero, these are presumed to be independent occurrences of the same mutation. The same would apply to the two mutants designated 155 and 201. The inset shows a representation of a section of DNA molecule drawn to scale. It can be estimated that mutants 274 and 201 are fourteen nucleotide pairs apart. (From S. Benzer, "Genetic fine structure and its relation to the DNA molecule," in "Mutation," *Brookhaven Symposia in Biology,* No. 8. With permission.)

the protein whose synthesis it controls. Since viruses are not only small, but contain a minimal amount of different kinds of molecules, some of which are extremely well characterized, they offer excellent experimental material for achieving this goal. The next few years probably hold in store many exciting findings relative to this problem.

The process of genetic recombination existent in several groups of viruses is the basis for various other interesting phenomena that have been observed by virologists. One of these is called mutual reactivation and consists of the following:

Virus particles can be inactivated by agents, such as ultraviolet light, which damage their genetic material and render them incapable of establishing an infection that results in the production of mature virus particles. If a bacterium is infected with two or more such inactivated particles, however, then successful infection is accomplished. What apparently happens in this case is the recombination of the undamaged parts of the genetic material of the inactive particles to supply complete undamaged genetic material necessary for the production of active virus particles. The individually inactive particles are still capable of injecting their DNA into the bacterium where the possibility for recombination occurs.

An interesting enigma is posed by the comparison of the genetic material contained in viruses and the genetic material contained in living cells. The current belief in regard to the composition of cellular genetic material is that it is composed exclusively of DNA. The function of transmitting the information contained in the DNA to the rest of the cell is attributed to the cellular RNA. No evidence has as yet been found for the existence of cellular RNA with autocatalytic property. We have seen, however, that many viruses possess RNA as their genetic material and this RNA definitely does have the property of autocatalysis. The question we may ask is whether and in what manner the RNA contained in viruses is unique so that it alone among the RNA's, appears to be imbued with the property of self-replication. The existence of viral genetic RNA presents another dilemma because, as detailed elsewhere in this book, the autocatalytic property of DNA is intimately associated with its double-stranded structure. The viral RNA's are all single-stranded, however, and thus, it does not appear likely that the method of RNA replication is similar to that of DNA. The problems raised by the discovery of genetic RNA are challenging and require active research for their clarification.

The virus-host cell interaction is of a rather specific kind. Certain species of virus grow only in a restricted range of host cell species. The reasons for this specificity are not altogether clear. One of the factors involved, however, is the ability of the virus particle to release its nu-

CHAPTER 6

HAROLD R. GARNER

Associate Professor of Bacteriology
Purdue University

Harold R. Garner was born at Marion, Indiana, in 1919. He received the A.B. degree from Earlham College in 1941. From 1942 to 1946 he served in the U.S. Army Medical Corps, first as a hospital laboratory technician and later as director of a pathology laboratory in Biological Warfare Research. He received his graduate training at Purdue where he was awarded the Ph.D. degree in 1950 with a thesis on the "Metabolism of *Streptomyces griseus* with special regard to the tricarboxylic acid cycle." He spent the year 1950–51 at California Institute of Technology as a Fellow of the American Cancer Society. From 1951 to 1957 he was a Scholar in Cancer Research of the American Cancer Society at Purdue University. Since that time he has been a member of the Department of Biological Sciences at Purdue.

Professor Garner's Research interests have centered on problems of biosynthesis and metabolism. Among his published papers are the following: "Fermentation of D-glucosamine by *Leuconostoc mesenteroides*," *Bact. Proc.*, 1958, 97 (with G. W. Jourdian and H. Koffler); "Metabolic relationship between cystathionine and methionine in *Neurospora*," *J. Bacteriol.*, 1960, 80:50–60 (with J. L. Wiebers); "Demonstration of laminarin in fungal cell walls," *Bact. Proc.*, 1961, 95 (with K. Horikoshi and H. Koffler).

CHAPTER 6

Bacteria: Reproduction and heredity

H. R. GARNER
Purdue University

INTRODUCTION: USE AS EXPERIMENTAL CELLS

Because of their ability to reproduce rapidly, bacteria are the organisms of choice today for the investigation of many of the basic problems of biology. A generation time of 20 minutes attained by some bacteria means that immense populations of cells can be obtained within a relatively short time. It means also that the enzymes (organic catalysts in the cells) responsible for producing all the materials making up the cell must be very active. The short generation time of a unicellular organism means that large masses of cells that are essentially identical can be produced under carefully controlled conditions. Fig. 6.1 shows graphically how a single cell reproducing at the rate of once every 20 minutes becomes more than 100 times as much living material in just over two hours. In the next two hours it would generate more than 10,000 times as much living material! In contrast to animals or plants where a given organ may consist of several kinds of tissues and a corresponding number of kinds of differentiated cells, this ability to obtain quantities of homogeneous material is a distinct advantage to the experimenter. In this chapter, we shall consider a selected few of the biological problems for which bacteria are helping to furnish the answers.

Reproduction in bacteria is of the simplest sort. Usually, when a cell gets large enough it divides into two equal parts by binary fission, and two individuals exist where one was previously. This is a very sim-

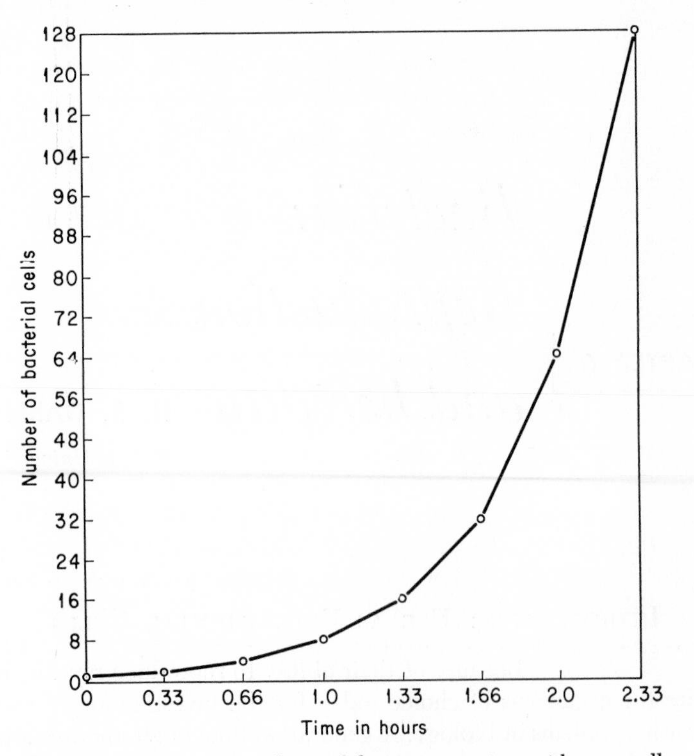

Fig. 6.1. Increase in numbers of bacteria starting with one cell having a generation time of 20 minutes.

ple statement of the overall process and does nothing to describe the multitude of chemical and physical events involved.

Some of these individual problems may be stated. How is the cell wall produced? How is it stretched without losing integrity, to cover a larger cell as protoplasm increases and eventually divided into two parts, each equal in every way to the original? What are the biochemical reactions involved in changing the relatively simple organic chemicals of food into the more complex compounds characteristically found in protoplasm? How are all these chemical reactions controlled and integrated into such an efficient whole? What are the differences which make some organisms able to use simple chemicals such as H_2

and CO_2 for energy and carbon, while others require a multitude of amino acids and vitamins before they can grow?

These are very broad statements, each embodying a multitude of lesser questions. It is a common observation in biology that an answer found using one organism may very well apply to many organisms, and that organisms that are phylogenetically similar carry out similar chemical and physical operations during growth. These interrelationships make it feasible to do basic research concerning the nature of cancer, the growth of cells, the control of growth and differentiation, with bacteria as the experimental cells.

Energy for Growth and Reproduction: Variations among the Bacteria

Bacteria include among their number examples of all of the major types of metabolic energy production. There are bacteria that use sugar as an energy source and can build all the chemical molecules they need from the carbon and chemical energy contained in these molecules plus various other inorganic molecules or atoms. Some bacteria are more fastidious, requiring a whole host of specific organic chemical compounds like the vitamins and amino acids required in the nutrition of man. Some are so fastidious in their nutrition that, as of now, we can only grow them by giving them blood serum or even living animal cells as a nutritive source. Still others are able to use very simple chemical compounds, such as CO_2 for carbon, and perform oxidation of molecules such as H_2 for energy to use in the synthesis of all the vitamins, amino acids, and other compounds needed for the synthesis of living protoplasm.

The process of respiration is the principal source of energy for many bacteria. In this process molecular oxygen from the air dissolves in the liquid surrounding the bacterial cells and then diffuses into the cells where it is available to the bacterial enzymes to accept hydrogen removed from a substance such as sugar. The sugar molecule is made of carbon, hydrogen, and oxygen atoms combined in such a way that the cell can obtain energy when these atoms are rearranged to form CO_2 and water. Removal of hydrogen is chemically the equivalent of oxidation, but in the cell an acceptor must be available for the hydrogen removed, in order for the enzyme involved to be restored to its original state so that it can repeat the process. The same enzyme molecule must remove hydrogen from many molecules of sugar and pass the hydrogen on toward combination with oxygen.

In the total process many individual chemical steps are involved. Biologically, this makes it possible for the cell to extract the energy of the sugar in the form of several small packets of chemical energy. The energy thus made available for use by the cell approaches that which is released in the form of heat when sugar is burned. It does not actually equal this amount because the cell is not a perfect machine and sometimes wastes part of the energy as it uses the remainder.

The final step in the transfer of hydrogen to oxygen produces water in some organisms. Water is a necessary part of protoplasm, so this is a very satisfactory end product. However, some bacterial enzymes produce hydrogen peroxide at this step. Hydrogen peroxide is toxic to cells and its accumulation would therefore be harmful. Fortunately, enzymes are usually available to convert peroxide to water. Bacteria that can grow in the presence of oxygen usually have the enzymes which permit them to deal with peroxide, but strict anaerobes often do not.

The anaerobes and some facultative organisms have the ability to grow in the complete absence of oxygen. This does not mean that they are incapable of carrying on chemical oxidation reactions. It does mean that instead of reducing oxygen by means of the hydrogen removed from a substance such as sugar, they must use the hydrogen to reduce something else. This something else may be some part of the products of sugar metabolism. The end result here is usually an incomplete utilization of the sugar and an accumulation of chemical by-products of metabolism as the cells break down more and more sugar molecules to obtain the energy required for synthesizing the compounds needed to build protoplasm. Examples of accumulated by-products of such partial oxidations are lactic acid and ethanol. The fermentation industries make use of this incomplete utilization of sugar and of the fact that living cells can often carry on enzymatically catalyzed chemical reactions cheaper and faster than extrinsic methods devised by the chemist. Lactic acid-producing bacteria are used in processing milk to make cheese. Still other bacteria help man by contributing by-products of metabolism to the manufacture of vinegar, pickles, ensilage, and kraut.

In many ways, the autotrophic bacteria are the most interesting in the way they obtain energy. The oxidation of hydrogen has been mentioned. Other bacteria can use H_2S or elemental sulfur with sulfuric acid as the oxidized product and with a resulting production of energy for the cells. There are even some bacteria that can make use of photosynthesis, thus deriving their energy quite directly from light.

It is not surprising that with such a wide variety of metabolic types available, bacteria can be found which closely approximate many of the kinds of cells found in other organisms. Likewise, it probably should not surprise us to find among the bacteria genetic mechanisms which result in a reassortment of genetic characteristics in much the same way as sexual mechanisms achieve it for higher forms. The rest of this chapter will concern some of these genetic processes.

Bacterial Heredity: the Nucleus

Seventy or more years ago the science of bacteriology began to develop as men like Pasteur and Koch were demonstrating that specific bacteria caused specific diseases. At that time there was a variety of ideas concerning the presence of nuclei in bacterial cells. Some held that there was no nucleus, while others were of the opinion that the bacterial cell, because it is so small, was all nucleus. Some variations on these ideas are still to be heard. However, it was recognized that cells reproduce and that the progeny usually have the same characteristics as the parent. It might be conceivable that the various parts of a living cell were each somehow capable of directing the synthesis of more of the same. By far more acceptable biologically is the idea that there is nuclear material which somehow directs the synthetic activities and controls the characteristics of the mature cell. Fig. 6.2 is a thin section of a bacterial cell, demonstrating that there is structural differentiation within the cell and, also, that nuclear material is well differentiated.

The question of nuclei was resolved by Robinow after he devised staining methods which were specific for the deoxyribonucleoprotein which is the important material in the chromosomes in nuclei of higher animals and plants. Using the phase microscope and photographing living cells at intervals, Mason and Powelson were able to show that these structures behave as nuclei by reduplication before cell division occurs (Fig. 6.3). The rod-shaped bacteria are often seen to have two or four individual nuclear bodies. Half of the number is in each daughter cell after cell division. In older cultures when growth is very slow, the majority of the cells may become uninuclear. Sometimes it is possible to disrupt the synchrony of nuclear division and cell division. A particular strain of *Escherichia coli,* when treated with ultraviolet light (U.V.), appears to lose the ability to divide into daughter cells. The nuclei continue to divide, and cell susbtance is produced, resulting in very long, snakelike cells with many nuclei. Fig. 6.4 shows a U.V.-resistant strain and a U.V.-sensitive strain after a few hours of growth on the surface of agar following treatment with U.V. After several hours, the effect of the ultraviolet wears off and the snakes break up into normal-sized cells.

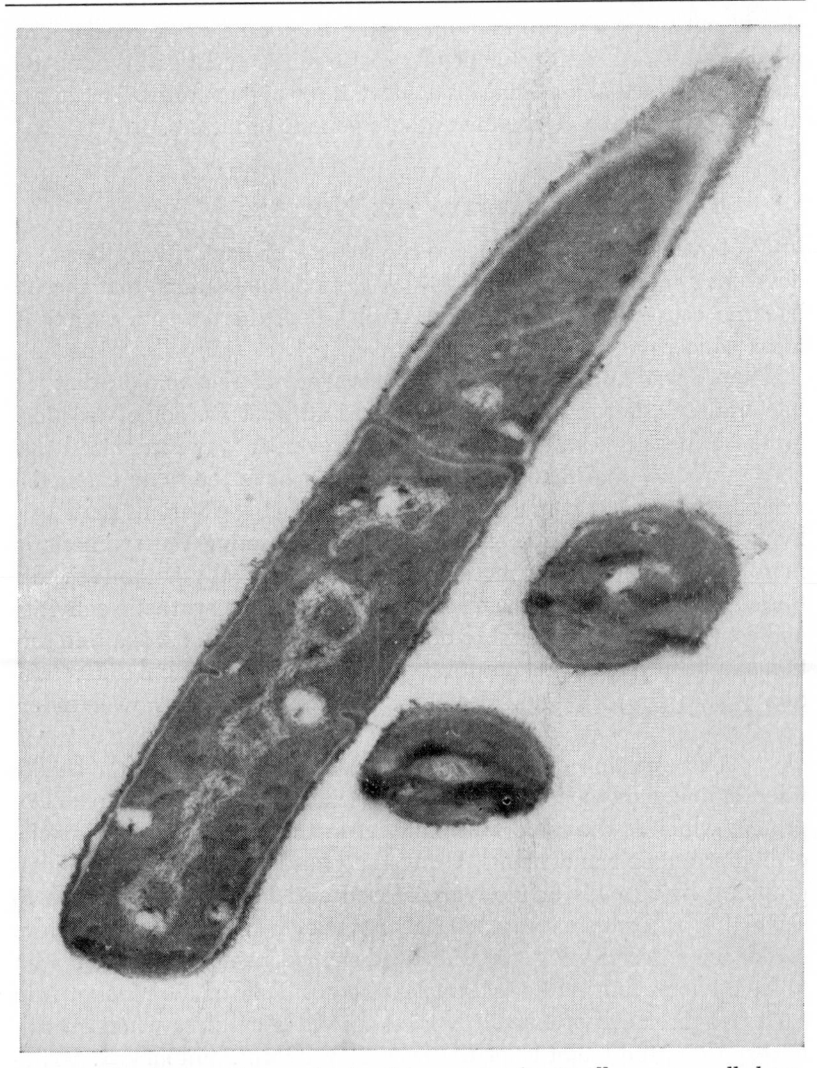

Fig. 6.2. An electronmicrograph of a thin section of a *Bacillus cereus* cell showing some of the structures visible inside the bacterial cell, including the nuclear apparatus. (From G. B. Chapman and J. Hillier, *J. Bacteriol.* *66*:363, 1953. With permission.)

Transformation: Pneumococci

Among the bacteria which cause pneumonia, there are many different types. These may be distinguished on the basis of specific serological reactions. The tests involve using antiserum reactions (the blood

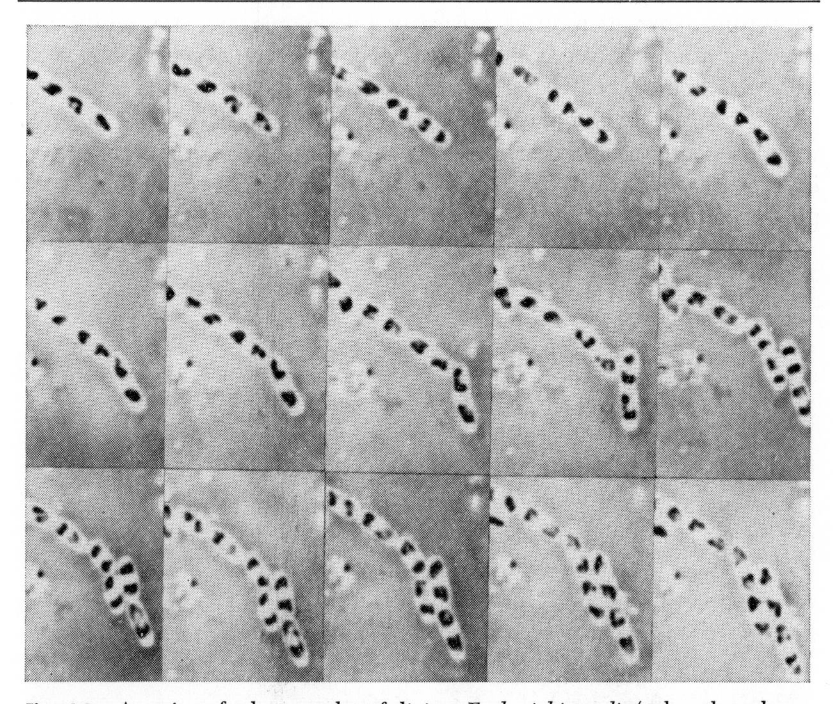

Fig. 6.3. A series of photographs of living *Escherichia coli* (taken by phase-contrast microscopy) showing the nuclear changes during cell division. The total elapsed time is 78 minutes from the first to the last photograph; the time of each frame starting at the upper left corner and reading left to right: 1 = start; 2 = 6 minutes; 3 = 15 minutes; 4 = 21 minutes; 5 = 30 minutes; 6 = 33 minutes; 7 = 36 minutes; 8 = 39 minutes; 9 = 48 minutes; 10 = 54 minutes; 11 = 57 minutes; 12 = 60 minutes; 13 = 66 minutes; 14 = 69 minutes; and 15 = 78 minutes. (From D. J. Mason and D. M. Powelson, *J. Bacteriol. 71*:474, 1956. Photograph appeared originally on the cover of *The American Biology Teacher, 19,* March 1957. With permission.)

serum of an animal after infection with one specific type of pneumococcus cells can cause this reaction). If cells of a strain of *Pneumococcus* isolated from a patient having pneumonia are mixed with this serum, and if the new strain is of the same type as that which was used to infect the animal, there will be a visible reaction (quellung reaction). But there will be none if the new strain is a different type from that used to bring about formation of the antiserum. Strains of *Pneumococcus* which do not show a visible reaction are said to be antigenically different. By having on hand a series of at least 100 known antisera, the medical laboratory can determine the "type" of the pneumococci involved in any new case of the disease. Before the advent of antibiotics, this typing was essential so that the patient could be treated with specific antiserum. Now, as soon as a case of pneumonia appears, antibiotics are often administered and typing is rendered impossible.

The serological types of pneumococci are involved in an example of genetic change observable among bacteria. To understand this we need a few more facts concerning the pneumococci. Virulent organisms are surrounded by capsules composed mostly of polysaccharide (a polymer of sugar units). When pneumococci are grown in the labora-

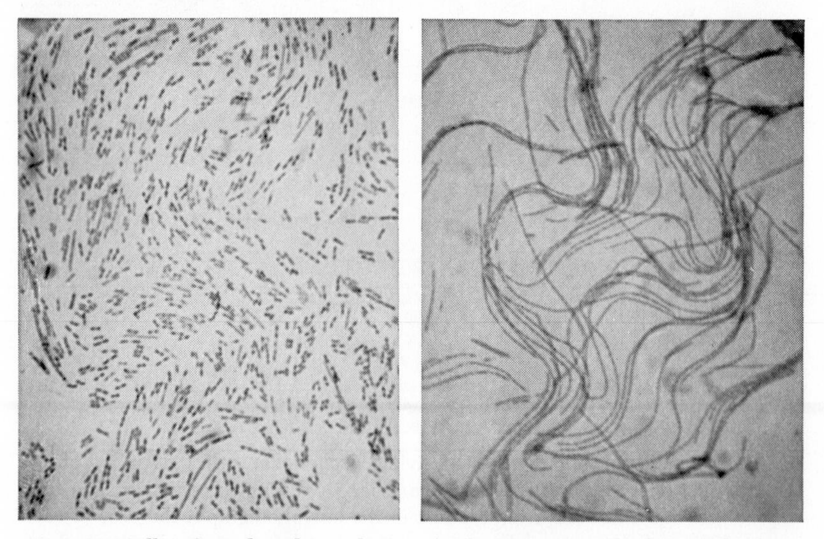

Fig. 6.4. Cells of *Escherichia coli* B/r (radiation-resistant), *left,* and of *E. coli* B (radiation-sensitive), *right,* streaked on agar following 25 ergs per mm^2 U.V. irradiation and incubated for 3 hours at 37° C. The cells are stained by De Lamater's method to show the nuclear apparatus. (From V. Bryson in W. Braun, *Bacterial Genetics,* Saunders, 1953. With permission.)

tory, occasional cells lose the ability to produce capsules and at the same time become avirulent (that is, lose the ability to cause disease). Such cells can be found and isolated by placing several cells on the surface of growth medium in a shallow dish. Each cell grows into a macroscopically visible colony. The colony growing from an unencapsulated cell is different in appearance from those colonies made up of cells with capsules. The opposite change, an unencapsulated cell becoming capsulated, has not been observed in laboratory cultures.

In 1928 Griffith undertook an experiment in which mice were inoculated with living avirulent pneumococci, together with some heat-killed cells of a virulent strain. Many of the mice died and were found to be infected with virulent pneumococci. These cells were of the same type as that of the dead cells injected into the mice, not like the type from which the living avirulent cells were derived (Fig. 6.5). Subsequent experiments proved that some part of the heat-killed cells was capable of effecting a change in the living pneumococci, causing them to become virulent. The reversal was of interest because this kind of change had never before been observed in the laboratory, and because virulence was inherited in further generations of the "transformed" cells.

A few years later it was shown that similar transformations could be carried out in test tubes. This permitted Avery, MacLeod, and McCarty to determine the chemical nature of the transforming

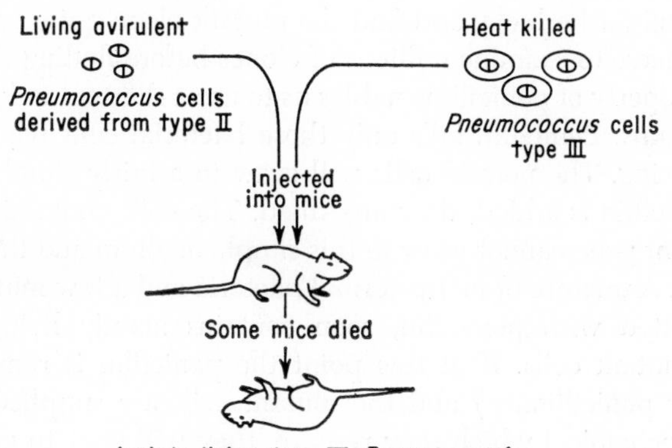

Fig. 6.5. Pneumococcus transformation in mice as demonstrated by Griffith.

principle. By a very rigorous process of purification and testing, they showed that the active material was highly polymerized deoxyribonucleic acid (DNA). This is chemically the same as the material of chromosomes that carry information from one generation to the next. In this case it appeared that the avirulent cells had absorbed DNA fragments capable of providing them with information on how to make a specific new kind of capsule and become virulent again. This particular DNA then became a part of the chromosome material, or at least was reduplicated at each cell division.

Biochemical Mutants: Identification

Beadle and Tatum showed that many mutant strains of *Neurospora* (red bread mold) could be obtained, each of which was deficient in ability to carry out the synthesis of a biochemical compound essential for growth of the cells. These "biochemical mutants" have been very useful in helping to elucidate the chemical details of the reactions the cells must carry on to grow. For some purposes it would be convenient to have biochemical mutant strains of bacteria. Penicillin makes it possible to obtain these mutant strains of some species of bacteria quite easily. Without penicillin the work involved in obtaining mutant strains is rather overwhelming. Suppose a normal gene changes to the desired mutant form with a frequency of one in a million. Without a selective method it would be necessary to examine clones (that is, a colony composed of many bacteria derived by reproduction from a single cell) derived from single cells, in the hope of finding a clone with the desired trait. One might be lucky and find the mutant clone quite soon, or unlucky and have to examine millions of clones before finding the one desired. A property of penicillin enables us to use a shortcut in locating the mutant strains. Penicillin kills only those bacterial cells which are actively growing. The normal cells will grow in a fairly simple medium, and if penicillin is added, they are killed. The cells containing the desired mutant gene cannot grow in this simple medium and therefore remain alive. A mixture of many normal bacteria and a few mutant bacteria, if treated with penicillin, soon contains mainly living but not growing mutant cells. If at this point the penicillin is removed (destroyed by penicillinase) and the mutant cells are supplied with the specific biochemical which they require, they will start to grow. Since the penicillin has been destroyed, the bacterial mutants are not killed while growing, and can be isolated in pure clones.

By using this method, many kinds of biochemical mutants of bacteria have been obtained. Some are unable to synthesize an amino acid needed to build protein molecules. Others are deficient in their ability to make vitamins or purines or other essential molecules. The mutant strains that can be obtained and studied are those which we can restore to near normal growth rates by feeding them the compounds which they can no longer make. Probably there are more potential mutant types, but these we cannot feed because we do not yet know the compounds they need, or because they need compounds that cannot penetrate the cell wall and thus must be produced within the cell.

Some other types of mutants may also be selected. A mutant which is more resistant to an antibiotic than the parent strain can be selected by adding the antibiotic to a growth medium containing both parent and mutant cells. In this case the susceptible cells are killed but the resistant ones can grow. In a similar way, bacteriophage (viruses that grow as parasites in bacteria) can be used to kill a culture of bacteria. If a few mutant cells with resistance to phage are present, they will continue to grow.

CHAPTER 7

GEORGE W. BEADLE, *President*

University of Chicago

George Wells Beadle was born near Wahoo, Nebraska, in 1903. He attended the University of Nebraska where he obtained the B.S. degree in 1926 and the M.S. degree in 1927. He then went to Cornell University where he joined the active group of corn geneticists under Professor R. A. Emerson. After receiving the Ph.D. at Cornell in 1931 he spent the next two years at California Institute of Technology, as a National Research Fellow, where he began his work on the fruit fly, Drosophila, in the laboratory of Thomas Hunt Morgan. In 1935 he spent a year in Paris working with Boris Ephrussi on certain inherited defects in eye-pigment production in Drosophila. After one year on the biology faculty at Harvard, Dr. Beadle joined the biology faculty at Stanford where he remained until 1946. During this period, he and E. L. Tatum made the now famous discovery, while working with the bread mold *Neurospora crassa,* that the synthesis of vitamins and amino acids is under the control of genes. In 1946, Dr. Beadle was appointed chairman of the Biology Division at California Institute of Technology. He served in this capacity until 1961 when he was appointed to his present position.

President Beadle has received honorary degrees from Yale, Nebraska, Northwestern, Rutgers, Kenyon, Wesleyan, Oxford, and Birmingham. He has received the Lasker Award (1950), Dyer Lectureship Award (1951), Emil Christian Hansen Prize (Denmark) (1953), Albert Einstein Commemorative Award (1958), Nobel Prize (1958), National Award, American Cancer Society (1959), and the Kimber Genetics Award (1960). He is a member of the National Academy of Sciences, Royal Danish Academy of Sciences, and The Royal Society. He has been president of the American Association for the Advancement of Science and the Genetics Society of America.

In addition to his many technical papers he is the author (with A. H. Sturtevant) of *An Introduction to Genetics,* Saunders, 1939.

CHAPTER 7

Structure of the genetic material and the concept of the gene

GEORGE W. BEADLE
University of Chicago

It is a basic characteristic of all living creatures that they are capable of reproducing their kind in a special manner. They do this by putting together an array of heterogeneous component parts or building blocks in ways that produce replicas of themselves. The parts are the chemical elements, either as elements directly or as molecules of varying degrees of complexity. In this way each successive generation is, so to speak, copied from a preceding generation.

It is often the case in plant and animal reproduction that the physical material directly carried over from one generation to the next is limited to a single cell only a fraction of a millimeter in diameter. In fact, it is known that in some of the subcellular and submicroscopic viruses the bridge between successive generations is reduced to a single large molecule.

It is obvious that whatever material does serve as the hereditary bridge between generations, it must somehow carry the information or specifications necessary to make new organisms. Thus in man, the fertilized egg must in a sense know that it is to develop into a person and not into a frog or an elephant. In fact, we know from studies of identical twins, the two members of a pair of which are known to develop from a single egg cell, that the egg must carry directions for growing into a very specific individul, not into just any person.

Let us examine the human fertilized egg. It does not appear to be very different from the elephant egg, or, except for size, to be so very different from the egg of a frog. It is about 1/300 inch in diameter —just large enough to be visible to the naked eye. It is the result of union of an egg and a sperm cell. The sperm is very much smaller than the egg.

The bulk of the spherical human egg cell is cytoplasm. Centrally located in the cell is the nucleus. Within the nucleus are chromosomes. Normally there are 46 per cell in man, 23 contributed by the mother and an equal number brought into the egg cell by the sperm nucleus. In both the cytoplasm and the nucleus there are other cellular structures but most of them will not be considered in this discussion.

For many inherited traits in cellular organisms the contribution from the two parents seems to be quantitatively equal. This suggests that the specifications for these traits must be carried in the nucleus both of egg and sperm, since the sperm cell contributes relatively little aside from its nucleus.

Let us therefore confine our attention mainly to the nucleus. In doing this we must be careful not to be misled into believing that the cytoplasm is unimportant. It is in fact indispensable; the egg nucleus is quite incapable of development without it. Furthermore, the cytoplasm must be quite highly specific. If the nucleus of one species of frog is transplanted to the egg of a related species, the nucleus of the recipient egg having previously been removed, development does not take place. The factor of possibly irreparable injury that might have been inflicted during the operation is excluded by the fact that transplantation of a nucleus from one egg into the cytoplasm of another of the same species permits normal development. This type of experiment shows that the cytoplasm must be species specific. This means that it, too, must carry hereditary specifications. A good deal is known about cytoplasmic inheritance, but we shall not here deal further with the subject.

What needs to be kept in mind is that an egg cell, if it is to develop normally, must remain in a proper environment. This means a specific chemical and physical environment. It means, too, that proper raw material in the form of food must be available at the right time and in the right amounts. For a human egg to grow into a mature person normally requires consumption of some ten tons of food.

We know that a large number of the total set of directions required to convert an egg cell into a person are contained in the nucleus. We will examine these directions in terms of the following five questions:

1) How did they come to be in the egg nucleus?

2) How are they written?

3) How are they copied or "reprinted," as they must be with each of the many cell divisions that intervene between the egg of one generation and the egg or sperm of the next?

4) How are they used in the growth and development of the egg cell into a person?

5) Do mistakes ever occur in these directions and, if so, what are they, how do they arise, and what is their result?

Mendel

The Augustinian monk Gregor Mendel was the first person to postulate that nuclear directions for development were made up of discrete units. Today we call these Mendelian units *genes*.

What is a gene and what does it do? You will recognize that this is a way of rephrasing the five questions posed above. Mendel studied inheritance in the ordinary garden pea and in so doing found evidence for the existence of seven separate and distinct genes. One had to do with the color of the flowers, one with the color of the seeds, one with the shape of the seeds, and so on. We now know that all organisms have genes. For example, two are known in man that specify how to make the two protein subunits of our hemoglobin molecules. There are many thousands more, only a few hundred of which have been investigated in any detail.

Mendel did not know that the units of heredity he postulated were in the nucleus of the cell, or that they were located in rod-shaped chromosomes within the nucleus. But he did formulate a set of laws according to which the units were transmitted from one generation to another and could thus specify certain characteristics in the pea plant. Although these laws have been extended and modified over the years, they still serve as useful first approximations to the ways of inheritance. Mendel was so far ahead of his time that none of his contemporaries appreciated the importance of his discovery. A third of a century after he published his results and his interpretation of them the climate of scientific thought had become favorable, and the rules of inheritance he proposed were soon confirmed for a variety of organisms.

It soon became obvious to a few biologists that chromosomes were transmitted in exactly the way Mendel envisaged for genes, assuming each chromosome to contain many genes. The final indisputable proof of the chromosome theory came from the experiments of the late Calvin B. Bridges, who worked on the small fly *Drosophila melanogaster* in the laboratory of Thomas Hunt Morgan and who showed that abnormal transmission of sex-linked genes was exactly paralleled by abnormal transmission of sex chromosomes.

We now know that the seven genes studied by Mendel are carried in the chromosomes of the pea plant, of which there are seven kinds. It is truly remarkable that each of the seven genes of Mendel appears to be located in a different one of the seven chromosomes. The a priori chance of this is exceedingly small. (See if you can calculate this from the laws of probability developed in beginning algebra, assuming that any gene is equally likely to be in any chromosome.) Had Mendel not been so lucky, his results might well have been complicated by linkage in a manner that would have frustrated him in arriving at a correct interpretation.

We can illustrate the principles of Mendelian inheritance with flower color. One of the genes Mendel studied involved this character. Each cell of the pea plant as we see it growing in the garden has two sets of seven chromosomes. In one pair of these is located this particular gene for flower color. The gene exists in two forms, called alleles—one for purple flowers, one for white flowers. The first form of the gene carries a message that somehow says "I am now a correct message for making flower pigment." The alternative form says, "I am not a correct message for making flower pigment." Let us designate the second message with a lower case letter *a* and the first with a capital letter *A*. The vegetative cells of the purple-flowered plant can then be designated *AA*, and those of the white-flowered line *aa*. The egg cells of the purple-flowered plants carry one chromosome of each kind and hence can be designated *A* in genetic constitution for the one gene we are considering. The sperm cells (in the pollen grains) of the white-flowered plant are then *a* in constitution. If pollen of the *aa* plant is put on the stigmas of the *AA* plant, the fertilized eggs will be *Aa*. That is, they and all cells that come from them by mitosis will carry one of each of the two forms of this gene. They will be hybrid and will be found on flowering to have purple flowers. This means the gene for pigment is dominant to that for absence of pigment. Or conversely the *a* form of the gene is recessive to its *A* allele.

When the hybrid plants produce eggs, each egg will receive either the *A* or the *a* form of the gene. It is a 50:50 chance affair. The same happens when sperm cells are produced—half will carry *A* and half *a*. If the plant is self-fertilized, the normal condition for the garden pea, four types of fertilized egg cells will be produced:

AA, *Aa*, *aA*, and *aa*

The first three will have purple flowers, the last one white flowers. This is the classical 3 to 1 Mendelian ratio.

The same principles apply in the case of man. In us, too, there is a gene concerned with pigmentation. The normal dominant form *A* results in an active melanin pigment-forming system; its recessive allele, *a*, results in an inactive system. As in the pea plant there are four kinds of individuals possible with respect to this particular gene,

AA, Aa, aA, aa

The second two are distinguished from each other only by the fact that one gets the *A* gene from the mother and the other from the father. The first three are normally pigmented. The fourth is an albino. Just as in the pea plant, when a woman of *Aa* type produces egg cells, it is a matter of chance whether in a particular egg she will transmit the *A* allele or its recessive counterpart. Each of the thousands of kinds of genes in a pea plant or a person is transmitted by this simple mechanism which it was Mendel's genius to discover without knowing about chromosomes, or mitosis, or meiosis. However, in a sense he predicted meiosis on genetic grounds.

Linkage is a secondary phenomenon that was unknown to Mendel. All genes in a given chromosome are said to be linked. They can be "mapped" by frequency of crossing over. Genes carried in the sex-determining chromosomes in man and other organisms behave somewhat differently in detail because of the fact that the so-called Y chromosomes may be inert for genes carried in its X chromosome homologue.

Chemical Composition of a Gene

Since chromosomes are made up largely of protein and deoxyribonucleic acid (DNA), it has long been supposed that the gene must be made up of one or the other or both of these substances. Proteins are large polymer molecules built of 20 kinds of amino acids arranged in linear chains of dozens to hundreds of amino acid subunits. The complete sequence of subunits has been worked out for only a few kinds of protein molecules. Insulin is one of these.

DNA molecules are also linear polymers. But they are built up of subunits called nucleotides. There are four of these. A single DNA molecule may be many thousands of subunits long. The exact sequence of nucleotides is not yet known in any naturally occurring DNA molecule.

Prior to 1940, or thereabouts, it was rather widely believed that genes were proteins; that the "language" of the gene was written as a code in which amino acids served as letters. This was believed because chemists knew that countless arrangements of amino acids were possible in reasonably sized protein molecules. They were less sure about the variability possible in DNA molecules. In fact, one view rather widely held was that DNA molecules were made of repeating segments of the four nucleotides, arranged in a single order within each segment, and joined linearly to form a monotonous and genetically uninteresting polymer.

Evidence that DNA is the primary genetic material

Over a period of some fourteen years, beginning in 1928, it was found that one serological type of pneumococcus can be "transformed" into another type by adding to it some pure DNA prepared from bacteria of the first type. The pneumococcus bacteria used in these experiments are pathogenic to man and to mice. They are responsible for one type of pneumonia. They exist in many serological types, each type inducing the production of unique type-specific antibodies by an infected animal. Type specificity resides in gellike coats of polysaccharide. These coats are not an essential part of the living bacterium and mutant strains occasionally appear that lack them. These coatless cells grow as characteristic "rough" colonies on a culture plate. They do not produce disease in a susceptible mouse; they are avirulent. They also show no reaction when used with type-specific antisera.

A coatless strain of pneumococci derived by mutation from say a Type II strain with a coat (which grows as "smooth" colonies) may occasionally back-mutate. When this happens, it almost always reverts to the smooth Type II from which it originally came. But if pure DNA prepared from a smooth strain of Type III is added to a rough ex-Type II culture under exactly the right conditions, the frequency of "mutations" to smooth virulent cells is enormously increased. And, even more important, the smooth virulent cells so produced are now of Type III. Their descendents now produce more DNA capable of transforming Type II into Type III. This process of transformation is illustrated diagrammatically in Fig. 7.1.

It is now widely believed that this transformation involves not only the entrance of DNA molecules from the donor Type III cells into the rough cells but its subsequent incorporation into the DNA directions to the recipient cell through replacement of corresponding defective DNA, which before mutation directed that Type II coats be made. This interpretation, which is not the only one possible but which seems the most plausible, assumes that DNA itself is the substance of the gene. It assumes that the original Type II bacteria contained a segment of DNA that specified Type II polysaccharide coat, that the mutation to rough involved some incapacitating change in this segment, and that this defective segment of DNA was replaced by DNA specifying Type III during the transformation. The particular segment of DNA that directs synthesis of the coat polysaccharide may be called a gene. In this case it is not known how large a segment this is—that is, how many nucleotide "letters" are involved in the DNA "sentence" that we call the gene.

Further evidence that the essential and irreducible component of a gene is DNA comes from studies on bacterial viruses (also known as bacteriophages, or more simply as phages). The bacterial viruses that multiply in the ordinary colon bacillus *Escherichia coli* (a bacte-

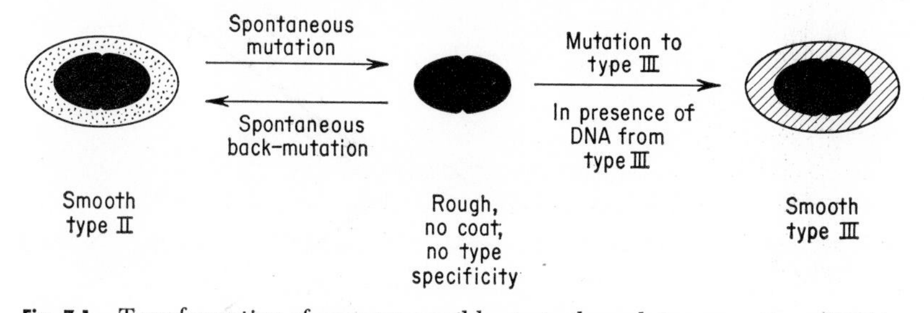

Fig. 7.1. Transformation of pneumococcal bacteria through incorporation of DNA.

rium often used by health laboratories as an indication of pollution of water by sewage) are now almost as widely used in genetic studies as is the better known fly, *Drosophila melanogaster.*

Coliphages, as these viruses are sometimes called, come in numerous varieties that differ in size, shape, serological properties, etc. A widely used "species" is called T2. Its individual units are submicroscopic tadpole-shaped structures with polyhedral heads and cylindrical tails (Fig. 7.2). Many mutant strains of the T2 phage are known. Some differ from the standard type in host specificity (many genetically different strains of the host bacterium are known). Others produce characteristically modified circular virus colonies on plates covered with an opaque layer of host bacteria. These virus colonies are called "plaques." In them many or all of the bacterial cells are killed and broken up, that is, are "lysed." Plaques may be large or small, clear or turbid, etc.

When a host cell is simultaneously infected with two genetic types of T2 phages that differ in two characters, the progeny may consist of both parental types of virus offspring and, in addition, of two new types that "recombine" the traits of the parental viruses.

The virus genetic material must therefore be made up of genes and also undergo a kind of mating process in the host cell by which new combinations of these genes are produced. In principle, this production of new combinations of genes is not unlike the phenomenon of recombination observed in peas and flies. Furthermore, just as chromosomes "maps" may be constructed for peas and flies on the basis of frequencies of recombinations for different pairs of genes, so can genetic maps be made for phage genes. In short, bacterial viruses have genes.

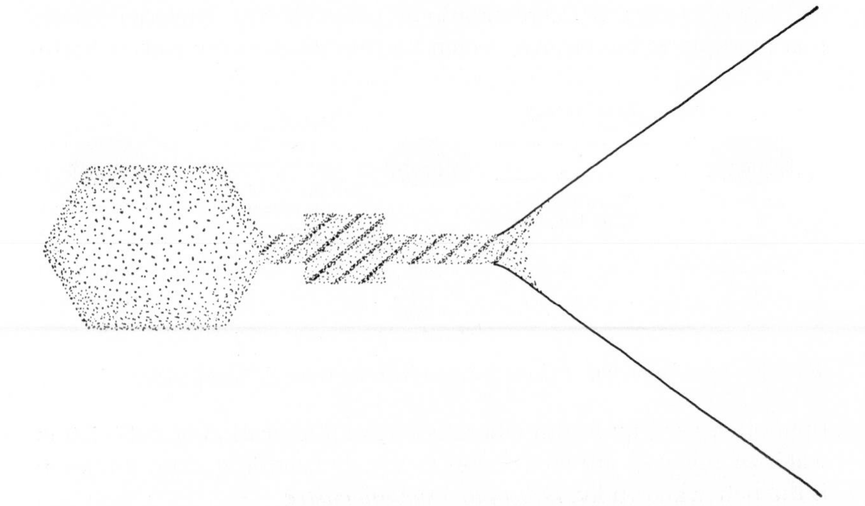

Fig. 7.2. Schematic diagram of "triggered" T2 bacterial virus consisting of a polyhedral head (which consists of a protein coat enclosing a single giant DNA molecule of molecular weight approximately 140 million), a protein tail sheath (contracted state characteristic of time of infection of host), a tail core (protein), and tail fibers. (Drawn from electron micrograph taken by S. Brenner and R. W. Horne at Cambridge University. With permission.)

What is a phage particle chemically? By osmotic shock treatment (shifting quickly from a salt solution to distilled water) phage particles can be made to separate into two components, protein and DNA. Electron micrographs show that protein makes up the head envelope and tail sheath, and strongly suggest that in intact particles the DNA is packed in the head. This conclusion is supported by other evidence—for example, resistance or susceptibility to degradation of protein or DNA by specific enzymes.

Electron microscopy indicates that during the infection process a T2 phage particle becomes attached to the surface of the host cell by the tip of its tail and that DNA is then "injected" into the host cell by a process that leaves the head coat and the tail sheath outside. After the injection these can both be sheared off in a Waring Blendor without interfering with the production of as many as several hundred daughter viruses in the infected host.

That the above process actually occurs essentially as described and as illustrated in Fig. 7.3 is most elegantly demonstrated through the use of radioactive labels on the DNA or the protein components of phage particles. Such experiments were first reported by Alfred D. Hershey and Martha Chase in 1952.

Nucleotides of DNA are made up of five kinds of atoms: carbon, hydrogen, oxygen, nitrogen, and phosphorus. In almost all proteins, on the other hand, there are sulfur atoms present, but no phosphorus. The remaining four atoms are common to both protein and DNA.

If phages are grown on a culture of bacteria that had previously been grown on a culture medium containing radioactive phosphorus (P^{32}) as phosphate, the phage DNA becomes radioactive and this can be detected with a proper radioactivity meter. If such labeled phages are now used to infect nonradioactive bacteria, and the virus coats separated from the infected cells just after the injection process (by use of a Waring Blendor followed by separation of cells and virus coats in a centrifuge) the cells are found to carry almost all the P^{32} label.

If, on the other hand, a comparable experiment is carried out in which the protein is labeled with radioactive sulfur (S^{35}), the great bulk of the label remains outside the host cells in the virus coats.

Thus it is clear that most of the DNA enters the host cell while most of the protein in virus coats and tails remains outside. The obvious conclusion is that the genes of the virus must be largely or wholly DNA. That the small amount of protein entering the host is not of continuing genetic significance is made clear by the fact that it is not carried over as intact molecules to daughter viruses.

Genes are DNA. And DNA obviously constitutes the directions for making daughter viruses, including their protein coats, from the raw materials in the bacterial host cell and with the use of at least part of the metabolic machinery of the host cell.

What about the genes of men and mice and flies? Are their primary messages also written in DNA? There is as yet no direct evidence of the kind that has been described for bacteria and viruses. Nevertheless, in the interests of economy in hypotheses, we assume that the DNA carries the essential genetic information in all cellular forms, in plants and animals alike.

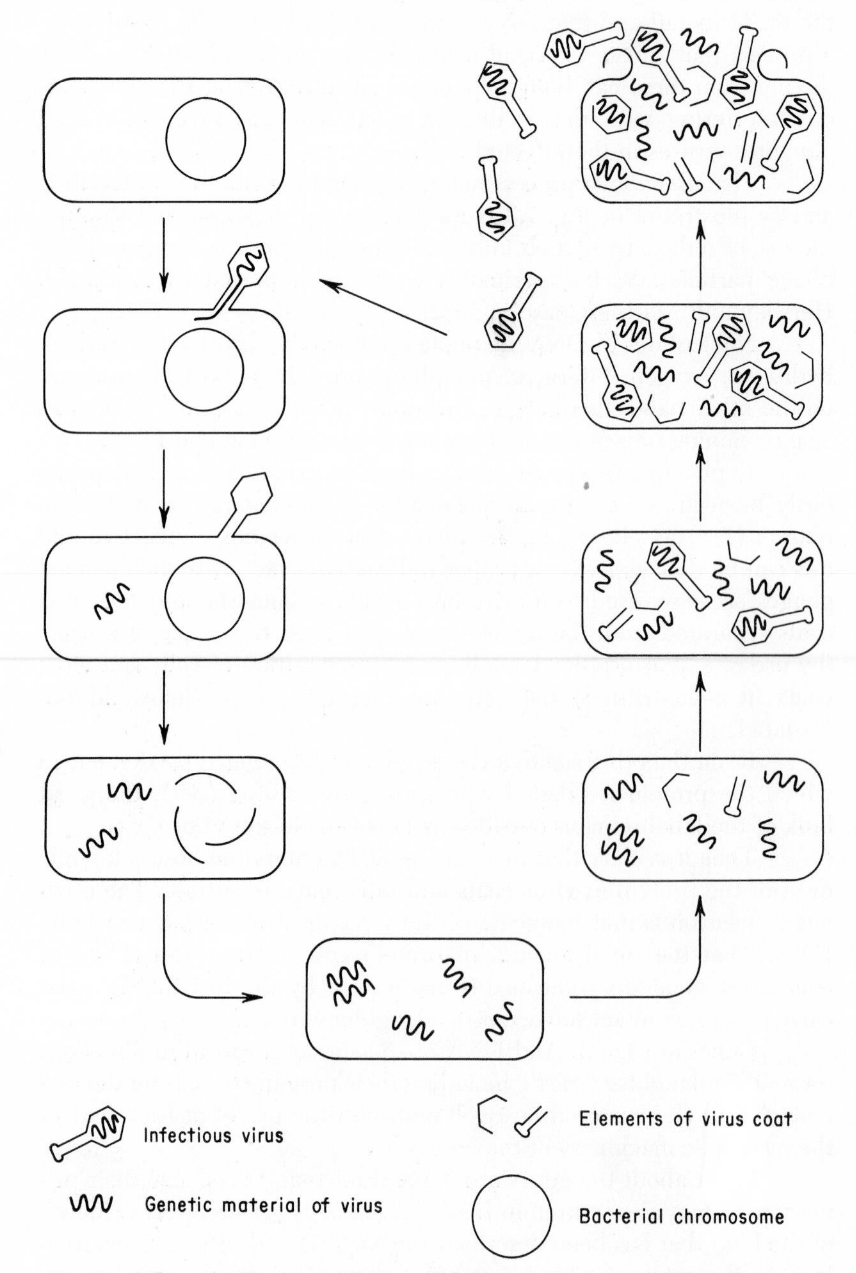

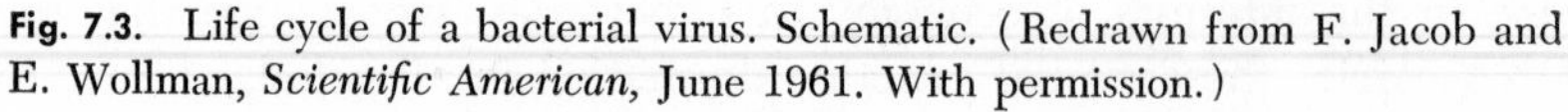

Fig. 7.3. Life cycle of a bacterial virus. Schematic. (Redrawn from F. Jacob and E. Wollman, *Scientific American,* June 1961. With permission.)

Chemical structure of DNA

Chemists and biologists have been interested in DNA for many years. But with the demonstration of its primary genetic significance in bacteria and viruses in the period 1944 to 1952, this interest was greatly intensified. In 1953 a major advance was made by a young (then 26 years of age) American biologist, James D. Watson, and an English chemist, Francis H. C. Crick. Using information then available about DNA from a variety of sources—such sources as general knowledge of the special arrangements of atoms in organic molecules of the types found in nucleotides, structure of the four nucleotides of DNA, relative frequencies of those units in DNA's of various kinds, and an ingenious model-building technique—Watson and Crick proposed a detailed structure for DNA that is now widely regarded as essentially correct. This structure generated extraordinary interest among biologists, and especially among geneticists, because it suggested such plausible answers to four of the questions asked at the beginning of this chapter, namely: what is the language of the gene? how are genes copied? how are they used in the control, development, and functioning of organisms? and what is the molecular basis of mutation? So useful has the Watson-Crick structure been in suggesting answers to these questions that it is thought by many to represent one of the most basic and important developments in all of twentieth-century biology.

What is the Watson-Crick structure? Although a complete appreciation of it and its biological and chemical significance depends on an understanding of some fairly sophisticated areas of organic and physical chemistry, the concepts involved can be stated in a relatively simple way. Their elegance and beauty should inspire every student of biology to learn the chemistry necessary for a deeper understanding.

According to the Watson-Crick structure, DNA consists of two parallel polynucleotide chains disposed in the form of a double helix such as is shown diagrammatically in Fig. 7.4. A so-called space-filling model is illustrated in Fig. 7.5. The paired chains are joined through the purine and pyrimidine components of the individual nucleotides by specific hydrogen bonding (Fig. 7.6). Members of paired nucleotides are complementary in the sense that adenine and thymine nucleotides are always paired with each other. The same is true of guanine and cytosine nucleotides. Nucleotides are oriented so as to give opposite direction to the two chains.

A four-unit segment is represented in two dimensions in Fig. 7.7.

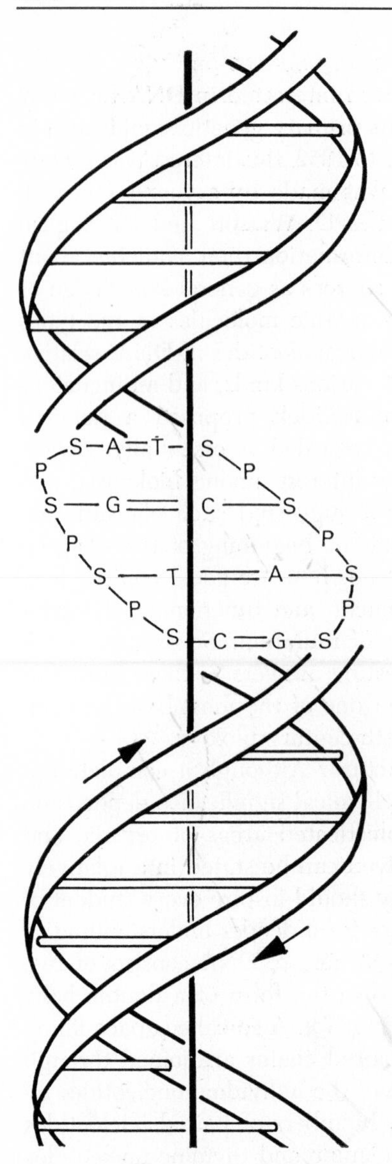

Fig. 7.4. The Watson-Crick structure of DNA schematically represented. The parallel spiral ribbons represent the paired polynucleotide chains. Hydrogen bonding is represented by transverse parallel lines. P = phosphate group, S = sugar unit, A = adenine base, T = thymine base, G = guanine base, C = cytosine base. Arrows indicate that polynucleotide chains run in opposite directions as specified by the sugar-phosphate linkages. (Redrawn from Watson and Crick, 1953.)

DNA as a code

How does DNA carry directions for the many activities that living creatures must carry out? The double molecule may be thought of as a 4-symbol code with each of the four kinds of pairs of nucleotides being one symbol. Information must somehow consist in a sequence of

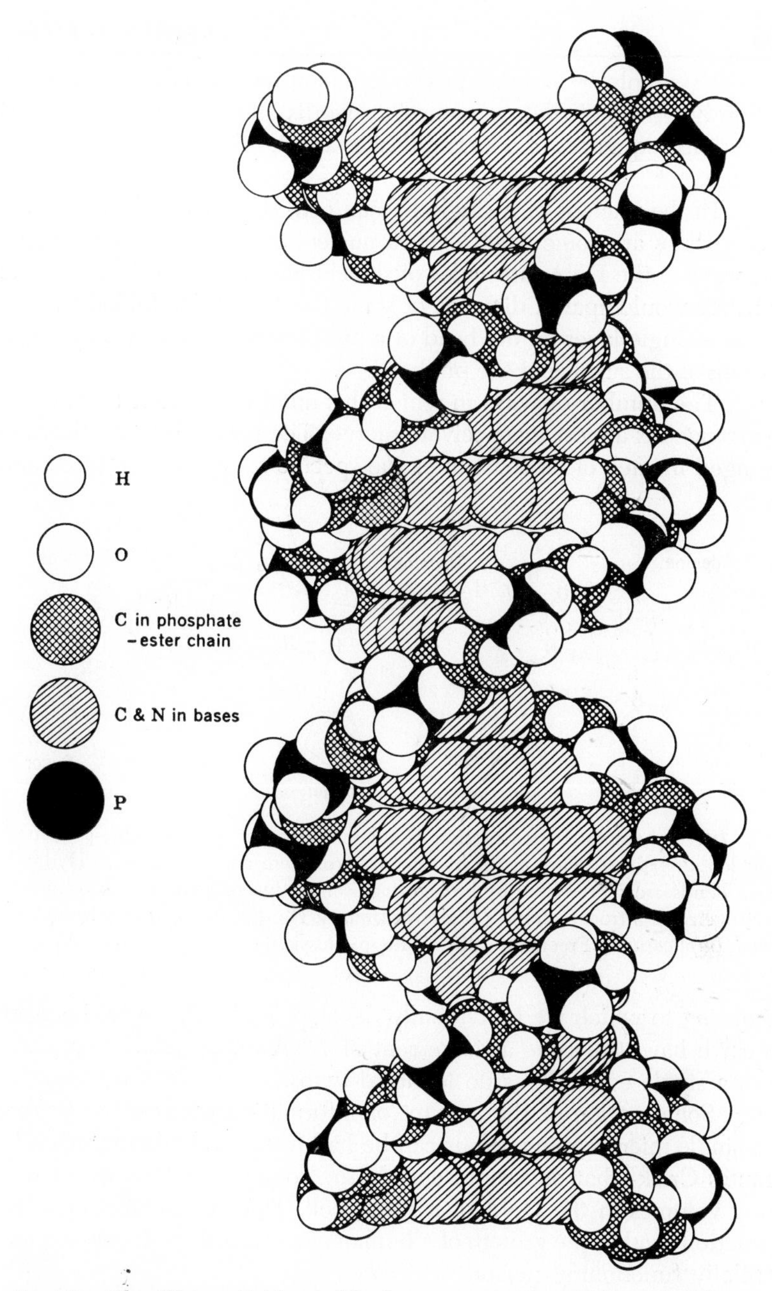

Fig. 7.5. The Watson-Crick model of a segment of a DNA molecule in which hydrogen, oxygen, carbon, nitrogen, and phosphorus atoms are shown as spheres. (From R. Sager and F. J. Ryan, *Cell Heredity*, Wiley, 1961. With permission.)

the four symbols or "letters," just as letters of our alphabet carry information by virtue of their sequences in words and sentences, or just as the various sequences of dots and dashes are significant in a telegraphic message.

In the nucleus of a single human cell, the fertilized egg for example, there are some 5,000,000,000 nucleotide pairs arranged in specific ways in the DNA molecules of the chromosomes. Stretched end to end they would span a distance of some five feet. Or if folded side by side in a single layer on the head of a pin they would cover only about 1/200th of the surface of the pin head.

The number of ways in which this number of DNA units could be arranged is almost inconceivably large. The particular way they are arranged in each of us constitutes the specific set of genetic directions

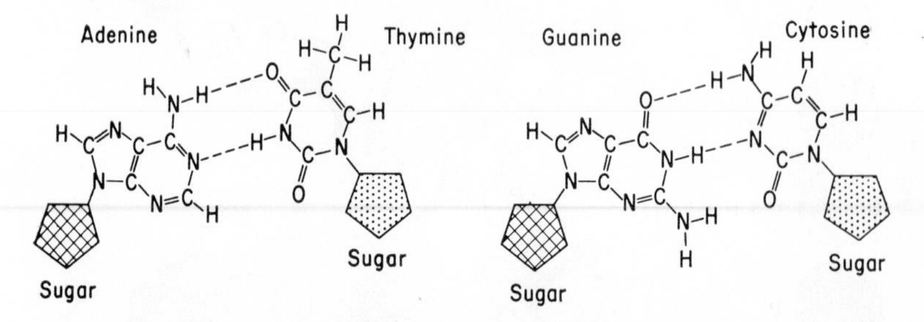

Fig. 7.6. Schematic representation of adenine-thymine and guanine-cytosine nucleotide pairs. C, carbon; H, hydrogen; O, oxygen; and N, nitrogen. Hydrogen bonds are represented by broken lines connecting oxygen and nitrogen or nitrogen and nitrogen atoms. (Redrawn from G. Hardin, *Biology: Its Principles and Implications,* Freeman, 1961. With permission.)

according to which we individually develop. Probably no two persons on earth have the same arrangement of DNA units, unless they come from a single egg cell, as do identical twins.

Some notion of the amount of information that can be packed in a single microscopic nucleus can be had from a calculation made by Francis Crick—that one could encode the contents of 1000 average library volumes in the DNA of a single cell. That is the amount of information used in the growth of a human egg into a fully developed and normally functioning person.

Another way of appreciating the miniaturization achieved in DNA code is through the realization that a pinhead completely covered with a single layer of DNA molecules lying side by side could contain information equivalent to a 200,000-volume library. This is a sizable college library.

Self-copying of DNA molecules

The Watson-Crick hypothesis immediately suggested to its authors how DNA molecules might be replicated by the double molecule's separating into two complementary single DNA chains, followed by synthesis of new partners against each of the single chains. In a sense each single chain "knows" what its new partner should be by virtue of the specific patterns of hydrogen bonding between complementary base pairs. The two single chains are presumed to act as templates against which complementary new chains are built up from a pool of

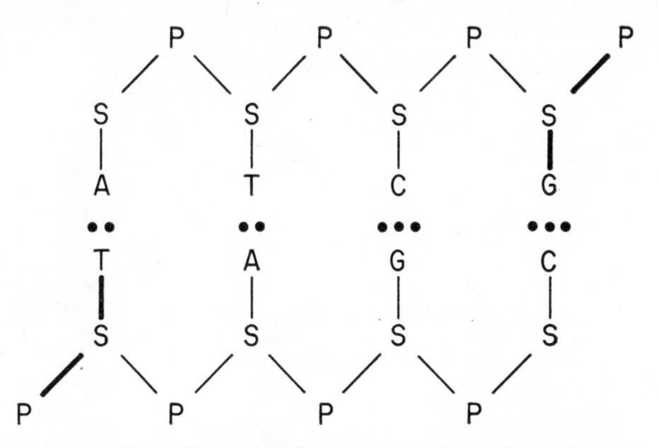

Fig. 7.7. Two-dimensional representation of a 4-unit segment of DNA. A, adenine; T, thymine; C, cytosine; G, guanine; S, sugar; P, phosphate. Hydrogen bonds are represented by dots. Orientation of nucleotides (two shown with heavy lines) gives opposite polarity to the two chains.

free nucleotides in the cell in which division is occurring. This process is schematically represented in Fig. 7.8.

Prior to the Watson-Crick model, few biologists could have imagined that the elementary molecular event underlying biological reproduction in organisms as diverse as viruses and man could be so simple. Today we believe it is. Aside from the elegant simplicity of the hypothesis, what are the reasons for believing it to be correct?

There are several lines of evidence that support the Watson-Crick hypothesis of DNA replication in the simple form described above. One of these involves labeling DNA molecules in such a way that old and new molecules can be distinguished. Radioactive phosphorous (P^{32}) has been used for the purpose, but there are some difficulties in this method that have not been completely resolved. The use of the heavy stable isotope of nitrogen (N^{15}) instead of the usual nitro-

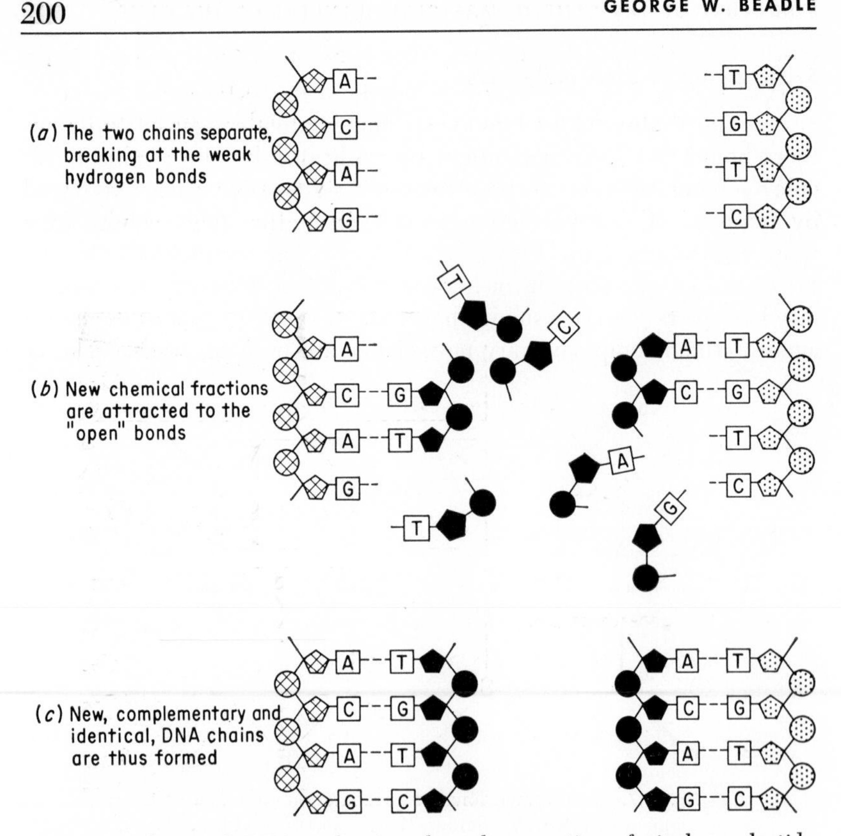

Fig. 7.8. Scheme of DNA replication through separation of single nucleotide chains followed by synthesis of complementary new chains. (Redrawn from G. Hardin, *Biology: Its Principles and Implications,* Freeman, 1961. With permission.)

gen-14 has proved useful in following the course of DNA formation in living cells.

Mathew S. Meselson, Frank W. Stahl and Jerome Vinograd have devised a method of banding DNA in a cesium chloride solution in the cell of an analytical ultracentrifuge. If a solution of this salt is spun at high speeds in such a centrifuge a density gradient is established in the cell. The salt molecules are thrown down in the cell by centrifugal force. But they are small enough to diffuse back even against the highly amplified force of gravity. The result is a density gradient—higher density at the centrifugal end of the cell, lower density at the centripetal end. If the density of such a solution includes that of DNA molecules, such molecules in the solution will form a sharp band at their proper density level. Those at lower density sink to their proper level and those at higher density float to the same level (Fig. 7.9*a*). DNA molecules are very large and thus diffuse little. They therefore form a sharp band across the cell. Its position (indicating density), dispersion (related to molecular weight), and amount can be determined by use of photography through an ultraviolet optical system built into the centrifuge. Nitrogen-15-labeled DNA forms a band clearly separated from the band formed by N^{14}DNA. A mixture of the two gives two cleanly separated bands.

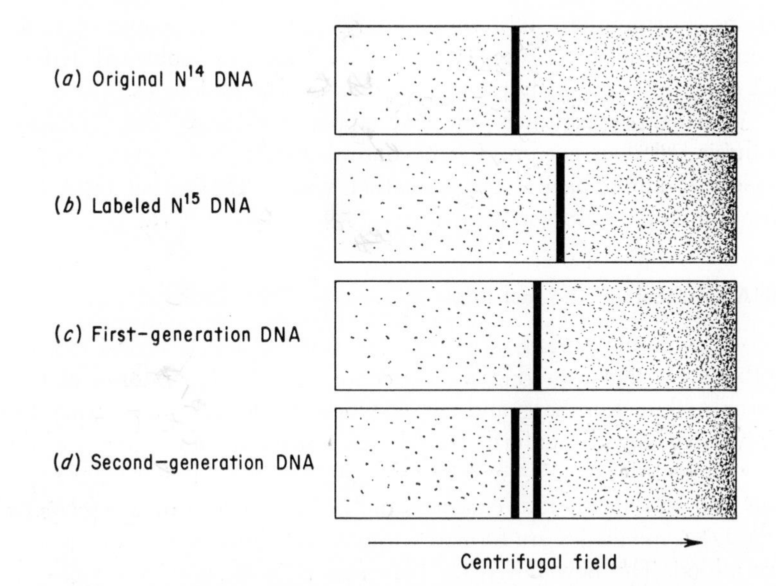

Fig. 7.9. Banding of light, heavy, and "hybrid" DNA molecules in analytical ultracentrifuge cells in the Meselson-Stahl experiment.

With this technique, Meselson and Stahl were able to perform the following experiment:

Colon bacteria were grown for many generations in a culture medium in which essentially all nitrogen was N^{15}. Their DNA thus became more dense by a factor of about 1 percent (Fig. 7.9*b*). Such cells were then washed and transferred to a medium in which all nitrogen was N^{14} and allowed to undergo one cell division, as determined by doubling of the number of cells. The density of their DNA molecules was found to be exactly intermediate between heavy and light DNA—as though they now were each made up of one heavy and one light chain. This was predicted by the hypothesis assuming separated single chains would remain intact (Fig. 7.9*c*).

When density measurements were made on DNA molecules removed from bacteria after exactly two generations in light medium, they were found to consist of intermediate ("hybrid") and light molecules in equal numbers. Again this was to be expected (Fig. 7.9*d*).

It was further found that hybrid DNA molecules from the first generation bacteria could be separated by heating into heavy and light units, equal in number, and with roughly half the molecular weight of the unheated molecules. It was later shown by Professor Paul Doty and his co-workers at Harvard University that from these single units double units could be reconstituted by slow cooling under proper conditions. Furthermore, if strands of DNA molecules capable of transforming pneumococci were so separated, they lost biological activity but regained it on being reconstituted as double molecules.

All this constitutes powerful support for the Watson-Crick hypothesis but does not prove it beyond all doubt. Nature is often perverse and might have evolved another way of replicating DNA that would give the observed results.

DNA synthesis in the test tube

Even more dramatic evidence in favor of the Watson-Crick hypothesis of DNA reproduction has come from the laboratories of Professor Arthur Kornberg and his co-workers formerly of Washington University now at Stanford. They have shown that in a solution of the four nucleotides of DNA as triphosphates, a suitable buffer magnesium ions and an enzyme that catalyzes the polymerization of DNA chains, new DNA molecules are formed without lag if primer DNA molecules are added. The new DNA has the same ratio of adenine-thymine to guanine-cytosine nucleotide pairs as the added primer. This ratio varies in native DNA's of different sources. There are other similarities between mother and daughter DNA molecules that support the conclusion that the order of nucleotides in the former is reproduced in the latter.

If the nucleotide solution is allowed to stand without primer for several hours, a spontaneously formed DNA appears. This consists only of adenine-thymine nucleotide pairs. If now this A–T polymer is used as a primer in a fresh preparation, daughter DNA containing only A–T molecules is formed without delay. The C and G nucleotides available for synthesis are excluded, as they should be if the copying is according to the Watson-Crick hypothesis. This spontaneously synthesized DNA is important and exciting in another way. It demonstrates that under favorable conditions DNA can arise without pre-existing DNA, as one must suppose it once did in the evolution of the primitive living systems that first appeared on earth some billions of years ago.

In the Kornberg system, DNA heated under conditions that separate the strands is a more effective primer than is double-stranded DNA. Similarly, native single-stranded DNA as found in the smallest known bacterial virus, ϕX174, is more efficient as a primer than is its double counterpart. It presumably reproduces in the test tube system like single chains derived from double helices, by directing the synthesis of a partner with a complementary nucleotide composition.

The genetically significant DNA of T2 virus appears to be in the form of a continuous double helix at least 120,000 nucleotide pairs in length, giving it a molecular weight of approximately 80 million. After injection into a suitable host cell this tremendous molecule replicates seven or eight times in a period of about ten minutes. This means a molecular generation every one and a half minutes. Considering that the two chains are wound around each other in a double helix with a total of at least 12,000 turns, one wonders how the two chains are able to separate. The manner is not known, but calculation would indicate that the energy requirement for untwisting is small if the molecule turns on its own axis in a manner like that of a spinning speedometer cable.

DNA in chromosomes

Professor J. Herbert Taylor of Columbia University has shown that DNA of plant chromosomes labeled with tritium (radioactive hydrogen) is distributed to daughter chromosomes, formed in the absence of label, as expected on the assumption that it was arranged as a single double helix per chromosome. Evidently the DNA molecules of a chromosome are arranged in some very special way, for the summed length of all the DNA molecules in a single chromosome is 1000 or more times that of the chromosome.

Significance of DNA replication

There is no other molecular structure known to science that permits a pattern-copy type of reproduction like that of DNA. DNA replication may therefore be the fundamental and unique molecular event underlying all biological reproduction in all living organisms from the smallest DNA viruses to man himself. If so, its appearance on primitive earth may well have been a decisive step in the evolution of living systems.

Translation of DNA information

How is the information written in DNA code used in the direction of life processes? A detailed consideration of this complex question is given in Chapter 2 of this book. It will suffice for our purposes to point out here that a hypothesis widely employed by geneticists and biochemists as a working basis assumes a sequence of events somewhat as follows:

Segments of DNA in the chromosomes—genes—transfer information to ribonucleic acid (RNA) presumably by a template mechanism during which RNA molecules, consisting of four nucleotides much like those of DNA (except that the sugar component is ribose instead of deoxyribose) are constructed against double DNA molecules or possibly against single DNA chains. In this way, possibly through the use of specific hydrogen bonding, the four nucleotides become arranged in RNA according to a pattern dictated by DNA nucleotide sequence. This informational RNA then moves to the cytoplasm where it becomes incorporated in submicroscopic structures called ribosomes (or microsomes). These are the site of protein synthesis. Each of the 20 kinds of amino acids becomes attached to a small coding segment of RNA. As these amino acid-RNA complexes come in contact with the ribosome, the coding segment of RNA to which they are attached serves as a kind of address tag coded to specific segments of the informational RNA template. They are thus properly ordered along the template and joined into protein chains by the formation of connecting peptide bonds. Presumably protein molecules synthesized in this way then peel off the template and the process is repeated.

In whatever way the genetic DNA achieves this remarkable feat of specifying amino acid sequence in proteins, it is abundantly clear that in many cases genes do function in determining protein structure, each gene species being responsible for one kind of protein chain. Hemoglobin molecules are protein in large part. In man, each hemoglobin molecule is built up of four protein chains, two of one kind and two of another kind. Each such chain is associated with a heme group. The two alpha chains are synthesized according to directions carried by one gene. The two beta chains are specified by a second gene well separated genetically from the first.

In the same way it is supposed that for every one of the thousands of specific protein chains in an individual there is in the nucleus a segment of DNA in which is coded the information required to arrange the many amino acids in proper sequence in that particular protein chain. This segment of DNA we define as a gene.

The DNA-protein coding problem

How is information in the 4-symbol DNA code translated into that of 20-symbol protein? No one yet knows in complete detail. It has

protein component of human hemoglobin. An inherited defect in this protein is identified with a substitution of the amino acid valine for the glutamic acid unit normally present in one of the 150 amino acid positions of the beta protein. The altered hemoglobin molecule containing this one-unit substitution in each of its beta chains is called S hemoglobin because red blood cells containing it become distorted—often sickle-shaped—under conditions of low oxygen supply. Persons who have only S hemoglobin suffer from "sickle-cell anemia." Their red blood cells have a reduced life expectancy and tend not to be replaced sufficiently rapidly to keep the hemoglobin content of the blood at a normal level.

Sickle-cell hemoglobin is inherited in a simple Mendelian manner. The gene that specifies normal beta hemoglobin protein has become altered in such a way that it now directs the synthesis of S hemoglobin with one glutamic acid unit replaced by valine. Presumably, a specific amino acid-specifying segment of the DNA molecule that is this gene has been altered. Since the instructional coding system is not known, we do not know the nature of this segment either before or after mutation. Using a hypothetical triplet code, we might imagine that an ATC triplet encodes glutamic acid and that an ATG triplet, changed only in the third nucleotide, encodes valine. The gene mutation would thus involve the C–G nucleotide pair in such a way that a 3-unit segment would be modified from

$$
\begin{array}{ccccccccccc}
A & - & T & - & C & \quad \text{to} \quad & A & - & T & - & G \\
\vdots & & \vdots & & \vdots & & \vdots & & \vdots & & \vdots \\
T & - & A & - & G & & T & - & A & - & C
\end{array}
$$

There are obviously two possible categories of mutation in such a system: changes in 3-letter "words" in such a way that they specify different amino acids, or changes of a kind that do not encode any of the 20 amino acids. These have been called "missence" and "nonsense" mutations. The first would lead to an amino acid substitution as in S hemoglobin over against normal hemoglobin. The second might perhaps lead to omission of an amino acid.

Like random typographical errors in a sensible typed message in English a random mutation in a gene is more likely to be unfavorable than neutral or favorable. Thus S hemoglobin is unfavorable. But, again like typographical errors, gene mutations are not necessarily unfavorable in an absolute sense. The word "not" may or may not be unfavorable as compared with the word "now," depending on the context in which it appears. Persons with one gene for normal hemoglobin and one for S hemoglobin have both normal and S hemoglobin in each red cell. In the presence of tertian malaria (caused by a protozoan parasite that spends part of its life cycle in human red blood cells), having part S hemoglobin as a result of the mutant gene is an advantage because it confers a measure of resistance to the disease. In the absence of malaria, however, the same mutant gene is unfavorable because it reduces the oxygen-carrying capacity of the blood to a degree that might be dangerous under special circumstances such as those attending onset of other diseases. Actually, S hemoglobin is pretty largely confined to populations and their descendants that live or have lived in areas in which malaria is or has been prevalent.

We can therefore say that whether a given gene mutation is unfavorable or favorable will depend on its particular context. There are both genetic and environmental contexts in which all genes function.

Although one must acknowledge the possibility that an allele of a gene unfavorable under most circumstances may, by trial and error—and perhaps over a series of many generations—find a context in which it turns favorable, it is still a valid generalization that most mutant genes will be unfavorable in most contexts. Such mutant genes are eliminated by natural selection by reducing the reproductive fitness of the organisms that carry them. They may impair fitness in either heterozygous or homozygous form, and the degree of impairment may be small or large.

By definition, mutant genes that increase fitness under specific conditions are said to be favorable. They are the raw material of evolution in that they are preferentially multiplied relative to their ancestral forms as long as the environmental and genetic contexts continue to favor them.

Fine Structure of the Gene

If we define a gene as a segment of DNA in which are encoded the complete instructions for ordering the sequence of amino acids in a single protein chain, it is obvious that mutations should be possible at many or all of the nucleotide pairs that made up the gene. There is now extensive experimental evidence that this is indeed the case. This evidence comes from studies of recombination of mutational sites within genes and is of the same kind as the evidence showing that chromosomes contain many genes arranged in a linear sequence. Thus in a particular gene in the T2 bacterial virus, designated *rII*, mutants having separate origins show recombination in doubly infected host cells. Thus if a virus carrying a gene designated

rII_1

– – – – – – – – – – –

where rII_1 designates a mutational site (presumably a nucleotide pair), and a virus carrying an allele indicated

$$\overset{rII_2}{\text{— — — — — — — — — — —}}$$

simultaneously infect a host cell, the 100 or so daughter viruses that are released some 20 minutes later may include a few viruses that are not mutant at all, designated

— — — — — — — — — — —

In actual experiments these are detected by testing daughter viruses in a special test strain of bacteria in which the two mutant strains will not multiply, but in which a nonmutant recombinant will. This is obviously a different strain of bacteria from the one in which the original virus "crop" was grown. The complementary double mutant

$$rII_1 \qquad rII_2$$

— — — — — — — — — — —

is expected, but it is not usually easy to detect because in most cases it is like the single mutants in not being able to grow in the test bacterial strain.

Such intragenic recombinants are low in frequency, usually less than 1 percent of the total population, but are readily detected and counted because very large populations of viruses can be plated on a culture of test bacteria on which only the nonmutant recombinants are able to produce virus colonies or plaques. The total number of viruses tested is determined by plating—after appropriate dilutions of virus solution—on bacterial plates in which both mutant and nonmutant viruses are able to grow.

The recombination frequencies for various combinations of *rII* mutant strains of the virus indicate a linear order of the mutational sites within the gene. Thus a map of mutational sites within a gene is constructed in much the same way as are maps of genes within the entire DNA molecule of the virus. Furthermore, one can make crosses that show the mutational sites within a gene to be in the same linear sequence as are the different genes of the total genetic material of the virus.

Thus we are able to visualize the genetic material of the virus as a continuous DNA molecule some 120,000 nucleotide pairs long, subdivided into some 20 to 100 functional units or genes, each consisting of perhaps 1200 to 6000 nucleotide pairs.

One immediately wonders how functional units are separated from one another in the linear sequence. The answer is not known.

Possibly there are separating segments of DNA that do not encode amino acids.

Genetic fine-structure studies like the above have been extended to bacteria, fungi, flowering plants, and multicellular animals. They all support the view that the gene is genetically divisible into subunits. Studies of this kind often involve the use of ingenious and highly interesting genetic techniques, many of them too special to be described here. In organisms with true chromosomes it is not known whether functional units of DNA, here defined as genes, are separated by non-DNA material, protein presumably, or are parts of large continuous DNA molecules.

Mendel's Concepts Modified

Mendel postulated that the hereditary units which he called "elements" and we call genes were discrete and particulate, that they were assorted and recombined independently of one another in sexual reproduction, and that the dominant and recessive forms of a given element were not cross-contaminated in the hybrid. Shortly after the rediscovery and reappreciation of Mendel's work, it was realized that his law of independent assortment was based on limited observations and needed to be modified to take genetic linkage into account. We now know that the concept of the purity of the gametes was also only a first approximation. We see from the results of intragenic recombination studies that the two alleles of a single gene can in fact recombine their subunits and thus become mutually modified in the hybrid. Until relatively recently this phenomenon was not detected, because the usual practice in classical genetics is to deal with hybrids in which differences between alleles of the same gene are confined to a single site. Obviously, intragenic recombination can be detected genetically only if two alleles differ in two or more mutational sites.

We now know, too, that Mendel's view of dominance and recessiveness was also oversimplified; that, in fact, if the more sensitive tests are used, the difference between a diploid organism homozygous for a dominant allele of a gene can often be distinguished from one heterozygous for such an allele and a recessive allele. Complete dominance in Mendel's sense is probably not the rule and may be rare or even nonexistent.

Despite these refinements, Mendel's interpretation of inheritance remains as one of the great achievements of modern biology. It is, of course, usual in science to approach true interpretations through a series of closer and closer approximations. One even doubts the possibility of arriving at any interpretation of nature that achieves final truth.

Arbitrariness of the Definition of a Gene

We have defined the gene as a functional unit of genetic material. We could instead define it either as a unit of recombination or as a unit of mutation. In fact, until recently it was assumed that the unit defined in all three ways was the same unit. We know now it is not. In a sense, any decision regarding which definition to adopt is arbitrary. The one chosen here coincides closely with the units Mendel dealt with and those that most classical geneticists since him have made use of in practice. No one of the three is easy to use operationally in a precise way. The functional gene is fully defined only if we know the molecular structure of the immediate gene products—RNA and protein. In no case do we yet know these in complete detail.

Clearly, in whatever way we define a gene, it is a fundamental unit of biology. Not only do the genes encode a large part of the specifications for the development and functioning of all living creatures, but they almost certainly played decisive roles at all stages of organic evolution from the time of the earliest appearance of living systems on earth to the advent of man himself. Today chemists, physicists, and biologists can talk about genes and work with them in molecular terms common to these three branches of natural science. In large part, this was made possible by the formulation of the Watson-Crick structure of DNA.

REFERENCES

Allfrey, V. G., and A. E. Mirsky, "How cells make molecules." *Sci. Am.*, September, 1961.

Beadle, G. W., "Physiological aspects of genetics." *Ann. Rev. Physiol.*, 22:45–74, 1960.

Jacob, F., and E. L. Wollman, "Viruses and genes." *Sci. Am.*, June 1961.

Sager, R., and F. J. Ryan, 1961, *Cell Heredity*. New York: John Wiley.

FRITS W. WENT, *Director*

Missouri Botanical Garden, St. Louis

Frits W. Went, son of Dr. F. A. F. C. Went, the well-known Dutch Professor of Botany at the University of Utrecht, was born in 1903. During his youth he lived next to the Botanical Garden and Botanical Institute of the University, in constant contact with plants and botanists, and this stimulating environment induced him to become a botanist himself.

After receiving his Ph.D. degree at the University of Utrecht in 1927, on a thesis describing the role of the growth hormone in the Avena seedling, he went to Java, where he was associated with the famous Botanical Gardens at Buitenzorg (Bogor) for five years. In 1933 he went to the California Institute of Technology at Pasadena, where he was Professor of Plant Physiology.

During his early years in California, he worked on hormonal control of plant growth, as well as on root formation and other auxin-affected phenomena, but his research interests gradually turned to environmental influences on plant growth. The results of over fifteen years of work in this field are summarized in a book, published in 1957, *The Experimental Control of Plant Growth.*

His other botanical interests, which developed in the course of extensive travels all over the world, lie in the fields of ecology, especially of the tropical forest and the desert, and of evolution.

His interests in botanical gardens are evident from his former membership on the Board of Governors of the Los Angeles State and County Arboretum, and his present position as Director of the Missouri Botanical Garden. He has lectured on his work in different parts of the world (twice as national Sigma Xi lecturer). He is honorary doctor at the Université de Paris, member of the National Academy of Sciences, Correspondent of the Koninklijke Nederlandse Akademie van Wetenschappen, Amsterdam, of the Academie des Sciences, Paris, and of the Academie Royale de Belgique, and president of the American Institute of Biological Sciences.

His published works include, in addition to many technical papers, *Phytohormones* (with K. V. Thimann), Macmillan, 1937.

What is growth? Actually, a number of very different phenomena are lumped under this general term. Here, however, we shall consider three of the several manifestations of growth:

1) Increase in size. This can come about simply by water uptake, as in a cactus plant swelling after a rain. This water uptake is not really growth, just as the swelling of seeds is not growth, for this water can be lost again with no ultimate gain in size or dry weight. Therefore we can refine our definition of growth as increase in volume by limiting it to an *irreversible increase in size.* For instance, the elongation of a young stem is largely due to water uptake; this growth is irreversible and therefore is true growth.

2) Increase in number of cells. This is the most significant type of growth. Each cell division is preceded by mitosis, which involves doubling the number of chromosomes and a twofold increase in the nucleic acids of the nucleus. It is also accompanied by increases in cytoplasm and other cell components, but these latter do not bear such a rigid stoichiometric relationship to increase in cell number.

3) Development and differentiation. In higher plants these phenomena are always accompanied by cell division, which now results not only in an increase in cell mass, but in special arrangements of the newly formed cells into different tissues and organs. This is the most remarkable type of growth, since it leads to the complexity of the plant body, and it is exhibited only by multicellular organisms.

Rather than discuss growth in terms of generalizations, let us examine what happens in the tip of a stem as it grows. The growing point or meristem of the stem is usually not immediately visible, but is surrounded and covered by the young leaves. It looks like a hill less than 0.1 mm wide (Fig. 8.1), consisting of isodiametric cells. Whereas the width of the meristematic hill may differ from plant to plant, the size of the cells of this meristem is about the same, whether they belong to a giant redwood tree or a miniature herb. In all fast-growing plants the meristematic cells are 10 to 15 μ wide, whereas in slow-growing ones, this size may increase to about 30 μ.

When the cells produced from these meristems have reached their final size, we again find that they are approximately of the same dimensions: the strongly elongated cells in stems and vascular bundles are up to 1 mm in length; other, isodiametric cells, are approximately 0.1 mm in diameter. Therefore differences in size that are found among different kinds of plants are largely caused by differences in the number of cells.

The cells of the apical meristem divide continuously, and thus produce more stem tissue. To produce the shapes typical for each species, these cell divisions in the apical meristem have to follow a very rigid schedule. Some of the general rules for development and differentiation can be stated very simply:

1) In ferns and mosses all cells of the stem are derived from a single tetrahedric initial cell, located centrally on top of the meristem.

2) In phanerogams there is no initial cell, but a whole group of

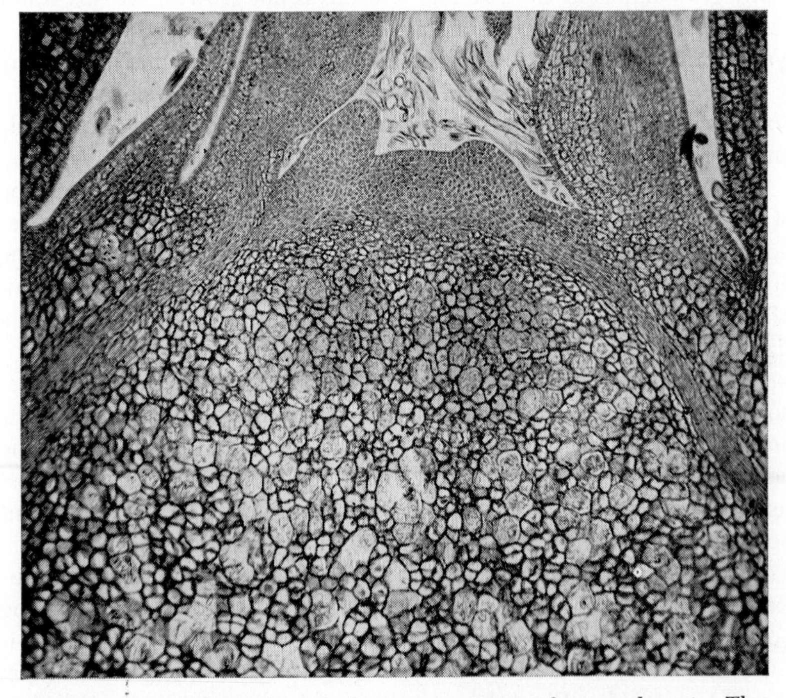

Fig. 8.1. Cross section through the growing point of an apple twig. The central flat part of the growing cone is the apical meristem. To the right a small hill indicates the first leaf; to the left a larger hill indicates the next older leaf. In the lower part of the section cells have stopped dividing and are enlarging. (From C. L. Wilson and W. E. Loomis, *Botany*, rev. ed., Holt, 1957. With permission.)

meristematic cells that divide continuously. In this apical meristem a central group of cells, the "corpus" in the form of an inverted cone, normally does not divide; but the tunica cells around this corpus are actively dividing.

3) The outer layer of cells, the periderm, divides only in radial direction, and thus remains one cell layer thick. In the mature plant this layer becomes the epidermis.

4) The next layer of cells, the periblem, divides also predominantly radially, but occasionally produces tangential walls. The cortex tissues are all derived from the periblem cells in the apical meristem.

5) The third layer of cells, the plerome, produces the cells of the central part of the stem, the central cylinder, containing all vascular elements.

When observing the growing point and the areas below it, it will be seen that just under the half-dome-shaped apex a number of small

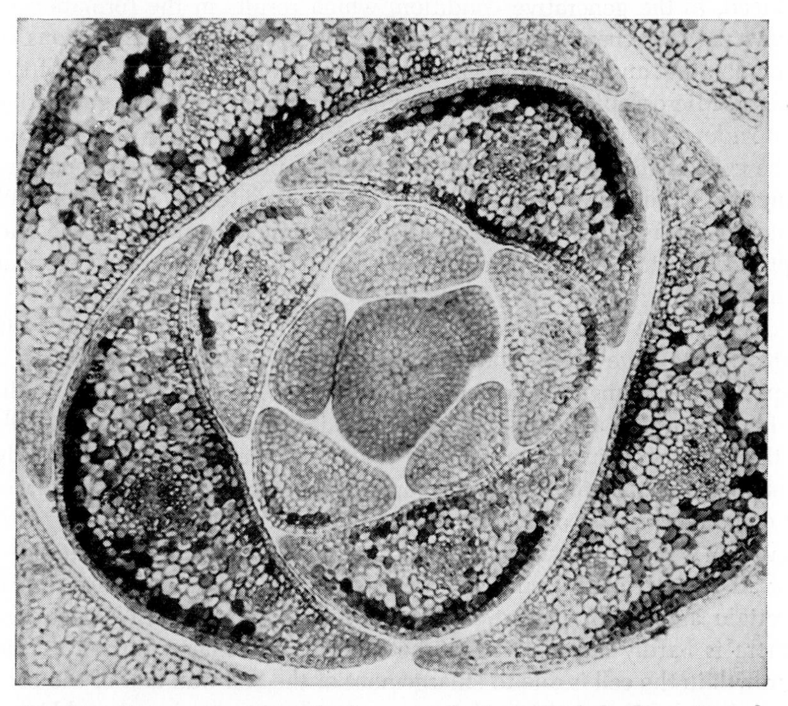

Fig. 8.2. Cross section through the young bud of Rhododendron. Central area is growing point with, toward upper right, the youngest leaf primordium attached, next oldest leaf to the left of meristem. Next oldest to the lower right, etc., in a spiral arrangement. (From C. L. Wilson and W. E. Loomis, *Botany*, rev. ed., Holt, 1957. With permission.)

hills appear, and also that they are larger the further they are removed from the apex. These are growth areas of increased mitotic activity, and they will give rise to leaves or flower parts. They appear in a regular sequence (Fig. 8.2), each next one approximately 137 degrees removed from the previous one. This results in a spiral arrangement of leaves around the stem.

Many experiments have been carried out to try to change the arrangement of cells of leaf and flower primordia in the apical meristem. In only very few cases has it been possible to influence this arrangement; therefore, we can say that the control of cell division in the apical meristem is largely under the influence of internal factors within the cells themselves, and that the environment has only a slight guiding influence on these divisions.

There is, however, one specific case in which the environment is able to cause a dramatic change in the apical meristem. This is when it is passing from the vegetative condition, in which just leaves are produced, to the generative condition, which results in the formation of flowers. This change can be brought about by marked alterations in temperature and by changes in the intervals of daily illumination of the plant. Microscopically, the development from vegetative to generative is evidenced by a widening of the meristem, and by an activation of the cells of the corpus. Once this has taken place, the whole arrangement of primordia just below the meristem is different, and instead of having the new parts arranged about the stem in spirals like the leaf primordia, the calyx, petal, stamen, and carpel primordia appear in whorls.

After a sufficient number of cell divisions in which most of the stem parts have been produced in the form of meristematic cells, a spectacular change occurs in these cells. Instead of continuing to divide, or instead of remaining small and isodiametric, these stem cells start to elongate in the direction of the axis of the stem. There is hardly any widening of the cells; they enlarge only in a longitudinal direction, and thus become long and narrow. This elongation stage of growth is macroscopically the most spectacular, and more than 9/10 of all stem growth occurs as a result of stem elongation. Although a certain amount of new cytoplasm is formed during cell elongation, there is hardly any growth of the nucleus: the major portion of the growth in the cell is due to enlargement of the cell wall and of the central vacuole. The cytoplasm becomes spread out over a larger and larger expanse of cell wall until it forms only a very thin layer. During this period of cell elongation, the cells are very strongly influenced by the environment, and the difference between a tall and a short plant of the same species is usually largely the result of differences in stem elongation.

The greatest advances in the knowledge of plant growth came when botanists began to investigate the problem of growth correlations. By "growth correlations" are meant interrelations between phenomena in plants, as when a particular event is always observed in conjunction with another one, or when the presence of certain parts is essential to growth in other parts. In botany we therefore use the term correlation in a strictly causal sense, in contradistinction to its statistical use, which implies only a mathematical and not a causal relationship.

Detailed information about the story of plant growth substances or growth hormones, which now follows, can be found in books like those of Went and Thimann, or in a more recent study by Audus (see References at end of chapter).

The earliest botanists had noted, for instance, that when a stem is cut into a number of sections or cuttings, new roots are formed at the basal end of the cutting, and not at the apical end. They therefore assumed that materials required for rooting flowed down in stems, resulting in root development at the base of the stem. A particularly clear case of such correlation was discovered and investigated by the great English biologist Charles Darwin (1880). Darwin was not only a great thinker, but he was also one of the best observers of nature who ever lived. When he was investigating plant tropisms—that is, the curvatures which plant parts produce under the influence of light or gravity—he noticed that after removal of the extreme tip of the stem or of the root, the parts below (which grow most rapidly) were unable to respond to light or gravity. An even more remarkable experiment was carried out when he illuminated only the extreme tip or only the lower part of grass seedlings. He found then that only when the tip was illuminated from one side was the seedling able to bend toward the light, whereas similar unilateral light falling on the lower part of the stem was ineffective in causing curvature. He also noticed that it was necessary to let light shine on one side of the seedling for only a short while in order to produce a curvature toward that light an hour later. From this he deduced that the perception of light was spatially and temporally separated from the plant's response to this light with a phototropic curvature. Darwin therefore showed for the first time that there exists a *correlation* between the stem or root tip and the growth zones in plants.

It took scientists almost 30 years to recognize the general significance and correctness of Darwin's observations, and only then did it become possible to advance further.

Since so much of the following work has been carried out with grass seedlings, specifically oats, it will be useful to describe these seedlings in more detail. Oat seeds, when buried in moist soil or sand, soon germinate. The seeds first swell, and within one day at 25° C the primary root emerges from the seed and becomes visible. Soon afterward, the shoot also starts to grow, and develops into a long tubelike organ, the coleoptile (Fig. 8.3), which grows straight up to a length of 50 mm as long as it remains in darkness. Once the tip of the coleoptile is exposed to light, it stops growing, and the enclosed folded first leaf pushes through a thin spot near the apex of the coleoptile, and thus the tender leaf is guided through the soil by the tubular coleoptile.

The coleoptile starts its growth on the second day of germination, grows faster on the third day, has a fairly constant high growth rate (about 1 mm per hour) on the fourth day, then reduces its rate and stops growing when the first leaf penetrates. This so-called grand period of growth—slow, fast, slow—is typical of all plant organs and thus the growth of the grass coleoptile exemplifies plant growth in general. Because of its simple cylindrical structure, fast growth rate, and great phototropic sensitivity, the oat coleoptile has become the favorite experimental object of plant growth study. Another advantage is that during the last and most rapid growth stages, practically no cell division occurs in the coleoptile, so that we are dealing here with only one type of growth: cell elongation.

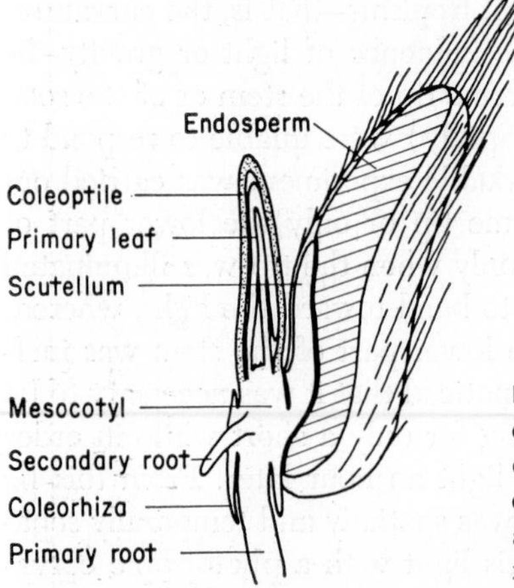

Fig. 8.3. Longitudinal section through an oat seedling showing the early stage of coleoptile growth 30 hours after beginning of germination. (Redrawn from F. Went and K. V. Thimann, *Phytohormones,* Macmillan, 1937. With permission.)

In 1911 Boysen-Jensen of Denmark published a very important paper in which he described how phototropic curvatures could no longer be produced in oat coleoptiles from which the tips had been removed; but that after the cut tip had been glued back onto the stump of the seedling, phototropic sensitivity was restored: that is, the phototropic stimulus can be transmitted across a wound gap.

Boysen-Jensen's experiments were repeated by Paal who fully confirmed them. In addition to Boysen-Jensen's finding, Paal (1918) discovered that even without illumination, there is a stimulus continuously moving from the coleoptile tip to the lower zones, which causes these lower zones to grow. He assumed, therefore, that the phototropic curvature in these coleoptiles was produced by redistribution of the normal downflow of a growth-promoting substance from the tip of the seedling toward the growing zones.

It was on the basis of the work of Boysen-Jensen and Paal that I carried out my own experiments with oat coleoptiles (Went 1928). Since it had been shown by Paal that a growth-promoting material was produced in the seedling tip, and since it had also been shown that this growth-promoting stimulus could cross a wound gap, even if there were a thin layer of gelatin between tip and stump, it was logical to assume that this growth-promoting material had to be in the gelatin on its way downward (Fig. 8.4). Therefore, the following experiment was carried out:

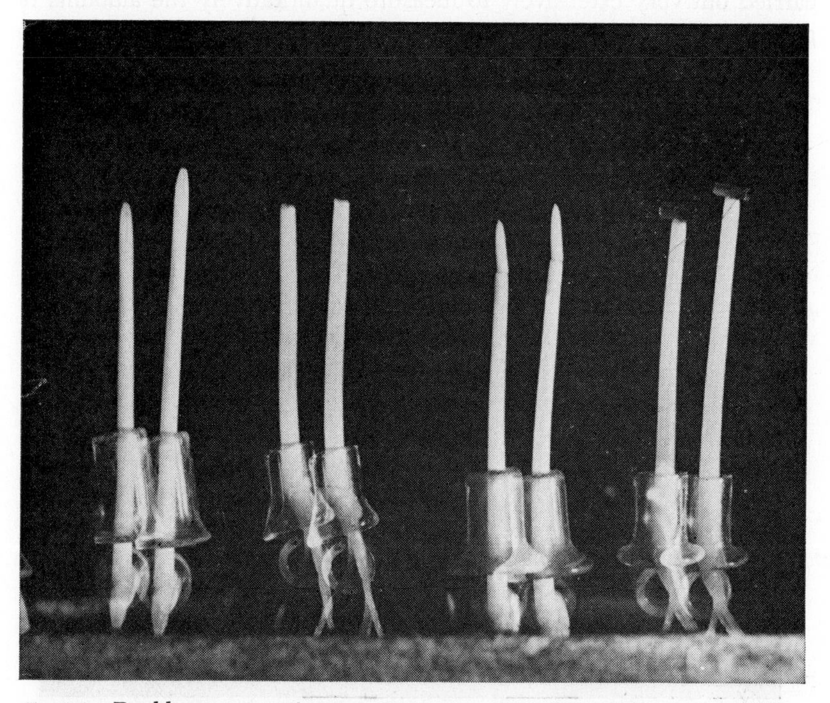

Fig. 8.4. Double exposure of series of four oat coleoptiles two hours apart. The left intact coleoptile shows growth of approximately 3 mm in 2 hours. Second from left decapitated coleoptile shows less than 1 mm of growth in 2 hours. Third from left decapitated coleoptile on which tip has been replaced shows 1½ mm of growth. On the right-hand plant, decapitated coleoptile on which an agar block with diffusate from tips has been placed shows 2½ mm growth in two hours. (Courtesy Edmund B. Gerard.)

A number of coleoptile tips were cut off and placed on a thin layer of gelatin, or agar (Fig. 8.5). After one or two hours the tips were removed and the gelatin was placed on the decapitated coleoptile stump. Whereas this had not grown much after the tip was removed, it did grow when gelatin on which tips had stood was put on the cut surface. A simple quantitative test was developed in which the gelatin (with tip diffusate) was placed on only one side of the cut surface. This resulted in increased growth of the cells underneath the gelatin (or agar) block only: the decapitated seedling therefore started to curve. I could then show that the curvature was directly proportional to the concentration of the growth-promoting substance in the agar (Fig. 8.6).

This biological test for the growth-promoting substance produced in the coleoptile tip is called the *Avena Test*, and it has been carried out very extensively to measure quantitatively the amounts of growth-promoting substances present in plants. It also became possible

Fig. 8.5. Agar blocks with coleoptile tips standing on them. Auxin diffusing into agar. (Courtesy Edmund B. Gerard.)

to assess the role of this growth-promoting substance in the general phenomenon of growth.

To give an idea how the Avena test is carried out in a routine manner, Fig. 8.6A is included. This shows rows of test plants lined up on a shelf in the Avena test room, which is kept at a relative humidity of 95 percent so that the agar blocks do not dry out during the 100-minute reaction period. Each row of 12 plants has received agar blocks with the same auxin concentration. The plants are now ready to have shadow photographs taken, from which the angle of curvature can be measured. This angle is proportional to the auxin concentration. The average curvature of 12 plants is used in each test to reduce the error due to individual variability of the plants.

One of the most intriguing problems this growth-promoting

material has posed is its chemical nature. In a series of brilliant experiments, two chemists, Kögl and Haagen-Smit (1931), isolated a sufficient amount of the growth-promoting material to determine its chemical composition. This substance was called "auxin," and it turned out to be present not only in all plants, but in the animal body as well; and it was found that many microorganisms produced it. Auxin-*a* was the first auxin to be isolated, and its properties seemed to indicate that this was

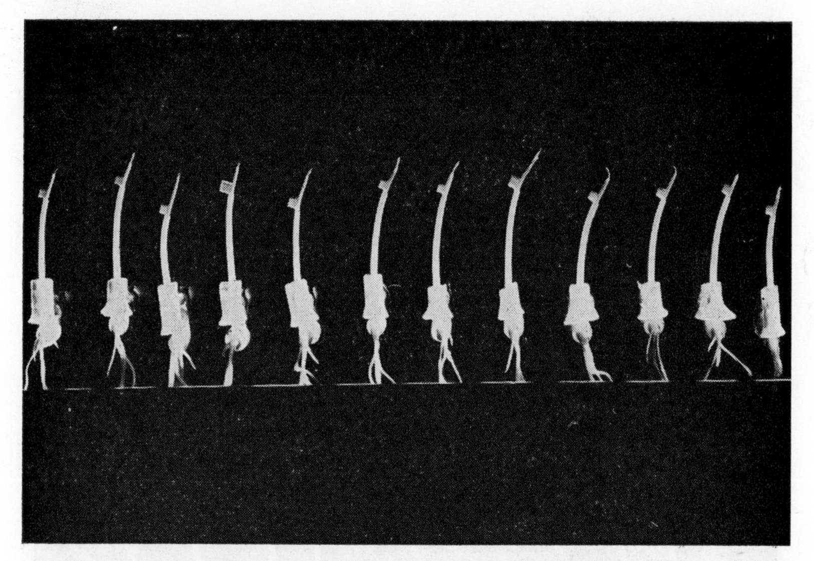

Fig. 8.6. Set of 12 decapitated coleoptiles on each of which an agar block has been placed unilaterally. The primary leaf protruding from the coleoptile is used for attaching the agar block. (Courtesy Edmund B. Gerard.)

the material that was produced in the tip of the oat coleoptile. The next substance with auxin activity to be isolated was indoleacetic acid, the abbreviation of which is IAA. This substance is easily synthesized and can now be bought from any chemical supply house.

This chemical identification of the auxins was entirely accomplished with the aid of biological tests, in which not the chemical properties of a substance, but its biological activity, was measured. The amount of auxin formed in one Avena coleoptile tip in the course of one hour is of the order of magnitude of one billionth of a gram, which precludes any attempt to identify it chemically. The presence and quantity of such a small amount can, however, be measured in the Avena test. In this way some basic properties of auxin, such as its light and heat stability, could be established, and its molecular weight determined through diffusion-rate measurements. Extraction of large quantities of auxin became possible when it was found that certain plant and animal products contained relatively high concentrations of it. These source materials were then extracted with organic solvents and precipitated with specific reagents; each time the effectiveness of the process was checked with the Avena test, and the most active material was concentrated further. In this way the auxin in the starting material had to be concentrated approximately a millionfold before it was obtained as crystals which then could be identified by regular chemical methods.

Fig. 8.6a. (Courtesy Edmund B. Gerard.)

The isolation of these auxins and their availability in large quantities raised a question as to whether it was possible to increase normal plant growth to an unheard-of degree by applying synthetic auxins. Calculation showed that theoretically one gram of indoleacetic acid could produce hundreds of miles of growth of a seedling. Rather to our regret, it turned out not to be so. For even though these substances were produced in the plant and would make the plant stem grow, no excessive growth could be produced by application of much larger amounts of the auxins. This is because growth is a very complex phenomenon in which a large number of chemicals interact to increase the size of cells. Auxin is only one of the factors contributing to growth, and while the concentration of auxin increases, other growth factors

cause growth by itself if it were applied as long as any auxin remained in the coleoptile stump. The difference between a true auxin and an auxin synergist could then be found by comparing their effectiveness when applied immediately after decapitation, and again several hours later. Consequently, the standard Avena test is always carried out by applying the test substance two hours after the first decapitation, and immediately after the second.

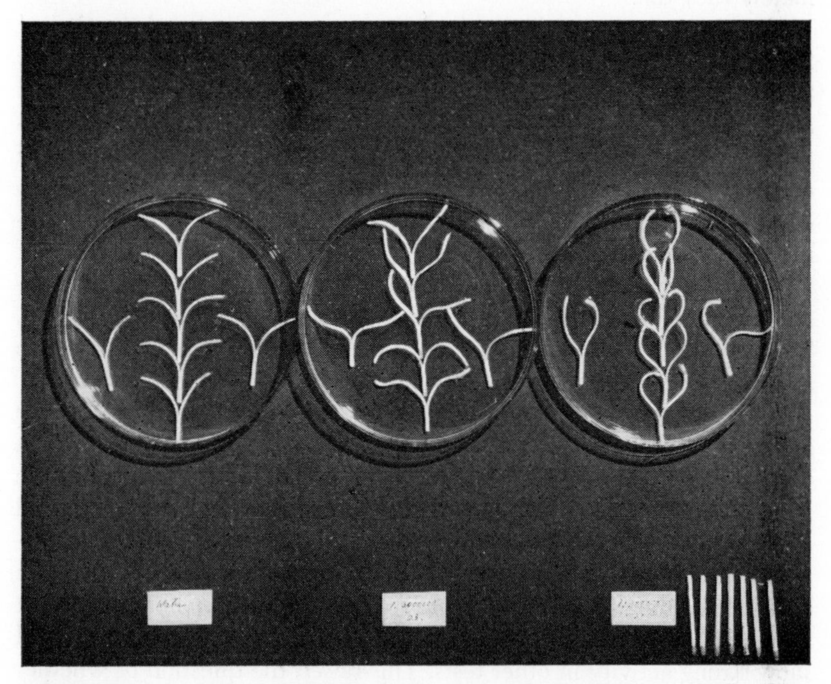

Fig. 8.9. Pea test for auxin. Etiolated pea stems split lengthwise and placed in petri dishes with (*left*) pure water, (*right*) 3 parts per million indoleacetic acid, and (*center*) 3/10 of a part per million of indoleacetic acid; photographed 7 hours after placing in solutions. (Courtesy Edmund B. Gerard.)

When indoleacetic acid is applied in the pea test immediately after splitting of the stems, or four hours later, very little difference in the response is found (Fig. 8.9). When the same comparison is made for 2,4-dichlorophenoxyacetic acid, the activity is seen to be greatly reduced in the pea stems decapitated and split four hours earlier. Presumably, the amount of native auxin in them has been depleted in the four hours between splitting and application. This indicates that 2,4-dichlorophenoxyacetic acid probably exerts its effects in the split pea test not by itself, as indoleacetic and naphthaleneacetic acids presumably do. This difference might explain why 2,4-dichlorophenoxyacetic acid (commonly abbreviated to 2,4-D) is used as a weedkiller, whereas the other two true auxins mentioned do not kill plants. All three at high concentrations initially produce the same symptoms: excessive growth of stems accompanied by bending of stems and leaf stalks. But whereas plants recover from high auxin doses and become quite normal after some time, the symptoms on the plants treated with 2,4-D worsen, leaf development is strongly inhibited, the plants start to wilt, and ultimately they die.

There are a number of hypotheses to account for the action of 2,4-D as a weedkiller (although, "weedkiller" is really a misnomer, for 2,4-D is very effective in killing broad-leaved plants such as mustard and other common weeds—and equally effective on tomatoes and especially cotton). One of the first to be advanced was that it increased carbohydrate metabolism to such extent that the plant burnt itself to death. Although occasionally 2,4-D application leads to increased respiration, this seems to be only a minor effect. Another suggestion was that 2,4-D was so much more effective than the natural auxins that it overstimulated all growth processes and the plant grew itself to death. This supposition is not borne out by comparison of activity in the standard tests.

Gradually, more and more substances were discovered to have auxin activity; that is, they could cause curvatures in the Avena or pea tests, or in general could make stem cells grow. This complicated the general picture of auxin activity. It has already been explained that all substances which are active in these tests have certain structural characteristics in common, and therefore can structurally take the place of auxin in the specific molecular configuration at the place of action. But some of these substances are not, or are hardly, active in one test and show strong activity in other tests. This raised the question of whether the same reaction was being measured in different tests. Table 8.1, for instance, shows the relative activity of five different substances in the Avena and the pea test. In each case the activity of indoleacetic acid is considered to be 100. We then see that in the Avena test this substance is many times more active than any other, whereas in the pea test naphthalene acetic acid, and indolebutyric acid are as active as indoleacetic acid.

Where they were investigated, these discrepancies in test performance could be explained on the basis of secondary properties of the active substances. In the Avena test, for instance, only substances which are translocated downward can cause unequal growth and a curvature, whereas in the pea test the stems are submerged in the solution and all cells can take up applied substances equally. It was shown that the transport downward in the Avena coleoptile of naphthalene acetic acid is many times slower than that of indoleacetic acid; this makes the former substance seem less active, but when it gets to the reaction locus it gives molecule for molecule the same amount of growth. *Cis*-cinnamic acid is not only slowly translocated in the coleoptile, but it is also a stronger acid than indoleacetic acid. Since only non-dissociated auxin molecules are able to take part in the growth reaction, *cis*-cinnamic acid seems less active, but if a correction is made for its greater dissociation, again equal molar activity is found.

TABLE 8.1

Activity of Different Auxins in Equimolar Solutions in Various Tests, with or without Corrections

	Indole acetic acid	Indole butyric acid	Napthalene acetic acid	Indole propionic acid	Cis-cinnamic acid
Avena test	100	5	2	0.3	0.05
Oat coleoptile section test (sections immersed in solutions)	100	100	50	2	2
Pea test	100	100	100	50	10
Pea test pretreated with γ phenyl butyric acid	100	100	100	100	20
Pea test pretreated, corrected for dissociation	100	100	100	100	100

The cases of 2,4-dichlorophenoxyacetic acid and of phenylbutyric acid are very peculiar. They are entirely inactive in the Avena test, and they are active in the pea test *only* when applied immediately after splitting of the stems. If one lets the split pea stems lie in water for four hours before applying the auxins, then indoleacetic acid is still fully active, but the other two substances are almost or completely inactive. This means that the two latter substances can produce only part of the reactions typical for indoleacetic acid. Another indication of a difference in the action of these substances is that they are synergistic; that is, the activity of one, indoleacetic acid, can be enhanced, up to tenfold, by the presence of the other two substances. Therefore it has been suggested that 2,4-dichlorophenoxyacetic acid, for example, is not in itself an auxin, but that it only enhances the activity of the native auxin in the plant. If at the same time 2,4-D inhibited the further formation of native auxin in the plant, its peculiar behavior (temporary overstimulation of various processes in which auxins take part) could be explained.

We can therefore conclude that, in spite of many complicating factors and effects and in spite of many conflicting facts still needing clarification, a fairly clearcut picture can nonetheless be drawn of auxins and auxin activity. It has been shown that the great majority of substances active as auxins have the same basic structure and the same basic molar activity. Departure from the basic structure leads to anti-auxins or synergists, inactive by themselves but enhancing or inhibiting activity of the true auxins. But thus far nothing has been said about another aspect of auxin activity.

One of the most amazing discoveries in the field of plant growth hormones is that the same auxin which had been shown to be essential for cell elongation was also responsible for a large number of completely different physiological effects. The first of these was the discovery of Thimann and Skoog (1933) that lateral bud inhibition by the apical bud was transmitted through the same growth-promoting substance that caused the stem to elongate under the apical bud. This meant that auxin could both stimulate and inhibit growth. The explanation for this phenomenon is not clear, although there is evidence that concentration differences are involved in the stimulation and inhibition of growth. Yet this does not seem to be the complete explanation for lateral bud inhibition. Because of the confused situation in this field, the problem will not be discussed in more detail.

The next discovery was made by Thimann and myself. We showed that the same extracts, which caused cell elongation, were effective in producing root formation, and it was finally shown that indoleacetic acid was able to produce root formation in exactly the same way that auxin does this in the intact plant.

Root formation is in many respects an entirely different phenomenon from that of cell elongation. It does not mean cell wall extension alone, but involves cell division and cell differentiation. Normally, roots develop as laterals from other roots, but occasionally roots can be produced on stems, which means that stem cells have to dedifferentiate, become meristematic, and then must differentiate into root cells. Whereas, potentially, most stem cells can give rise to roots, actually it is almost exclusively the cells of the pericycle, the cell layer just inside the endodermis of a stem, that change over into roots.

Fig. 8.10. Lemon cuttings. The two at left were treated with water, the two at right with indoleacetic acid; photographed two months after auxin application. (Courtesy Edmund B. Gerard.)

In the process of making cuttings or slips from a plant, stems are cut into sections, each having at least one node with bud, and usually one or more leaves. The bud and leaves are essential in the rooting of the cutting; without them no roots are produced. But they are unnecessary when auxin is applied (Fig. 8.10). Therefore the auxin normally formed in buds and leaves is essential to the formation of roots on stems. In this case auxin has a morphogenetic effect and causes tissue differentiation. Organ formation occurs always in the pericycle cells near the basal cut surface, even if the cutting is turned upside down or auxin is applied near or at the apical cut surface of the cutting. This polarity in root formation is due to the polar transport of auxin.

This polarity phenomenon was first demonstrated in the Avena coleoptile. When an agar block containing some auxin is placed on one end of a cylinder cut from a coleoptile, then auxin can be collected after an hour or less in a pure agar block placed on the other end of the coleoptile cylinder—but *only* when the auxin is applied on the apical end; no auxin moves from the base toward the tip (Fig. 8.11). This polar auxin transport was afterward demonstrated in stems and other plant parts as well, at least as long as the auxin moves through living

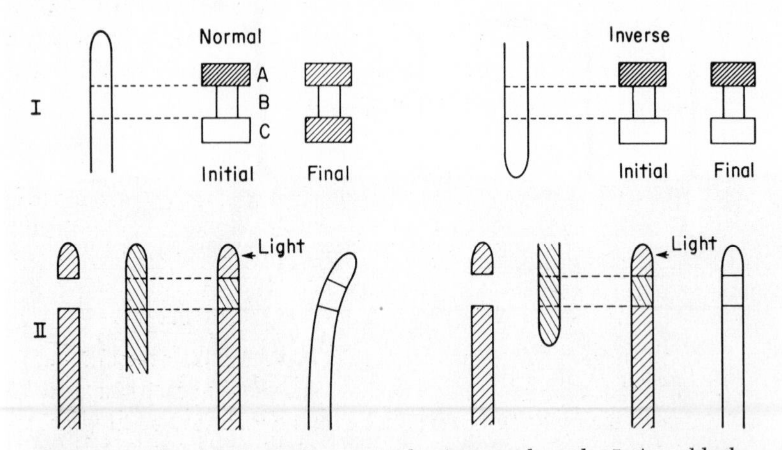

Fig. 8.11. Polar transport of auxin in the Avena coleoptile. I. Agar block, A, containing auxin, is placed on coleoptile section, B, resting on plain agar block, C. Degree of shading indicates auxin content of agar. Left side, normal transport; right side, section inverted—no transport. II. Transmission of phototropic stimulus through introduced section of coleoptile. Left side, stimulus passes normally placed section; right side, does not pass inverted section. (Redrawn from F. Went and K. V. Thimann, *Phytohormones,* Macmillan, 1937.)

cells. When it enters the transpiration stream, auxin may be carried up as well. But since in the intact plant the native auxin travels only in living cells, it always moves downward.

When a plant is treated with high auxin concentrations, the polarity is upset, and then roots may be induced wherever the auxin is applied. That phenomenon is now being used extensively by growers to make cuttings of hard-to-root plants. The basal cut surface of a stem cutting is dipped in an auxin solution or in talc mixed with finely powdered auxin (often naphthaleneacetic or indolebutyric acid); it can then be placed in the rooting frame, and after several weeks or months, roots will develop near the basal cut surface where the auxin was applied.

Another phenomenon in which auxin is prominently involved is the production of parthenocarpic fruit. Normally, an ovary does not develop into a fruit unless seeds are produced. However, when auxin is applied to the unpollinated ovary, the ovary will swell and develop into a near-normal fruit that contains no seeds. The most spectacular of these developments is the production of parthenocarpic watermelon which, amazingly, has not found public favor; at least, the melons are not available to the public. On the other hand, the tomato parthenocarpically produced by spraying the inflorescences of young plants with auxins, is a commercial means of increasing fruit set in early spring, before proper pollination of the flowers occurs. The spraying of auxin on flowers also makes it possible to produce holly plants with berries, in the absence of male trees in the neighborhood.

Fig. 8.12. Citrus trees with fruit dropped off in front of them. Left tree not sprayed, right tree sprayed with auxin. (Courtesy Edmund B. Gerard.)

Auxins are, at present, used extensively to prevent preharvest fruit drop, especially in apples. This phenomenon is related to the prevention of abscission of leaves when they are treated with auxins. A preharvest spray of apple trees will keep the ripe apples firmly attached to the branch, so that they do not drop off prematurely and become bruised when they hit the ground (Fig. 8.12).

Much work is being carried out on the effects of auxins in the prevention of abscission. As has been noted, certain effects of auxins can be counteracted by chemical substances that are closely related to auxin but differ structurally in a rather slight degree from the actual auxins. Such substances, or antiauxins, apparently get adsorbed to the same surfaces to which the actual auxins have to be adsorbed, before they can exert their effect. Since, however, they are chemically different, they do not produce the same reaction as the auxins, and they therefore clog the auxin reaction mechanism by usurping the place of the normal auxins. In this way, certain antiauxins have been used to defoliate cotton plants, for instance, before they are picked with a mechanical harvester.

Other processes or reactions enhanced by auxins include protoplasmic streaming, water uptake, and protoplasmic permeability. The effect of auxin on callus tissue growth will be mentioned later. It will not be possible to discuss all these different processes, but we must draw a few general conclusions from these facts. Either auxins are amazingly versatile substances, which can take part in the dozen or more physiological processes just enumerated, or else all these processes are dependent upon the same master reaction that sets all of them in motion, in much the same way as such processes depend on respiration. This master reaction has not unequivocally been found as yet. Whereas in general auxin, applied in concentrations that are physiologically effective, can be said to increase respiration in most tissues, there is definitely no stoichiometric relationship between the increased growth and the extra respiration. Conversely, it is possible to decrease growth with a number of inhibitors (iodoacetate, fluoride, dinitrophenol, etc.) without influencing respiration to the same extent. Therefore we can say that there is no special respiratory pathway along which auxin directs growth.

Even if auxin is not directly involved in respiratory processes, its mode of action suggests that it acts as a coenzyme, and therefore a study was made of possible substrates which might be used by the auxin enzyme. Again, no special substrate for the auxin reaction has been found, although in special cases one or another acid (such as citric acid) was found to increase auxin-induced growth.

Another approach involved trying to identify special enzyme systems that are formed or increased upon auxin application, or that parallel auxin concentration of tissues, or that are active especially in areas of greatest auxin and growth activity. Actually, there are several enzymes that increase greatly in effectiveness upon auxin application (ascorbic acid oxidase, pectin methyl esterase, and peroxidase). Since the pectin methylesterase in tobacco pith tissue cultured with auxin was connected especially with cell wall particles, this seemed to be a promising approach; but no such enzyme production was found in other tissues treated with auxin, and this tobacco tissue action would only explain auxin effects on cell walls and not on the dozen other auxin actions.

The case of increased peroxidase formation under the influence of auxin is interesting, because an indoleacetic acid oxidase is formed this way. Thus indoleacetic acid application produces an enzyme which destroys the substance that activates it. This is an interesting case of a self-regulatory mechanism and is a perfect example of a chemical feedback system.

As a general conclusion we can therefore say that the biochemical study of auxin action has given us much interesting information but has not elucidated the major problem, that of a principal biochemical reaction which is set in motion by auxins and which causes its effects. It is therefore very unlikely that auxin produces its manifold effects by setting in motion one master reaction. Yet we can try to approach this problem also from another angle.

In my first work on auxin I had already made it clear that it could produce its effect only in conjunction with other specific growth factors. In all subsequent work this general principle was borne out, and the idea expanded into my general hypothesis of calines. This assumes that there are specific growth factors, calines, in each part of the plant, and that they can be activated through combination with auxin. When auxin combines with caulocaline it induces stem elongation; when it combines with rhizocaline root formation is induced, etc. Thus the specificity of auxin action would be due to the specific caline with which it combines. Auxin could then be considered as a coenzyme for a number of calines. Although in much recent work the existence of unspecified growth factors combining or acting in conjunction with auxin is indicated, in no case has the actual caline been extracted. Thus this viewpoint has remained purely hypothetical; I mention it here because it clarifies in my own thinking the baffling problem of multiple auxin action.

Auxins are also called hormones because, in their typical functions, they are produced in the stem tip or young leaves, and produce their effects somewhere else, after being translocated there. They are effective in very low concentrations. This makes them comparable in function with animal hormones. Whereas in animals correlation between different parts of the body can be accomplished both by nerves and hormones, plants have no nerves, and therefore have only hormones or chemical messengers to integrate the various organs and parts. Whereas correlations between different organs in a plant are most easily studied, it must be evident that there are many other and subtler correlations in the plant body. Neighboring cells, for example, must be interrelated so that they grow at similar rates and form coherent tissues. During the past 25 years the nutrient requirements of plant tissues have been studied, and in the last few years growth studies of isolated individual cells have also become possible.

When plant tissues are removed from their natural cellular environment, they usually fail to grow, just as they cease to grow in the intact plant (Fig. 8.13). If a sufficiently large piece of stem or apical bud or root is placed in a medium containing sugar and salts, some growth may occur, either a continuation of the original growth (such as the stem tip or root), or a production of undifferentiated cells, a so-called callus. Such a callus is rather irregular, like a foam, and soon stops growing. Two Frenchmen, independently of each other, discovered that it was possible to obtain continued growth of such a callus provided some auxin was applied to the medium containing sugar and salts. When a small piece of callus from a stem segment of tobacco or a root section of carrot was cut off and placed in a flask with agar containing 2 percent sucrose and 10^{-6} molar indoleacetic acid, such a piece grew in the course of weeks or months into a cell mass of 1 to 5 cm diameter. This callus can be subcultured indefinitely by transferring a small segment to a new medium (Fig. 8.14). But when the subcultured piece is too small no growth occurs.

In general it had been found, also in animal tissue cultures, that only fairly large conglomerations of cells show continued growth; that is, normally the neighboring cells are necessary for growth. Then, one after another investigator succeeded in making individual cells grow and divide. This was accomplished in three different ways:

1) By confining cells to the smallest possible volume of nutrient medium in capillaries.

2) By providing a cellular environment by placing the individual cells on established tissue cultures, separated only by the thinnest possible permeable membrane (tissue paper).

3) By enriching the culture medium with further special growth factors.

All three methods have in common that they tend to increase the concentration of growth factors around the growing cells by preventing diffusion away from them, or by providing the factors from other cells or from the medium. A similar situation prevails in embryo growth. Egg cells or very small embryos could not be grown in culture media, but they developed between the mother cells of the uterus. As more cell growth factors became known, smaller and smaller explanted embryos could be grown to seedlings.

In a number of cases it has now been possible to produce callus cultures starting from a single cell. By the proper procedures it is even possible to induce such callus cultures to produce new shoots and

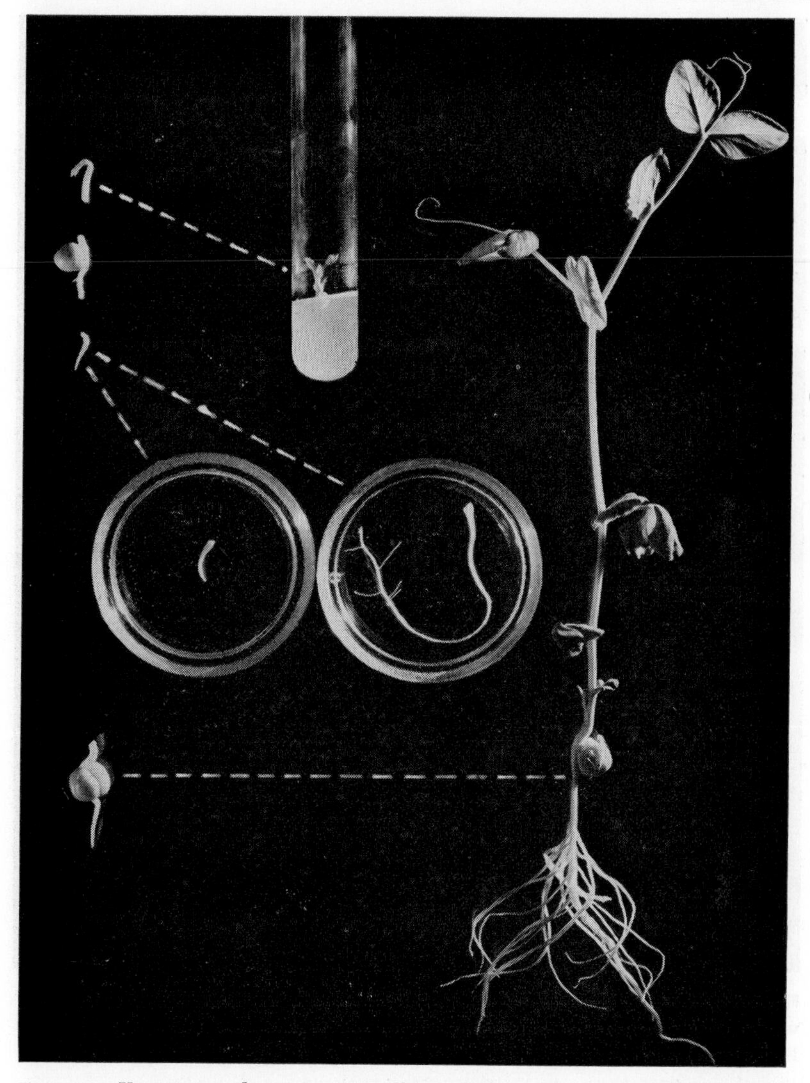

Fig. 8.13. Young pea plants. *Left:* seedlings at beginning of experiment; *right:* after a two-week growth period. The lower pea was left intact and grows into a normal plant. The upper plant was divided into three parts. The stem tip was transferred aseptically to a test tube containing nutrient agar, resulting in a very small amount of growth. The root tip was transferred aseptically to a nutrient medium containing Vitamin B_1. This has produced growth comparable to that in an intact plant. (Courtesy Edmund B. Gerard.)

Fig. 8.14. Carrot tissue placed aseptically in nutrient medium. *Left:* after few weeks of growth; *right:* subcultures from the first callus. (Courtesy Edmund B. Gerard.)

eventually complete plants (Steward 1958). The main advance in method which made this possible was the isolation of a number of growth factors from coconut milk. Plant embryos normally develop inside the maternal tissue of the ovary, with or without the interposition of endosperm. But in the coconut, the embryo develops in the big cavity of the nut, which is filled with endosperm, the liquid part of which is coconut milk. Consequently the coconut embryo can grow only if the coconut milk contains all growth factors that normally come to an embryo from the ovule tissues.

that cannot produce essential factors, such as biotin and other vitamins, and thus become dependent on the medium to supply these growth factors, or they have to depend on other cells of the same species. Then such cells have necessarily to grow in conjunction with each other, and one group of cells can grow only to the extent that the other cells produce an excess of the essential growth factor. In general this seems to be the pattern for plant development.

If we draw a simplified picture of a plant, indicating schematically the stem ending in a bud and carrying young and old leaves and a root system, then we know the following interrelationships in such a plant: sugar is formed in the mature leaves and is moved throughout the plant to all other metabolizing and growing areas (Fig. 8.16). The extent of growth, however, is not controlled by the amount of sugar; it is controlled by hormones which are produced in other parts of the plant. Thus root growth is limited by the amount of Vitamin B_1 produced in the leaves. Stem growth is controlled by auxin produced in the stem tip of the very young leaves and by an as yet unidentified factor coming from the root system. The existence of this factor can easily be established by cutting off stems. This almost immediately stops all growth in spite of a sufficient supply of auxin from the stem tip. As soon as new roots develop on this stem, growth is resumed. Another way to induce growth on cut stems is to graft them onto an active root system. As soon as new vascular connections have been established between scion and stock, the stem starts to grow again. All efforts to extract the active principle coming from the root system have failed thus far, and therefore this root factor can only be labeled as factor X, or as caulocaline.

Growth of the young leaves is dependent on the older, preexisting leaves, as Gregory established 35 years ago. We still do not know much about the factors produced by the older leaves to cause the expansion of young leaves. Some experiments indicate that purines and purine derivatives are effective. For instance, adenine has been found to produce surface growth of young pea leaves. A relative of adenine—kinetin (furfuro-adenine)—is a very active growth factor in tissue cultures, and it especially induces cell division in them. When supplied in the proper concentration, it is able to induce bud formation on tobacco tissue. If the same tissue is treated with indoleacetic acid rather than with kinetin, roots are produced. There is a very delicate balance between the concentration of kinetin and indoleacetic acid in the regeneration of roots and shoots in such tobacco tissues.

A fairly large number of other growth factors have been discovered during the last 20 to 30 years, but in most cases the hormonal nature of these substances is doubtful, or else their effectiveness is not

The first of the growth factors to be isolated from coconut milk and similar products was kinetin, and now a number of others have been isolated and identified. One other growth factor for plant cells and organs, which was first isolated from the culture liquid of several Fusarium species, is gibberellin. It has been extracted from seeds, but we have no clear picture as to its formation or action in the plant. It causes, in conjunction with auxin, cell elongation, and can cause excessive elongation of stems of many plants. In general the elongation equals that produced by certain genes in corn and peas. Many genetic dwarfs can be made to develop normally when gibberellin is applied. Therefore, gibberellin and its near relative, gibberellic acid, act very much as growth hormones in plants, but their hormonal nature has not been established as yet.

One of the great problems in development is whether genetic changes occur in cells which differentiate from the meristematic state and become leaf or flower or root cells. This question can now be answered with the aid of tissue cultures from individual cells. The results obtained thus far indicate that a completely normal plant can be produced from a tissue culture derived from a single cell, indicating that the cells used were still omnipotent and had all genetic possibilities contained in the zygote. Therefore the cell differentiation accompanying the development of a plant is not due to nuclear changes, but involves only the cytoplasm, and under the proper conditions is reversible. But we need much more specific evidence, of the kind that could be collected if individual cells from leaf, stem, root, or flower can be made to produce calluses, and if these calluses can then produce complete plants.

A special case, in which differentiated tissues can be made to grow indefinitely, is that of isolated roots. Ever since Haberlandt, now almost 60 years ago, unsuccessfully tried to grow plant organs or tissues *in vitro*, botanists have tried to do the same and, as described in the previous section, have succeeded with plant tissue cultures. Before these successes, White and other botanists were able to grow isolated root tips in synthetic media.

When whole seedlings were placed in a synthetic medium containing sugars and salts, they could be grown to large size plants, even in near darkness. However, when the root tip of such a seedling was cut off and placed in the solution under sterile conditions, then growth of the root soon stopped. Therefore, some factor was translocated from the rest of the seedling to the root to make it grow with sugar. White succeeded for the first time in making such isolated root tips grow in solution by adding a small amount of yeast extract to the medium. Yeast extract is one of the most complex mixtures known, since it contains practically every substance necessary for the growth of cells. The question was, therefore, which of the thousands of substances present in yeast extract was effective in root growth. Both Robbins and Bonner succeeded in replacing the yeast extract with a single substance, Vitamin B_1, or thiamin; this, in concentrations of one part in 100 million, made pea and tomato roots grow.

It was soon found, however, that a medium containing only sugars, salts, and Vitamin B_1 was insufficient for unlimited growth of root tips, so that after a few transfers to a new medium, the growth rate of these roots dropped off. It was then found that, in addition to Vitamin B_1, most roots require small amounts of Vitamin B_6, or nicotinic acid, or both. With such a medium, continued growth for many years has been achieved through successive biweekly subcultures. Quite a large number of roots have been investigated in this manner, and it was found that the nutrient requirements of roots for continued growth *in vitro* are slightly different from root to root. Flax roots, for instance, need only Vitamin B_1. Pea roots can be grown continuously in Vitamin B_1 plus nicotinic acid. Tomato roots require Vitamin B_1 plus Vitamin B_6 for optimal growth, whereas certain other roots require all three of these growth factors simultaneously. Since most grass roots have not been established in continuous culture, it would seem that they require an additional growth factor which as yet has not been discovered.

In the intact plant, roots apparently not only get sugars for their growth from the above-ground parts, but they also receive their Vitamin B_1 and other growth factors from the tops. It has been established that Vitamin B_1 is produced in leaves and that it is transported downward in the phloem. Therefore, Vitamin B_1 has to be considered as a root growth hormone. It is produced in the tops and has its effect on the root system. Very small amounts are required for optimal growth. We can, therefore, say that Vitamin B_1 is a vitamin in the case of animals which receive it from plants, whereas in the plant, Vitamin B_1 is a hormone.

There are a certain number of plants which cannot be grown unless Vitamin B_1 is supplied to them through the soil. This has been established for Camellias. Their roots require Vitamin B_1 for growth, but the tops of Camellia shrubs are unable to supply the required amount. Therefore, to obtain root growth in Camellias, it is necessary to grow them in a root medium which supplies small amounts of Vitamin B_1 (Fig. 8.15). This Vitamin B_1 can be supplied through leaf mold or other organic matter in the soil, perhaps through bacterial action. Other forest floor plants, such as Azaleas, seem also to have lost the ability to synthesize Vitamin B_1 and therefore have become dependent for their growth on external supplies of Vitamin B_1. Therefore, Vitamin

Fig. 8.15. Camellia rootings treated three months earlier with indoleacetic acid. The three at the right were treated with Vitamin B_1 two months before the picture was taken; the three at the left did not receive Vitamin B_1. (Courtesy Edmund B. Gerard.)

B_1, which is a hormone for most plants, is still a vitamin for Camellias and Azaleas. However, most other plants which do not continuously grow in a medium relatively rich in Vitamin B_1, such as forest soil, continue to produce it in their tops.

Vitamin B_1 is known to be a coenzyme for carboxylase, and so it has been wondered whether perhaps the effect of Vitamin B_1 in the root system is to produce a carboxylase in the respiratory cycle. Th evidence thus far is inconclusive on this point, but in any case, roo growth has become dependent on the above-ground parts of the plar through the inability of root cells to synthesize an essential cell constit ent—namely, Vitamin B_1. This indicates the general principle by whi an organism emerges from a mere conglomeration of independent cel As long as all cells are able to produce all essential growth fact themselves, like many microorganisms, then such cells can grow in pendently of each other and do not form an organism. The mom however that some of the cells lose the ability to produce an essen growth factor, they become dependent on other cells—either on cell a different species, as is the case in a number of yeasts and bact

universal. Whereas auxin is a general hormone effective in almost all higher plants to which it has been applied, this is not true of some of the other growth substances. A typical example of an exception is traumatic acid. This substance was discovered in extracts of stringbeans. These extracts will cause the formation of a wart of tissue on the parenchyma cells lining the seed cavity of the stringbean. Whereas traumatic

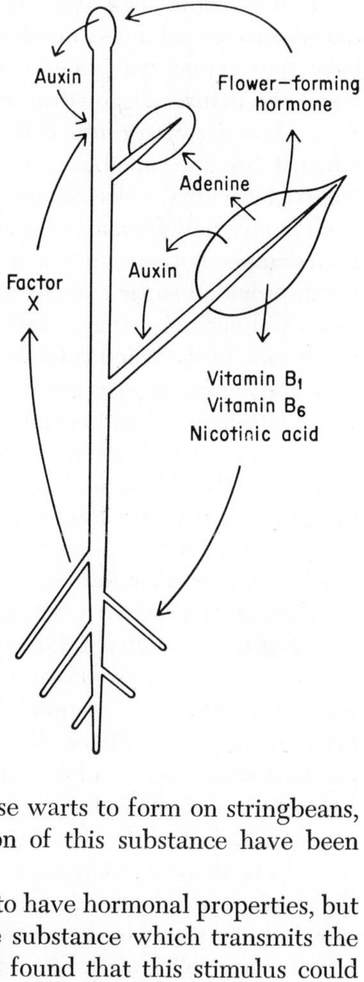

Fig. 8.16. Interrelationships between the organs of a plant. Arrows indicate in which organ a specific substance is produced and the region to which it is translocated to perform its function. The sugars coming from the mature leaf are not shown. Indicated in downward sequence are apical bud, growing stem, growing leaf, mature stem, mature leaf, and root system. (Redrawn from F. Went, "The regulation of plant growth," *Science in Progress,* second series, Yale University Press, 1940. With permission.)

acid is thus very active in inducing these warts to form on stringbeans, very few effects due to the application of this substance have been found in other plants.

Another substance which seems to have hormonal properties, but which is not effective in growth, is the substance which transmits the stimulus in *Mimosa pudica.* Ricca had found that this stimulus could be transmitted by a diffusible material, and many investigators have tried to isolate the effective substance produced after stimulation in this sensitive plant. It is formed in the stimulated cells of a leaf, and it is translocated, at least partly, in the transpiration stream to other parts of the plant where it causes the leaf joints to react. This substance apparently has its effect on the semipermeability of the cytoplasm of *Mimosa* cells.

Let us now evaluate what we have learned thus far about growth. We have seen that there are interrelations between the different parts of a growing plant—correlations which make it possible for the plant to develop as a unit, and to grow proportionately. We have also found that these correlations are the work of hormones, which in plants are rather simple chemical substances, necessary for all cells, but produced only by a limited number of cells and organs. Even though we have thus found out about correlations, we have not learned much about the nature of growth in respect to the individual cell.

Investigations into cell growth received a powerful stimulus when it bec .me possible to grow detached plant organs or even detached individual cells *in vitro,* without contact with the rest of the plant body. But the major conclusion from this type of work was that such detached organs grew just as they would have grown on the intact plant, provided sugar and the already known hormones were supplied, but it did not tell us more about the intricacies of the growth process. In the case of detached cells the situation seems more exciting, because they can be made to grow in a way different from the way they do when left in the intact plant. But on looking closer, we found that 1) the growth factor requirements for growth of detached cells are again primarily sugar and auxin; and 2) all cells which can be made to grow this way are de-differentiated, and all are vacuolated parenchyma cells, forming undifferentiated callus masses, which look very much alike whether derived from carrot roots, tobacco stems, orchid seedlings, or Jerusalem artichoke tubers. That is, morphologically they have lost their identity so far as their mother plants are concerned.

Yet, there are some most promising possibilities along this experimental approach to the problem of growth. In the first place, a number of new growth factors have been identified that are necessary in one or another tissue culture. In this way it was found that certain tobacco cells, although growing slowly in a simple medium, would grow many times faster with kinetin added.

The more restricted the system of growing cells, or the smaller the tissue transplant, the greater the need becomes for specialized growth factors, and in the future we can expect the discovery of a number of other cell growth factors.

In the second place, we are finding out more about what makes these undifferentiated cells from a callus culture change over into specialized cells. This work is still in its infancy. In a few cases (probably not surprising, after what has been said above) auxins induced differentiation of xylem elements in a callus or in regenerating vascular bundles; but this is not a general phenomenon. In other cases, investigators succeeded in inducing completely differentiated stem or root growing points on callus cultures. Interesting though it is, this growing point induction cannot be pinpointed and it still is a matter of chance as to which cell or cell complex will suddenly change into an apical or root meristem. But here lie some most interesting problems for future solution.

The problem we know least about is the interrelationship existing between individual cells. In callus cultures there are few if any interactions between adjoining cells so that the result is not an organism but a formless agglomeration of cells. In the normal plant body a sieve tube is always accompanied by a companion cell; stomata are differentiated in the epidermis in very specific spots, related to veins and mesophyll cells; and differentiation of leaf and flower primordia is all but haphazard. And even though the egg cells of oak and tomato may look alike, or the callus cells of an orchid and a carrot are indistinguishable, once they differentiate they give rise to entirely different, rigidly specific forms.

The problem of species specificity in cell differentiation, making a tomato cell produce a tomato plant, is a genetic one, and is related to the different kinds of proteins and other macromolecules inside the cells, and the potentialities based on the genes contained in the nuclei. This type of specificity does not pass from cell to cell and cannot be changed by growth factors or hormones.

Different varieties of apples and pears can be grafted on the same quince root stock, and each variety will retain its full individuality so far as form and taste are concerned. Therefore the growth factors essential for specific differentiation of cells are not transmitted from cell to cell, or, if they are at all, it is to a *very* limited extent only. They are cell locked; they are not hormonal in character, and they have not been studied in plants as yet. There are, however, some extremely interesting observations on record to indicate that an attack on the problem of specificity in cell differentiation is approachable experimentally.

Occasionally an abnormal leaf or flower grows on an otherwise normal plant. Such a teratological structure indicates that the *potentiality* for such aberrant development exists in the plant. If it were possible to induce it by some experimental means we might then have a tool to attack the form-giving process in plants. The so-called ever-sporting varieties, studied first by Hugo de Vries, have been used in this attempt. Some of these varieties, which usually form normal shoots, can under conditions of excessive feeding be induced to produce fasciations (ribbonlike widenings) of stems, or to have carpels instead of stamens.

A more promising approach to the problem is through the use of insect or fungus galls. Under the influence of the gall organism completely new structures can develop, of a kind not normally occurring in the attacked plant. The first gall used for such studies was the crown-gall, produced by *Bacterium tumaefaciens.* Work with this has produced much important information about growth in plants, but the crown-gall is a rather undifferentiated mass of cells, much like a callus culture.

An example of specific differentiation of plant cells due to a gall organism is stamen formation in female Melandrium plants. Normally their flowers contain *only* an ovary. But under the influence of a rust fungus, 5 stamens develop in each female flower, even though the anthers are not filled with pollen but with spores of the rust. Thus far no investigator has succeeded in replacing the fungus with an extract to produce these stamens, but it seems a fascinating problem. More remarkable still are the galls produced by insects, particularly gall wasps, on leaves, stems, roots, flowers, and fruits. Such a gall is a completely new, and often highly complex, structure on an otherwise normal plant. Not only is a new structure produced, but new types of cells occur that are not otherwise present in the host plant.

The most intriguing part of gall formation is that it can be produced at will by the action of the insect. Therefore cells can be made to divide and differentiate by the insect's depositing an egg—with or without further secretions of the mother insect—on the host plant at the proper place and time. On the same species of oak different gall wasps can produce a great variety of galls: large stem or leaf galls, round or oval, hollow or solid, lignified or parenchymatous, small root or stamen galls. Some of these gall wasps produce hairy galls whereas others are smooth or scalloped, and they may survive long after the rest of the leaf on which they were formed has died. These highly differentiated structures seem to be produced in almost the same way other plant structures arise; only in the case of galls the form-inducing propensities of the nucleus are replaced by materials derived from the gall insect.

In the few cases which have been investigated (the Pontania gall on willows and the Hormaphis gall on *Hamamelis,* Lewis 1958) it would seem that nucleic acids produced by the insect are involved. If this can be satisfactorily established we would have a completely new group of growth factors, which thus far have eluded experimental approach because normally these acids are intracellular products. Thus gall insects would provide a powerful new tool toward the study of cell differentiation and organ development.

Another tool in the study of cell differentiation has been neglected during the last decennia. This is the grafting technique. By grafting one plant onto another we obtain plants with a split personality, and we can let leaves and flowers be supplied with water and nutrients derived from a root system of a different species. But, as has been pointed out, this usually does not lead to any changes in either top (scion) or base (stock). This means that the hormones traveling from scion to stock and vice versa are the same in the graft partners. It is possible, however, to bring the cells of different graft partners in much closer contact. When a new bud differentiates on the surface of a graft, occasionally the growing point consists partly of cells from one and partly of cells from the other graft partner. Thus part of the stem developing from such a mixed meristem is typically the one species, and part is the other. Even though separately the two species would grow at different rates, when joined they adjust their growth rates to each other. And not only do the cells of the two species grow equally, but some are altered by the neighboring cells of the other species.

There is another excellent source of research material for the study of growth phenomena. That is materials available from geneticists. In their studies of the hereditary behavior of a particular species, they usually turn up a large number of mutant forms which differ in growth or differentiation from the wild-type plant. Since geneticists can reduce the differences between plants to a single gene, and such a gene may control only a single specific reaction in the chain of events which results in growth, comparison of the growth of a mutant form with the wild-type norm can furnish valuable clues to the growth process. The work on dwarf-corn varieties is a good example. All but one of the corn dwarfs can be made to develop into a normal-size plant by gibberellin applications. The exception responds to auxin.

There are two other growth phenomena in plants which are often attributed to the action of hormones: flowering and vernalization. In neither case, however, have active extracts been obtained. Investigators had assumed that the floral stimulus was a hormone because it can be transmitted across a graft union from the leaves, where perception takes place, to the growing points that become transformed into flower primordia. When a nonflowering scion is grafted onto a flower-induced stock, and when the scion is maintained in a light regime such that it would not flower, then the grafting will cause it to flower. Therefore something is produced in leaves and is transmitted to the growing points. But it could be something different from a specific substance.

After writing all this down, just 35 years after I started work in the field of plant hormones, I cannot disguise a slight disappointment that more progress has not been made in understanding so many of the growth processes that seemed to come into our grasp with the discovery and isolation of the first plant hormones. With the enormous increase in research workers since discovery of the herbicidal properties of auxin-related substances 20 years ago, one would have expected an equally remarkable deepening of our insight into the basic processes underlying the growth and herbicidal responses of these substances. This has not taken place, and it is amazing that as yet no satisfactory theoretical explanation can be given for the tremendous physiological activity of substances like 2,4-dichlorophenoxyacetic acid. For the young scientist, bent on deepening our insight into plant responses, however, this should be a spur to jump in, and with a fresh approach and new enthusiasm, bring these growth problems closer to a solution. And even if, for some obscure reason, the solution of 2,4-D action should prove too elusive, I have in the last pages indicated a number of problems in the general field of control of plant growth that are awaiting solution and will undoubtedly yield to an imaginative and vigorous attack.

REFERENCES

AUDUS, L. J., 1959, *Plant Growth Substances.* London: Leonard Hill. 2nd ed.

BOYSEN-JENSEN, P. "La transmission de l'irritation phototropique dans l'Avena." *Bull. Ac. Roy. Danmark,* No. 1:3–24 (1911).

DARWIN, C., 1880, *The Power of Movement in Plants.* London: Murray.

KÖGL, F., AND A. J. HAAGEN-SMIT. "Über die Chemie des Wuchsstoffs." *Proc. Kon. Ak. Amsterdam, 34:*1411–1416 (1931).

KOEPFLI, J. B., K. V. THIMANN, AND F. W. WENT. "Phytohormones: Structure and Physiological Activity." I. *J. Biol. Chem. 122:*763–780 (1938).

LEWIS, I. F., AND L. WALTON. "Gall formation on Hamamelis virginiana resulting from material injected by the aphid Hormaphis hamamelidis." *Trans. Am. Micr. Soc., 77:*146–200 (1958).

PAAL, A. "Über phototropische Reizleitung." *Jahrb. wiss. Botan., 58:*406–458 (1918).

STEWARD, F. C. "Growth and organized development of cultured cells. III. Interpretations of the growth from free cell to carrot plant." *Am. J. Botany, 45:*709–713 (1958).

THIMANN, K. V., AND F. SKOOG. "Studies on the growth hormone of plants. III. The inhibiting action of the growth substance on bud development." *Proc. Nat. Acad. Sci., 19:*714–716 (1933).

WENT, F. W. "Wuchsstoff und Wachstum." *Rec. trav. botan. Neerland., 25:*1–116 (1928).

WENT, F. W., 1940, *Plant Hormones.* Am. Assoc. Adv. Science, Pub. *14:*147–158.

Went, F. W., and K. V. Thimann, 1937, *Phytohormones.* New York: Macmillan.

Wildman, S. G., and J. Bonner. "Observations on the chemical nature and formation of auxin in the Avena coleoptile." *Am. J. Botany,* 35:740–745 (1948).

IAN M. SUSSEX

Associate Professor of Botany
Yale University

Ian M. Sussex was born in Auckland, New Zealand, in 1927. He graduated B.Sc. and M.Sc. from Auckland University College, and Ph.D. from the University of Manchester, England. After doing postdoctoral research at Harvard and in France, he returned to New Zealand to take up a teaching appointment at Victoria University College, Wellington. In 1955 he came back to the United States as Assistant Professor in the Biology Department of the University of Pittsburgh, and in 1960 was appointed Associate Professor of Botany at Yale University.

Among his publications are the following: "Morphogenesis in *Solanum tuberosum* L.: Experimental investigation of leaf dorsiventrality and orientation in the juvenile shoot," *Phytomorphology,* 1955, 5:286–300; "Experiments on the control of fertility of fern leaves in sterile culture," *Botan. Gaz.,* 1958, 119:203–208 (with A. T. Steeves); "A study on the effect of externally supplied sucrose on the morphology of excised fern leaves in vitro," *Phytomorphology,* 1960, 10:87–99 (with M. E. Clutter).

Plant morphogenesis

CHAPTER 9

IAN M. SUSSEX

Yale University

In its development from a single-celled zygote a plant grows continuously, producing new cells which become specialized to mature as a variety of tissues and organs, each with its own distinctive form. It can readily be seen that growth is not a simple repetition of cell production and specialization. There is, in fact, a regular and orderly development through a succession of dissimilar stages, each of which has its own distinctive appearance. Thus the embryonic plant gives way to the seedling and this to the adult, which may differ markedly from the earlier stages in growth rate, degree of branching, shape and spacing of leaves, pigmentation, and many other features. Later reproduction, senescence, and finally death complete the life history of each plant, and each of these stages in turn has its own distinctive appearance.

A study of the external appearance and the internal structural complexity of such a plant lies within the province of morphology and anatomy. However, for some time there has been an awareness among botanists that it is necessary to push on beyond this descriptive ap-

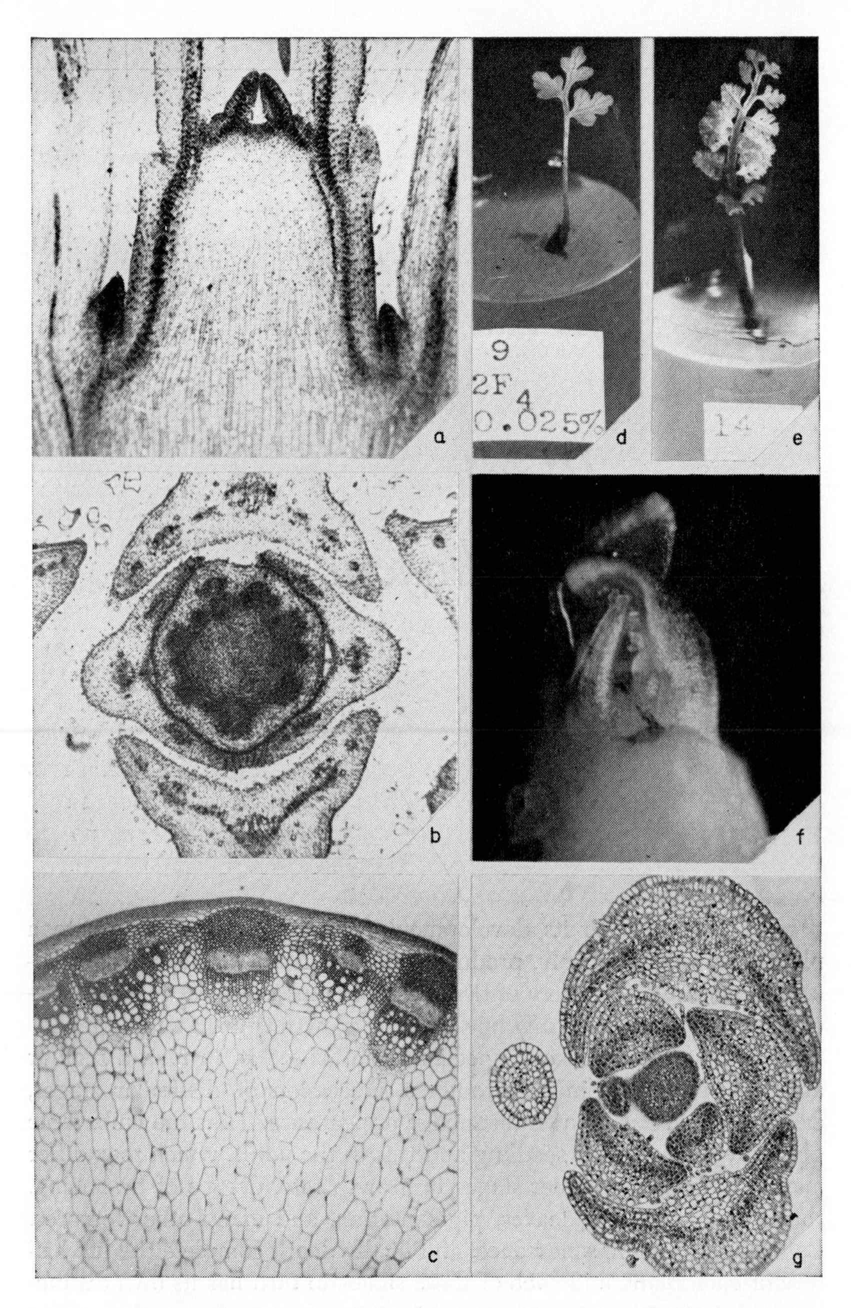

Fig. 9.1. *a:* Longitudinal section of the shoot apex of sunflower. *b:* Transverse section of sunflower stem just below the apical meristem. *c:* Transverse section of mature sunflower stem. *d:* Excised fern leaf growing on 0.025 percent sucrose medium. *e:* Excised fern leaf growing on 0.5 percent sucrose medium. *f:* Potato apex after surgical operation, showing incision scar and radial organ at front left. *g:* Section of apex in (*f*) with experimentally produced radial organ at left.

proach to plant form and to examine the factors that underlie it. This is not to say that descriptive studies have no place in modern botany; they continue to be an important means by which we measure developmental responses, and in this new sense anatomical studies take their place alongside physiological, genetic, and other approaches to plant form. The descriptive account of plant form and the analysis of those factors, both internal and external, by which form is regulated constitute the study of plant morphogenesis, which is sometimes called experimental or causal morphology.

In recent years it has become clear that we can study the morphogenesis of structures at many different levels of organization. Thus it is possible to speak of the morphogenesis of a cell or of a cell organelle as validly, if not yet as knowledgeably, as we can discuss the morphogenesis of a shoot or of a leaf. And perhaps with increasing knowledge of the surface shapes and of development of the biologically important macromolecules we shall also learn to speak easily of molecular morphogenesis.

Before examining some of the specific results which have been obtained in studies of plant morphogenesis it is necessary to consider briefly the way in which a plant grows. As we have already said, new cells are produced by the division of pre-existing cells more or less continuously throughout the life of the plant. A plant originating as a result of sexual reproduction begins its life as a single cell, the fertilized egg or zygote, and thus there is cell continuity from one generation to the next. The first few divisions of the zygote result in a spherical or elongated group of cells, all of which undergo division and all of which appear to be identical. Sooner or later, however, cell division becomes restricted to certain terminal regions called meristems. The intervening cells mature and become differentiated as organs of the embryo.

In the seedling and adult plant there is a meristem at the tip of each bud and root, and others in developing leaves, in corky tissue, and between the bark and the wood of trees. Not only are meristems the centers of production of new cells but they also act as determiners of the early morphogenetic patterns in the new cells. This is seen most clearly in the vegetative shoot apex in which a regular sequence of leaves and buds, each occurring in a predictable position, is initiated at the margins of the meristem (Fig. 9.1a). Internally in the shoot the earliest stages of cell differentiation are influenced by the meristem. Immediately below the apical meristem the initially more or less homogeneous cells start to differentiate so that three zones become distinct. There are outer and central zones of enlarging cells and between these a ring of small cells (Fig. 9.1b). The enlarging cells will continue differentiating as the marginal epidermis and cortex and the central pith. The ring of small cells differentiates into a variety of tissues, each specifically related to various parts of the shoot. Cells in those parts of the ring that underlie leaf positions differentiate as the conducting vascular system, the xylem and phloem, and are continuous with the vascular system of both the leaf and the root. Cells in intervening parts of the ring usually enlarge and become indistinguishable from the cortex and the pith (Fig. 9.1c). In the differentiation of the ring tissues the initial stages are related to the apical meristem; the later stages are apparently related to and controlled by the developing leaves.

In some plants development is very different from that just outlined. In unicellular and colonial algae and fungi, and in the gametophytes of many of the higher plants, the mature state is characterized by the complete absence of cell divisions. These plants resemble most animals in completing their morphogenetic development during their early growth.

Because morphogenesis deals comprehensively with the origin and development of plant form, no single technique or method is adequate for examining all its aspects. Techniques derived from a variety of disciplines including histology, anatomy, physiology, cytology, and genetics must all play their part. Of the various experimental methods that have been employed perhaps the two most successful have been (1) surgical operations in the vicinity of a meristem, by which parts are removed or partially isolated by incisions and the resulting developmental changes followed; and (2) sterile cultures in which detached, aseptic portions of a plant are grown under controlled nutritional and environmental conditions (Fig. 9.2).

Direct physiological studies of morphogenetic events are difficult to carry out because of the small size of some of the meristems and the inaccessibility of others. However, considerable information is available concerning the role of certain metabolites, and it has been possible to make direct applications of plant hormones externally onto some meristems. If, as now seems probable, morphogenesis is to be explained in molecular terms, and particularly in terms of the functioning of nucleic acids, it is important that detailed cytological and genetic studies form a part of any morphogenetic study. Yet it is just in this area that experimental studies have made least progress. Recently microorganisms, because of their advantage in possessing a relatively short life cycle and easily controlled sexual cycles, have seemed to offer a way to explore this relationship in more detail.

Turning now to some specific examples we shall see how interest in particular aspects of morphogenesis has arisen and to what extent it has been possible to provide satisfying answers.

that the evidence points to the sides of the apical meristem as the functional center and that the extreme tip is inactive; but most American and British botanists who have looked into this problem think that the very tip of the apex is the controlling center. Punctures of this ultimate terminal region made with very fine needles result in the cessation of growth of the apex. Later, growth is resumed by buds that develop from lateral parts of the apex. This seems to indicate that an intact tip is necessary to the normal functioning of the apex.

Despite the very considerable damage done to a meristem by operations of the kind described, the new shoot which develops is always normal in its general morphology. Most noticeably it possesses a characteristic symmetry. Just as each organ has its own symmetry, leaves usually being dorsiventral and stems radial, so each shoot is also symmetrical in the regular sequence of leaf spacing along its length. The regularity of leaf spacing with each leaf occupying a predictable position on the stem results from the regularity of leaf origin and spacing at the margins of the shoot apex. This raises such questions as why leaves are developed by the shoot apex while the root apex produces no comparable structures and how the regularity of leaf production is accomplished.

Concerning the first of these questions, about all that can be said is that we just don't know. However, since only one or two examples of truly leafless stems are known, production of leaves seems to be an almost invariable attribute of shoot apices. We do know quite a lot about the factors that determine the position a new leaf will occupy. Very careful observations of a shoot apex during the time when a new leaf is being formed show that in species with a spiral sequence of leaves the new leaf arises at a point on the apical margin some distance down from the summit and between two slightly older leaves. The evidence seems to indicate that these three reference points, the apical summit and the two adjacent leaves, may determine just where and when a new leaf will emerge. A possible hypothesis would be that a new leaf will develop when the apical summit and the two leaves have become separated by some critical distance through growth enlargement in the shoot. Tests of this idea have usually involved the surgical removal of one of the adjacent leaves. When this operation is carried out, the new leaf usually emerges closer to the position of the removed leaf than would normally be the case. This has been taken as evidence that we are not dealing simply with physical space available for leaf initiation, rather, it seems that removal of the leaf destroys some influence exerted by it that tends to inhibit production of a new leaf in its proximity.

From many experiments of this kind performed on several different species of plants, a general conclusion has emerged that each young leaf and the center of the shoot apex are surrounded by "physiological fields" of unknown composition that prevent the formation of a new leaf within their boundaries. New leaves emerge only in those positions which become cleared of physiological fields by enlargement of the shoot. The fact that it is experimentally possible to cause a new leaf to emerge in an unusual position indicates that all parts of the apical margins are potentially leaf forming, but that leaves emerge only in certain areas and then become surrounded by their own physiological field, thus preventing the formation of other leaves nearby.

An obvious test of the existence of physiological fields would be to cut off a newly emergent leaf from a plant and regraft it into a position lying within the field of another leaf. Its further development ought then to be inhibited. Unfortunately, this experiment is not possible at the present time because, in contrast to the situation in many animal embryos, it has so far proven impossible to graft tissues within the apical region of the shoot.

A system of physiological fields like that just described would account for the rather perplexing fact that leaf formation is a local event, and that a new leaf does not enlarge so much that it engulfs the whole apex. The new leaf will enlarge laterally only until it encounters the physiological fields of adjacent leaves. In this connection it is of interest that there are records of plants in which one leaf did engulf the whole apical margin. These so-called funnel leaves develop in plants damaged by virus attack, radiation, or by applications of chemical growth regulators, all of which might be expected to upset the normal physiological-field distribution.

The hypothesis of physiological fields surrounding the apex and young leaves would explain the continuation of any particular leaf sequence at the apex. However, in many plants the first few leaves of the seedling are produced in opposite pairs and only later are leaves produced spirally. Just how the transition from one kind of leaf arrangement to another is made is difficult to explain.

When the physiological fields are mapped it can be seen that each leaf occupies the central position within its field. Similar mapping of fields surrounding lateral bud initials or flower initials indicates that each young developing organ is the center of growth in the field. From this observation it is possible to make the general statement that the functioning of any shoot meristem, whether vegetative or reproductive, involves the production of a sequence of lateral growth centers in positions determined by the distribution of pre-existing physiological fields. The problems then to be solved relate to the subsequent development of the lateral growth centers as leaves, bud scales, spines, flowers, or any of the other organs characteristically produced by the shoot of a particular species.

Of the various developmental pathways available to a new growth center, that leading to a vegetative leaf is the most usual and has been studied in most detail. Of particular interest is the way in which symmetry and shape are developed during growth. When the leaf first emerges at the apical margin it is little more than a hemispherical mound of dividing cells and only later, as growth continues, does it become recognizably dorsiventral and leaflike. Anatomical studies of leaves at successive stages of development indicate that this is achieved by differing rates of growth along the two major leaf axes. One might inquire as to the way in which a group of cells that had previously been part of the apical meristem undergo a change in developmental fate and produce a leaf. There is no complete answer to this question but some experiments, again of a surgical nature, suggest certain of the changes that are involved.

If either the position at which a leaf growth center is about to develop or very young hemispherical growth centers are isolated from the apical meristem by an incision, then the growth center does not develop as a leaf but as a radially symmetrical structure. In the ferns in which this operation has been performed the isolated growth center develops as a shoot apex and itself produces a succession of lateral leaf primordia; in angiosperms a similar operation results in the development of a radial organ of limited growth which has characteristics intermediate between those of stem and leaf (Fig. 9.1f,g). The same experiment, repeated at a later stage when the leaf is already dorsiventral, fails to disturb its development. Evidently lateral growth centers have early potentialities for radial development but these are gradually suppressed and growth becomes dorsiventrally distributed. It appears that the apex of the shoot inhibits the side of the leaf growth center nearest to it and that this leads to the establishment of the asymmetric growth pattern.

In many plants, and especially in the ferns, leaves produced on plants of different ages differ considerably in their form, those of juvenile plants being smaller and simpler than the leaves of the adult plant. Because of the considerable differences in photosynthetic tissue volume during development, it has been suggested that the nutritional status of the plant may in part, at least, regulate leaf development. Evidence for such a view comes from experiments in which young fern plants have been grown in sterile culture on media containing different amounts of sucrose or glucose. Plants grown on media containing low concentrations of sugar produce leaves like those of soil-grown juvenile plants; those grown on sugar concentrations of about 1 percent or higher have leaves that are larger and bear more pairs of pinnae and in general resemble the leaves of more adult fern plants.

From these experiments it is difficult to conclude that the carbohydrate content of the plant directly affects leaf development. Sugars also affect the growth of the shoot apex, stem, and root; and it is not immediately obvious which effects are the direct result of sugar availability and which are indirect results.

A direct effect of sucrose on leaf development can be obtained by growing, in sterile culture on media containing different amounts of the sugar, fern leaves removed from the plant at early stages of development (Fig. 9.2). Leaves that develop on media containing less that 0.1 percent sucrose are like those of juvenile plants; those that are grown on media containing more sucrose are like those of the adult plant (Fig. 9.1d,e). In some cases it has been possible, by using high concentrations of sugar, to produce sporangia on excised fern leaves, thus opening the way for a study of fertility.

So far we have been considering the development of plant organs that lend themselves to external inspection. However, important morphogenetic events occur within the plant, and for some of these, rather precise information is available that relates development to specific factors. The maturation of cells as xylem elements has attracted considerable interest, and the chemical control of differentiation of this cell type has become fairly completely known. Because xylem differentiation in the intact plant begins within the apical bud where it is often difficult to carry out really critical experiments, most of the experimental work on xylem differentiation has been done on older parts of the plant and involves the redifferentiation of previously mature parenchyma cells as xylem. Care must be taken in extending these results to cover cases of xylem differentiation in normal situations.

If a notch is cut into the young elongating part of a stem deep enough to sever one or more of the vascular bundles (Fig. 9.1c), then new xylem cells are differentiated from pith parenchyma and continuity of the vascular strand is restored around the region of the cut. However, the differentiation of new xylem cells in this experiment depends on the presence of growing leaves on the stem above the cut. When such leaves are removed, the number of new xylem cells is drastically reduced. If low concentrations of indoleacetic acid, a naturally occurring plant auxin, are fed into the stem through the stump of a severed leaf, a large number of xylem cells is differentiated. It is presumed, therefore, that the tip of the shoot produces an auxin, possibly indoleacetic acid, which controls differentiation of xylem in the stem. Recently it has been shown that indoleacetic acid applications of the above type can also cause phloem cells to be differentiated when vascular bundles are severed. This raises the very interesting question of how a single substance can cause multiple effects. We shall return to this question later.

In other experiments sterile cultures of root or stem tissues were made and buds grafted into the cultured tissues. This resulted in the production of xylem, and sometimes of phloem, in the previously homogeneous tissue. Often these new cells were differentiated in a circular form reminiscent of the vascular cylinder of the stem. Again, if the incision into which the grafted bud would have been placed was filled with agar containing auxin, xylem cells were differentiated in the underlying tissue.

Returning to the possibility that a single chemical may have multiple effects within the plant, we can cite experiments on the effect of indoleacetic acid applications to tobacco pith growing in sterile culture. When pith is placed on an agar medium which contains two parts per million of the auxin, the cells do not divide but enlarge considerably, often becoming more than a millimeter in diameter. If the same concentration of auxin is supplied internally into cylinders of pith through small glass pipettes inserted in the apical end of the tissue, the cells undergo numerous divisions and some of them differentiate as xylem cells. These cells are all of the same genetic constitution, they were supplied with the same concentration of auxin, and the different responses may be explained by the different location of the responding cells in the tissue mass. In one case the cells were superficial, in the other internal. Whether the significant difference in cellular environment in this case is chemical or physical is not yet known, but it is from experiments of this kind that we hope to learn more about the processes that lead to tissue differentiation.

It cannot be claimed that the preceding discussion has provided complete answers to any of the questions we have asked. However, there do appear to be common factors underlying the development of such different structures as the fern spore, the zygote, free-floating cells, and growth centers that develop into all the morphologically distinct organs of the plant. What at first sight appear to be rather minor factors—such as the presence or absence of physical restraint of the zygote and spore, the transient one-sided relationship between developing leaf and apex, the cutting off of internal and external cells in a tissue culture—may have a profound effect on future morphogenetic events by directing development into one of several alternative pathways. The basic similarity in all of these events is that the distribution pattern of cell division and maturation is determined at early stages of development, and to a large extent this predetermines the subsequent morphogenesis. It is therefore necessary that morphogenetic studies should center on these early stages and that attention should be paid to the effect of environment as a determinant of planes of cell division and maturation.

This is not to say that we should discontinue the search for understanding of chemical aspects of morphogenesis. To do so would be foolish. But we should not expect to find a unique set of chemical factors controlling each individual morphogenetic event. Rather, we should endeavor to understand how localized regions of the apex, or of any tissue, can so modify their environment, or be modified by it, that they will respond differently from adjacent tissues to the chemical milieu of the plant.

Earlier in this chapter I said that I would give interpretations of morphogenetic processes that had been found satisfying by workers in this field. You will have to decide whether the explanations are satisfying to you. If they are you may want to carry out experiments which might extend and broaden these explanations. If you do not find the explanations satisfying there is, then, the even greater challenge of attempting to find answers to these questions which may ultimately lead to a better understanding of plant development.

REFERENCES

SINNOTT, E. W., 1960. *Plant Morphogenesis.* New York: McGraw-Hill.

STEWARD, F. C., and H. Y. M. RAM, 1961. "Determining factors in cell growth: Some implications for morphogenesis in plants," Ch. 5 in *Advances in Morphogenesis,* Vol. I. M. Abercrombie and J. Brachet, New York: Academic Press.

WARDLAW, C. W., 1952. *Morphogenesis in Plants.* London: Methuen.

WETMORE, R. H., "Morphogenesis in plants—a new approach," *Am. Scientist, 47*:326–340, 1959.

CHAPTER 10

MAC V. EDDS, JR., *Chairman*

Department of Biology
Brown University

Mac V. Edds, Jr., was born in Newark, New Jersey, in 1917. He attended Amherst College where he received the B.A. degree in 1938 and the M.A. degree in 1940, with his major field, experimental amphibian embryology. He was awarded the Ph.D. degree from Yale University in 1943 where he worked on experimental mammalian embryology under J. S. Nicholas. From 1943 to 1945 he was Research Assistant to Paul Weiss at the University of Chicago. He served as Instructor and Assistant Professor of Anatomy in the University of Pittsburgh Medical School during the period 1945–47. Since 1947 he has been in the Biology Department at Brown, serving as Assistant and Associate Professor, as Professor, and as Chairman since 1960. In 1954 he was Visiting Associate Professor of Biology at Massachusetts Institute of Technology; in 1956–57 he was Research Associate in Biology there.

He served as Instructor in the Woods Hole Embryology Course from 1951 to 1955, and as Director of the Course from 1955 to 1960. He has been Managing Editor of the journal *Developmental Biology* since 1958.

His research has been concerned primarily with the development and regeneration of the nervous system and the development of collagen. Among his research publications are the following: "Collateral nerve regeneration," *Quart. Rev. Biol.,* 1953, 28:260–276; "Development of collagen in the frog embryo," *Proc. Nat. Acad. Sci.,* 1958, 44:291–305; "Embryonic systems for the study of biochemistry of morphogenesis," *Fourth Int. Congress Biochem.,* 1959, 6:210–219.

Animal morphogenesis

CHAPTER 10

M. V. EDDS, JR.

Brown University

Background

None of the great problems of biology has ever been solved; each has merely been rephrased and subdivided into smaller problems which seem at least as difficult as those from which they derive. This is not a denial of progress, but a reminder that while knowledge advances by asking ever more precise questions of nature, the ultimate answers still elude us.

From the beginnings of recorded history, man has asked the question which remains the central problem of development: How does the egg give rise to a new adult? For two millennia, at first with agonizing slowness, then at a rapidly accelerating pace during the past century, students of development have sought to refine their answers to this question. Description of what can be seen to occur during development was, of course, the first task. In a number of organisms, the transformation of the egg into the adult has now been described in minute detail.

These details comprise a catalogue of progressive structural and functional changes which are recorded in numerous monographs and textbooks. Included are events at several levels of organization—all the way from the molecule through the cell and tissue to the whole organism. There are countless opportunities for further descriptive investigation, and information on the development of many animal and plant groups is still regrettably incomplete. Even in the case of forms where development has been studied frequently and intensively, many crucial observations remain to be made. But there is already available an impressive array of descriptive data, as even the beginning student can attest.

In what sense, then, does the central problem of development remain unsolved if one can so often specify in detail the steps followed by an egg as it becomes an adult? The crux of the matter is that we can so rarely explain what we can so amply describe. An interminable array of examples could be listed, but let the reader ask any such questions as these:

By what means does a sperm penetrate an egg surface? Why, generally, does only one sperm penetrate? What causes the streaming movements of cytoplasmic materials when an egg is activated? What directs the union of the pronuclei? Where do the fibrous components of the cleavage spindle come from? Do they move the chromosomes? How? What is the mechanism behind the deceptively simple subdivision of the cytoplasm during cleavage? What determines that blastomeres shall cleave synchronously? Or asynchronously? Why are some blastomeres larger than others, even in some eggs with little or no yolk to impede division? What factors lie behind the rearrangement of cells during gastrulation? How are the movements accomplished? What integrates the various movements throughout the embryo so that all parts share in a harmonious and orderly whole? By what means do the various cells of the gastrula start to become visibly different from one another? Do individual nuclei become different? Individual cytoplasms? Does the genome remain the same in all cells? What makes the neural plate fold; the notochord cells vacuolate; the neural crest cells migrate; the mesoderm segment; or the ear placode invaginate? What determines the conversion of mesenchymal cells so that some become muscle cells and start synthesizing myosin, while others become fibroblasts and make collagen or chondroitin sulfate? How do young nerve cells spin out their axons, some extending into the peripheral portion of the embryo, others remaining to course up or down the central nervous system?

There will be found no definitive answer.

Consider a much-studied case, the formation of the eye. How are the several previously separated components brought together in an orderly spatial and temporal sequence with lateral forebrain, surface epidermis, head mesenchyme, blood vessels, and nerve fibers all sharing in the process? Once together, what cues do these components follow so that one forms lens, another iris, another sclera, another retina? What keeps the components in balance so that each becomes a proportional and appropriate part of the finished organ? Why does the entire organ grow only to some typical size, then enter a steady state in which positive and negative growth processes are equalized?

These questions are representative of hundreds like them. All have one thing in common. We really do not know their answers. In each case, it is possible to give partial answers, based sometimes on established facts, sometimes on calculated guesses. Many of the questions are interrelated; a partial answer to one may shed light on another. Seventy-five years of ingenious experimentation by hundreds of investigators permit answers framed in terms of embryonic inductors and fields, segregation of special cytoplasms, nucleo-cytoplasmic interactions, competence, metabolic gradients, and the like.

Recent evidence permits assertions that sound more sophisticated. They deal, for example, with the microvilli at the cell surface; the *de novo* synthesis of DNA or RNA; the changing molecular configurations in the mitotic spindles; the emergence of new macromolecular constituents; the correlation of new enzyme patterns with emergent structures or functions; the important role of both small and large molecules in the microenvironment of developing cells; the time course followed during the synthesis of specific proteins, and a host of others. But in each case, the new information serves as much to raise new questions as to clarify old ones.

We have thus been led to a crude, general understanding of development. The broad outlines of the problem seem to be coming into focus. But we cannot point to a single instance in which we know the precise mechanism underlying even the simplest developmental event. We are surfeited with theories; almost everything can be "explained," granted a few hypotheses. Our intellectual ancestors would perhaps be pleased that we have come so far in clarifying their riddles. But they would be amused, too, that we still tread a path they knew well, and still look forward with excitement to new answers to old questions.

There is, of course, nothing unique in the state of affairs just outlined. All branches of science have passed through it, are in it, or will eventually enter it. But this uncertainty, this sense of future discovery, this opportunity to glimpse previously undetected clues in the ever-changing panorama of development—all make the embryo an especially seducing challenge to all who have grappled with it. The "mystery of development" is no idle phrase to those who have minds and eyes to think and see with. They recognize its implications on every side, and, confronting each new discovery by the biochemist or the microscopist or the physiologist, they ask: How did *that* reaction or structure or function come to be?

Just as new discoveries pose new developmental problems, so they contribute new methodologies to be used in seeking their solutions. Indeed, if one were to single out the most characteristic feature of developmental studies during the past two decades, it would be the cross union effected between the more classical methods of embryology and the newer techniques now revolutionizing nearly all branches of biology.

Consider the major changes which have occurred since, roughly, 1940. The electron microscope has become a powerful biological tool; polarization and other types of light microscopy have undergone profound refinement; methods for isolating and analyzing various components of cells have been developed; the whole field of radioisotopes has flowered; new, more accurate, and faster chemical procedures now permit even the undergraduate student to carry out analyses which were previously undertaken only by the most skillful chemists at great cost in time and labor. The biologist now shares his problems with many other scientists, as for instance with the physicist or the physical chemist. Even the recondite techniques of x-ray diffraction and the outlandish properties of liquid helium have become his allies. On every side, cooperative, multidisciplinary investigation is becoming more and more common.

As if these changes did not provide the embryologist with enough new grist for his mill, the horizons within his own field have expanded. The embryo is after all not the only developing object, however much this may at times be forgotten. Limbs, nerves, worms, and starfish also develop when they regenerate. The bud of a hydra or a tunicate develops; so does the gametophyte of a fern. A tumor is a developing system, as is a healing wound or a root tip. A microbial population, a culminating slime mold, a protozoan undergoing postfissional reorganization—all these and many more *develop*. Ultimately, general theories of development must account for all such cases. Budding cannot be dismissed as "simple," as textbooks too frequently imply, nor can the aberrant ontogenies of several invertebrates be set aside as merely evolutionary blind alleys. All must eventually be explained, and all lie within the domain of developmental biology—which itself is no more than a new term to describe a new emphasis on the unity of a body of phenomena which biologists of an earlier day clearly recognized as belonging together.

Meaning of Morphogenesis

Having painted a broad picture of what we should like to know about development, and of what we now do or do not know, let us proceed by dealing more specifically with a few key questions, taking as our starting point the title of this chapter, "Animal Morphogenesis."

Just what is "morphogenesis"? A dictionary would tell you that the word has two roots, the one (*morphē*) meaning form, the other (*genesis*) meaning beginning or origin. The same source might state that morphogenesis is the production of the structural as opposed to the functional characters of an organism. However, in biology the term morphogenesis has a rather long history, and its meaning has slowly broadened as the various "structural characters" of organisms have become better known. Thus, although at first used mainly in relation to the development of those grossly visible structures which are the concern of the anatomist, morphogenesis has for some time been applied to the origin of microscopic form as well. More recently still, it has become appropriate to inquire about the morphogenesis of structures visible only with the electron microscope.

In point of fact, it would be equally good practice to speak of the morphogenesis of any biological entity which has a specific shape, even if that shape, as in the case of molecules, for example, had to be inferred from indirect measurement or analysis. The reflective reader will already have noticed, then, both that the term morphogenesis could be used in a nonbiological sense, and that in biology its meaning may differ greatly, depending on the particular level of organization to which it is applied. Thus, the morphogenetic events associated with a protein molecule, a mitochondrion, a neuron, a bone, a wing, a horse, or an ant colony are obviously different, however they may blend into one another.

The beginner, and even the experienced student, often fails to appreciate these distinctions, and consequently falls short of real understanding. Indeed, many of the other terms we shall have to use here suffer from the same lack of precise usage because they were coined when knowledge was less complete, and have been retained as knowledge grew. One of our main concerns, therefore, will be to consider morphogenesis at a variety of levels, and to consider how events at one level grade over into, or give rise to, events at another level.

When one pauses to reflect on the morphogenesis of a whole organism, it quickly becomes apparent that the various changes in overall form occurring during development are the consequence, not of factors outside the organism, but of factors within it. This is not to say that morphogenesis proceeds independently of, or without relation to, the immediate environment. Indeed, the dependence of the developing organism on various physical and chemical factors in its environment may be illustrated in many different ways. Thus, the presence of appropriate amounts or ratios of oxygen, carbon dioxide, water, inorganic salts, hydrogen ions, and, in some cases, organic nutrients are critical. By experimentally varying one or more of these parameters, profound, and sometimes rather specific, modifications of morphogenesis can be produced. Lithium salts, for instance, cause grave distortions of gastrulation in many embryos. In the echinoderm embryo, treatment with lithium causes cells normally destined to form the ectodermal surface of the larva to be diverted into endodermal structures of the digestive system.

Not infrequently, materials produced by an organism and added to the immediate environment have a feedback effect on the type of morphogenesis displayed by that organism. An excellent example is provided by *Hydra,* which normally reproduces either sexually by producing eggs and sperm, or asexually by developing lateral bulges or buds from the body wall which then pinch off and become independent young *Hydra.* Carbon dioxide accumulating in the environment from the respiratory activity of the adults appears to "trigger" the sexual mode of reproduction.

Physical stability of the environment is also crucial, as may be illustrated, for instance, by the defective morphogenesis encountered after a developing bird or mammalian embryo is deprived of the amniotic fluid that normally bathes and supports it. But the point about all of these environmental factors is that while they are essential for normal morphogenesis, they permit rather than determine or direct the structural patterns which finally emerge. Thus, a fish egg develops into a fish, not because of the particular set of environmental circumstances under which it develops, but because of factors within itself that find opportunity for expression in a favorable environment.

It is not at all easy to specify in detail just what this latter, almost self-evident, statement really means. Evidence accumulated in genetic investigations during the past half-century permits the general statement that genes derived from the reproductive cells of the parents, and present in the chromosomes of the fertilized egg, determine what the egg shall become. But the exact mechanism whereby this determination is brought about is little known, and is currently the subject of renewed speculation and research. Later we shall have more to say on this subject, but first let us remember that in jumping from the whole organism to the gene, we have passed over several levels of organization that must first be considered.

Morphogenesis of the whole organism is a resultant of many different processes. Moreover, each component part of the animal—the tail, heart, limbs, eyes, feathers, muscles, kidneys, etc.—has its own morphogenetic history, which is of course closely integrated in time and in space with that of all other parts.

Obviously, the morphogenesis of a limb is different from that of a kidney. One involves bones, muscles, and nerves; the other tubules, glomeruli, etc. But when one proceeds below the level of the whole limb or the whole kidney and begins to examine events at the tissue and cellular levels, the differences become less striking than the similarities. A crude analogy will help make the point. A mason presented with building stones may, according to his preference, shape them into a garden wall or the lining of a well. The two end forms, so different in overall shape, are achieved with the same stones that are handled, moved about, and cemented together in similar fashion. The final difference is a consequence solely of the way the stones are packed relative to one another.

In the development of the limb or the kidney, there are no micromasons to go about fitting each cell into its proper place. The cells must do the job themselves. They provide not only the building materials, but also the blueprints and the motive force to achieve their proper spatial interrelations. This assertion is not just based on a logical inference; it has been repeatedly demonstrated experimentally. To be specific, the rudiments of limb and kidney, when removed from a chick embryo and cultured briefly in the presence of the enzyme trypsin, disintegrate into the component cells. If the trypsin is washed off, the cells remain alive and healthy. Cell suspensions derived from both limb and kidney can then be mixed so that a completely scrambled suspension results. When such mixtures are placed in an appropriate tissue culture medium, the individual cells move about in amoeboid fashion making random contacts with their neighbors. When two like cells meet, they remain together; when unlike cells meet, they soon separate and pursue independent courses. This characteristic behavior leads, within a few hours, to the formation of aggregates, each containing many cells but all of one type; for example, limb cartilage or kidney tubule.

Thus, by an active process of self-sorting, based on the capacity of embryonic cells to remain mobile until they encounter and "recognize" others of their kind, large clusters of similar cells are formed. Having achieved this state, the individual cells continue to demonstrate that they are the masters of their own fates. They rearrange themselves in typical patterns, as appropriate, fashioning kidney tubules or limb cartilages, and other structures which are found in a typical limb or kidney.

What we have said here in essence is this. During the course of embryonic development, the various cells derived by cleavage of the egg become subtly different from one another. Though the differences are generally not visible at first, each cell has "learned" its appointed role in the structure of which it will be a part. Thereafter each cell proceeds to fulfill that role, subject only to further "directives" or "inductions" which reach it from the neighboring cells that are to share in the final product. In this view, then, cells form organisms, and not vice versa.

This is a conclusion with the most profound consequences, both biological and philosophical. It is like saying that morphogenesis proceeds from the inside out, not from the outside in. It says that the incredibly rich variety of organic forms is a consequence of individual cellular activities, and that the cells themselves, not the "organism as a whole," direct and specify those activities. It says that whatever one's view of the ultimate source of order in living nature, the ordering proceeds upward through the cells into the organism, not downward from the organism into the cells.

Most beginning students of biology are deeply conditioned by what they have learned, for example, about the capacity of the whole organism to adapt to its surroundings; or about the integrative function of the nervous system, whereby the various parts of the organism are made subservient to the whole. Some readers may therefore sense a logical contradiction in the argument advanced above. Yet there is no paradox. The animal does display these adaptive and integrative properties; they are its hallmark. But they have arisen, like the structures which are their physical basis, from the prior activities of individual cells joined together in a common undertaking, the blueprint for which inheres in the cells.

In developing an argument like this, it is unfortunately necessary to use words like "learn," "recognize," "know," which the unwary reader may accept as implying that cells behave consciously, or like some human agency. This would, of course, be a gross error, and a mere warning should suffice to avoid the trap. We have only some preliminary guesses as to how cells do what they have been observed doing, but we have every reason to deny that the mechanism of their behavior is in any sense "human."

Cellular Reproduction

Now that we have described the ability of cells to construct entities larger than themselves, entities in which have emerged new properties not possessed by the component cells, it becomes of more than casual interest to inquire about the relation between a cell and *its* component parts. Is it possible, in other words, to dismember cells and to isolate nuclei, mitochondria, microscomal particles, and the various other granules, vesicles, and membranous organelles which make up what we used to lump under the single term "protoplasm"? And if this is possible, can these components reassemble into recognizable cells?

The answer to the first question is "Yes." Indeed, this is the basis of much recently acquired information about the function of various cell components. The answer to the second question is "No—at least, not yet." There are reasons for thinking we never shall be able to design the necessary conditions making it possible for cellular components to reassemble themselves. But, equally, there are reasons for thinking that we may.

First, the negative side of the argument. The most common means of cellular reproduction is, of course, mitosis. In this complex series of events, all of the crucial subcellular organelles are duplicated *within the parent cell,* and are then distributed more or less equally during division to the two daughter cells. Unlike the tissue and organ rudiments already discussed, new cells are not formed normally by a gathering together of previously separated component organelles. Thus, the argument would go: Only cells can make cells; and cellular components, though perhaps retaining in isolation some of their functional properties, can never reconstitute the cells from which they have been derived.

This is a cogent argument, and it may be true. But consider the other side. We come to a real paradox when we start thinking about subcellular parts at the molecular level. Every reader will know that, given the proper conditions, atoms spontaneously interact to form molecules. Sometimes, the necessary conditions are rather special, involving, for example, unusual catalysts or temperatures. In other cases, the interaction will proceed unless special measures are taken to prevent it.

Further, modern biochemistry is replete with examples of cell-free enzyme preparations which will catalyze the formation of large, complex molecules from smaller and simpler molecules. The macromolecules thus synthesized *in vitro* include even those of greatest interest to the biologist, nucleic acids and proteins. As a consequence, it is now generally believed that the innumerable chemical reactions which together make up "metabolism" follow rules which, at least in broad outline, are familiar to the chemist.

The living system is unique in three ways. First, the reactions are linked together in complex patterns of time and space. Second, the space allotted to individual reactions within the cell is very small. And, third, a corollary of the second, only relatively minute amounts of substance are involved at any given time in any given reaction within a cell.

It is often said that all these reactions occur *in* the cell, as though the cell were some kind of kettle containing a complex brew. Or, to make the metaphor more modern, it is said that certain reactions occur *in* the subcellular particles called microsomes—namely, those reactions which involve RNA as a template for the linking of amino acids into proteins. Again there is the implication that the microsome is a little pot containing various substances that are made to interact with one another. This is another of those false pictures into which we are trapped by incautious use of little words. It is more accurate, and much more revealing, to say that microsomes are composed of molecules, some large, some small, which interact to form new molecules, some large, some small.

This is not just a play on words; the difference between the two ways of expressing the matter is as great as the difference between understanding and misunderstanding. All of the subcellular organelles revealed by the electron microscope are aggregates of particular molecules. The aggregates are, of course, highly organized in the sense that specific kinds of molecules of varying size and complexity are arranged in strict and orderly patterns. Moreover, it is highly unlikely that some of the molecules play "structural" roles, while others are "functional." At this level, the distinction between structure and function becomes meaningless.

To return to the paradox, how is it that molecules can interact *in vitro,* and cells do the same, yet subcellular organelles cannot? Why not inquire whether, for example, microsomes could arise outside of cells from the "spontaneous" aggregation of a random mixture of their component molecules? Although no one has succeeded in providing the necessary conditions for this to occur, there are good reasons for believing that the trick will someday be accomplished. Only two lines of evidence, one directly related to microsomes, and the other indirectly, will be discussed here.

First, it is possible by appropriate chemical treatment to break up microsomes previously isolated *in vitro.* Each microsome apparently gives rise to smaller particles of unequal size and weight. The subparticles have molecular weights of the order of several millions, and thus are still very large in molecular terms. Upon the simple addition of magnesium ions, the subparticles may reunite and begin again to synthesize protein from amino acids added to the system. This implies either that Mg^{2+} serves to bind the subunits together, or that Mg^{2+}

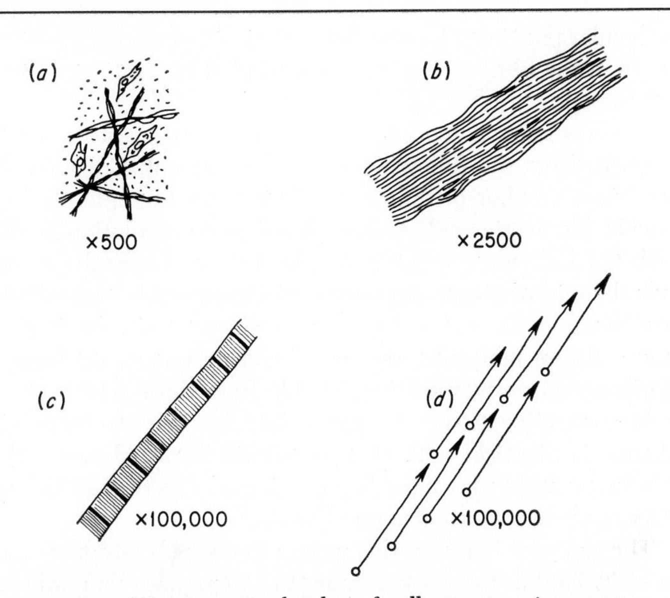

Fig. 10.1. Diagrammatic sketches of collagen at various magnifications. The general arrangement of collagen fibers and fibroblasts, as they appear in connective tissue seen with the light microscope, is shown in (*a*). In (*b*) is a collagen fiber as visualized at the highest resolution obtainable with a light microscope. One of the fibrils composing the fiber in (*b*) appears in (*c*) highly magnified with the electron microscope; note characteristic pattern of cross bands which repeat every 600 to 700Å. The arrows in (*d*) symbolize collagen molecules which are about one-third of a micron in length but only some 14Å wide. The molecules pack in a specific array to produce the banding pattern.

somehow changes the subunits in such a way that they can become linked.

The second line of evidence takes us farther afield, and deals with the protein collagen, a substance which is normally fashioned into the collagenous fibers of the various connective tissues of the animal body. Collagen is another macromolecule; it is rodshaped, weighs about 350,000 and measures roughly 14 by 3000Å. The collagenous fiber that can be distinguished in the light microscope is an assemblage of submicroscopic fibrils; each fibril in turn is an orderly array of collagen macromolecules. As Fig. 10.1 shows, the macromolecules are packed in the fibril in a linear manner, with their "heads" all pointing in the same direction. Further, each macromolecule is displaced one-fourth of its length relative to its neighbors on either side. The resulting structure is so regular as to be essentially crystalline. As a consequence of the specific molecular packing, electron-dense regions occur periodically along the length of the fibril giving it a cross-banded appearance in the electron microscope.

We now know a good deal about the morphogenesis of these intricate fibrils from the following simple experiment. Collagen may be dissolved in a number of different reagents, for example, in weak organic acids like acetic acid. A clear, homogeneous solution is obtained in which the individual macromolecules are randomly dispersed, and in which there is, of course, no trace of collagen fibrils. If small changes are then made in the pH or in the concentration of salts in the solution, the collagen molecules rapidly aggregate and again form fibrils. The fibrils are in no way distinguishable from those which occur naturally in connective tissue. In particular, the fine structure of their cross bands is identical with that of natural fibrils, showing that the collagen macromolecules have become joined together in the specific and characteristic pattern of normal fibrils.

The collagen case is the most exhaustively studied and best known of its kind at the present time. But there are other substances—for instance, paramyosin isolated from the adductor muscles of molluscs—which behave similarly. We are thus forced to the conclusion that the building of complex macromolecules into some of the orderly and intricate patterns revealed by electron microscopy is not a process which is necessarily dependent on the presence of cells. The molecules are of course first synthesized in cells, and may normally remain within cells as in the case of paramyosin. But the experiments described demonstrate that such molecules can interact with one another in specific fashion, and, without depending on any external source of order, form structures that we once regarded as linked intimately with "cellular activity."

Studies of morphogenesis at the level of aggregates of macromolecules are in their infancy. No one can say how much more information will be obtained about the origin of structure from investigations of this kind, but to many students of morphogenesis, the implications and possibilities seem challenging. At the least, these studies confirm the general point of view set forth in this chapter—namely, that order in living systems is imposed from the lower levels of organization to the higher.

The genetic code, which is discussed in Chapter 7 of this book, may be thought of as controlling the synthesis of a host of different species of macromolecules, each with typical shapes, and bearing reactive chemical groups at specific sites that are subject to variation according to local chemical or physical conditions. These features, among others, give each molecular species a unique set of interaction properties which allows it spontaneously to form selective associations with others of its kind, or with related molecules. As a consequence, supramolecular structures of many different kinds and degrees of organizational complexity emerge.

Now that this account has taken so much credit away from the "organism as a whole," and given it over to the molecules of which the organism is composed, it is both appropriate and necessary to emphasize how far we still remain from a solution to the problems of morphogenesis. Quite aside from the difficulty of explaining in detail what accounts for the various molecular properties, or how they arise, we must insist that the *in vitro* formation of fibrils from collagen macromolecules is not the same as the formation of cellular organelles, or of cells. The highly coordinated organization of a cell, its orderliness in space and time, its regulatory and adaptive properties—all these and more still elude our efforts to explain. The cooperative behavior of cells, enabling them to form supracellular aggregates possessing still other properties of selective association into organs and organisms, is for the moment even more mysterious. It is also more difficult to account for in molecular terms.

It is often remarked that the properties of table salt inhere neither in sodium nor in chlorine but in their combination. It is further said that no amount of information about sodium or chlorine alone would ever permit one to predict the properties of sodium chloride. Is this not an overly pessimistic view? The "new" properties which emerge when any subunits combine must be based on properties within the subunits. They cannot have come from nothing.

The fundamental task facing the student of living systems is to detect and understand those properties of subunits at every level which by interacting lead on to new properties at higher levels. No single approach, no single point of view—whether it be molecular, cellular, or organismic—will suffice to yield the required answers. There is no room for chauvinistic defenses of particular techniques or attitudes. What is needed is a host of bright minds acquainted with the problems, industrious hands anxious to work, and, not least, willingness to be content with the excitement of the chase itself, for success is never assured.

REFERENCES

De Robertis, E. D. P., W. W. Nowinski, and F. A. Saez, 1960, *General Cytology*, Chapter 1. Philadelphia: W. B. Saunders.

Loomis, W. F., "The sex gas of Hydra." *Sci. Am.*, April 1959.

Moscona, A. A., "Tissues from dissociated cells." *Sci. Am.*, May 1959.

ONCLEY, J. L., 1959, *Biophysical Science—A Study Program.* New York: John Wiley.

ROSE, S. M., "Feedback in the differentiation of cells." *Sci. Am.,* December 1958.

SCHMITT, F. O., "Giant molecules in cells and tissues." *Sci. Am.,* September 1957.

SUSSMAN, M., 1960, *Animal Growth and Development.* Englewood Cliffs, N. J.: Prentice-Hall.

ZAMECNIK, P. C., "The microsome." *Sci. Am.,* March 1958.

CHAPTER 11

EDGAR ANDERSON

Curator of Useful Plants, Missouri Botanical Garden and Professor of Botany, Washington University

Edgar Anderson was born at Forestville, New York, in 1897. He received his undergraduate training at Michigan State (B.S., 1918) and did his graduate work at the Bussey Institution of Harvard University (Sc.D., 1922) under E. M. East. He had a joint appointment to the staffs of the Missouri Botanical Garden and the Henry Shaw School of Botany of Washington University from 1922 to 1931. During these years he investigated the species problem in the genus Iris. From 1931 to 1935 he was on the staff of the Arnold Arboretum of Harvard University, visiting the Balkans in 1934 to obtain winter- and drought-hardy strains of Holly, Ivy, Yew, and Boxwood. In 1935 he returned to the Missouri Botanical Garden and Washington University. He carried out a cytological survey of the American Tradescantias and monographed them jointly with R. E. Woodson, Jr. This led to a field and experimental study of the role of interspecific hybridization in evolution. The methods worked out in these studies were further developed for studies of variation and evolution in weeds and cultivated plants with particular reference to maize. His published works include, in addition to many technical papers, *Introgressive Hybridization,* Wiley, 1949, and *Plants, Man and Life,* Little, Brown, 1952.

CHAPTER 11

The role of hybridization in evolution

EDGAR ANDERSON

Missouri Botanical Garden and Washington University

Before we can begin to discuss the role of hybridization in evolution we shall have to have a minimum vocabulary of a dozen or so specialized expressions for dealing with the ancestors and the offspring of hybrids. Along with this useful shorthand, we need to acquire a general understanding of what happens, generation by generation, when hybrids are made between two species. For our purposes there is nothing better to start with than a discussion of two species of flowering tobacco and the hybrids between them. The flowers are large, and the differences between the species are clear-cut; they are easily described and lend themselves well to diagrammatic illustrations.

Though they belong to the same genus as common tobacco, these two species are not suitable for smoking and are termed "flowering tobaccos" or "nicotines" by gardeners. So excellent are they for scientific analysis and demonstration that for two centuries our understanding of the laws of hybridization have continued to be illuminated by study of these two species, *Nicotiana alata* and *Nicotiana Langsdorffii* and their hybrids. The first of these is the common sweet-scented night-flowering nicotine of old-fashioned gardens, frequently referred to in seed catalogues and among gardeners as *Nicotiana affinis,* though *Nicotiana alata* var. *grandiflora* is now its accepted scientific name. The second is a botanical curiosity, named after the Captain Langsdorff who first brought back to European gardens seeds of this other South American nicotine with flowers like tiny bright green bells. We can set out the main differences between the two species in tabular form:

Nicotiana alata	*Nicotiana Langsdorffii*
flowers white,	flowers bright green,
large (6 inches long)	small (2 inches long)
corolla flaring to a	corolla scarcely flaring
5-pointed star	not at all star-shaped
night-flowering	day-flowering
sweet-scented	no perfume
inflorescence slightly	inflorescence much
branched	branched

Since these two species were used as parents we shall refer to them as the P_1 generation, that is, the *parental generation.* Crosses between these two species are called the F_1 (or *first filial generation*); seeds grown from the F_1 plants produce the F_2 (or *second filial generation*), they in turn give rise to the F_3 (the *third filial generation*), and so on. If we take one of the F_1 plants and cross it with either of the parental species, we term this a *first back-cross;* if these plants are crossed back to the same parental species we obtain third, fourth, and fifth back-crosses and so on. Were we to produce the back-crosses by repeated crosses back to *Nicotiana alata,* we would refer to that species as the *recurrent parent* and to *Nicotiana Langsdorffii* as the *nonrecurrent* parent. Similarly in a set of repeated back-crossing to *Nicotiana Langsdorffii* we would speak of that species as the recurrent parent and of *Nicotiana alata* as the nonrecurrent parent. See Fig. 11.1.

With these useful terms agreed on, it is now a simple matter to generalize the results of this species cross.

1) The F_1 plants (*Nicotiana Langsdorffii* and *Nicotiana alata*) are uniform and intermediate between the two parents. They bear medium-sized flowers, opening a yellowish-green and fading to an ivory white. Their pollen is pale blue, fading to almost ivory. The flowers were somewhat flaring and five-pointed, though by no means so deeply and beautifully cut as in *Nicotiana alata.*

2) The F_2 plants on the contrary are exceedingly variable from plant to plant. If they are grown by the hundreds, an occasional plant is indistinguishable from *Nicotiana alata.* At the other extreme are

plants with little greenish flowers almost as small and green and blue-pollened as those of *Nicotiana Langsdorffii.* In between are various intermediates, combining in diverse ways the contrasting characteristics of the two parental species. One finds such odd recombinations of the parental types as short, star-shaped flowers of purest white, with bright blue pollen, or slender star-shaped flowers of light yellow green with ivory pollen. Unless grown by the hundreds and carefully catalogued, we cannot ordinarily find any two plants which are precisely alike in flower and inflorescence. However, the various F_2's produced by crossing different F_1's are essentially alike in so far as one can make precise comparisons between different lots of such variable plants.

3) The results with the F_3's varied according to what F_2 plants had been selfed or crossed to produce that particular F_3. Very rarely did an F_2 plant, pollinated with its own pollen, produce an F_3 population of plants all very much like it and closely resembling one another. Most of the F_2 populations varied much less among sibling plants of a cross than did the F_2's. Generally they tended to resemble the F_2 plants from which they were derived and did not vary greatly among themselves in any particular F_3. Occasionally, however, there would be an F_3 population whose variation from plant to plant reminded one of that obtained among sibling F_2's.

The dramatic difference in variability between the uniform first generation and the highly variable F_2's cannot be overstressed. For two hundred years it has not ceased to amaze those who have made crosses between species of animals or species of plants. When, however, with any one of these species crosses we attempt to follow all the variables at once, we learn that in spite of the bewildering variability of the F_2, the outstanding fact about the whole assemblage is the extent to which *the characters which went into the cross together tend, on the average, to stay together.* In our example of the two nicotines we were crossing

a large,		a small,
white,		green,
star-shaped,	with	unlobed
flower		flower
with ivory pollen		with blue pollen

If we sit down with one flower from each of fifty to a hundred F_2 plants and sort them out we shall find

1. The white-flowered plants *on the average* are larger than the green-flowered ones (white and large size went into the cross together).
2. The star-shaped flowers *on the average* are whiter than those which are least lobed (white and star-shaped went into the cross together).

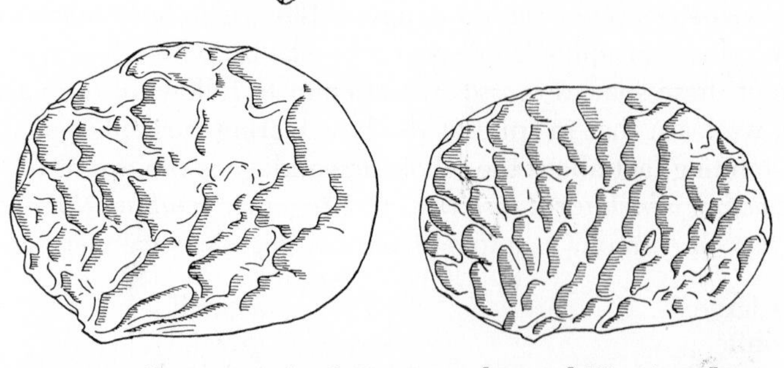

Fig. 11.1. *Above:* Details of *Nicotiana alata* and *Nicotiana Langsdorffii.* To the same scale one flower of the former and two of the latter, with and without a calyx. A seed pod of each somewhat enlarged but to the same scale. Seeds of each highly enlarged. *Nicotiana alata* to the left; *Nicotiana Langsdorffii* to the right. (Redrawn from E. Anderson and R. P. Ownbey, "The genetic coefficients of specific difference," *Annals of the Missouri Botanical Garden, 26,* 1939. With permission.) *Facing: Nicotiana alata* and *Nicotiana Langsdorffii* and their hybrid descendants, all to the same scale. From above to below: 5 flowers each of the two species, F_1, F_2 and backcrosses to each parent. (Redrawn from E. Anderson, *Introgressive Hybridization,* Wiley, 1949. With permission.)

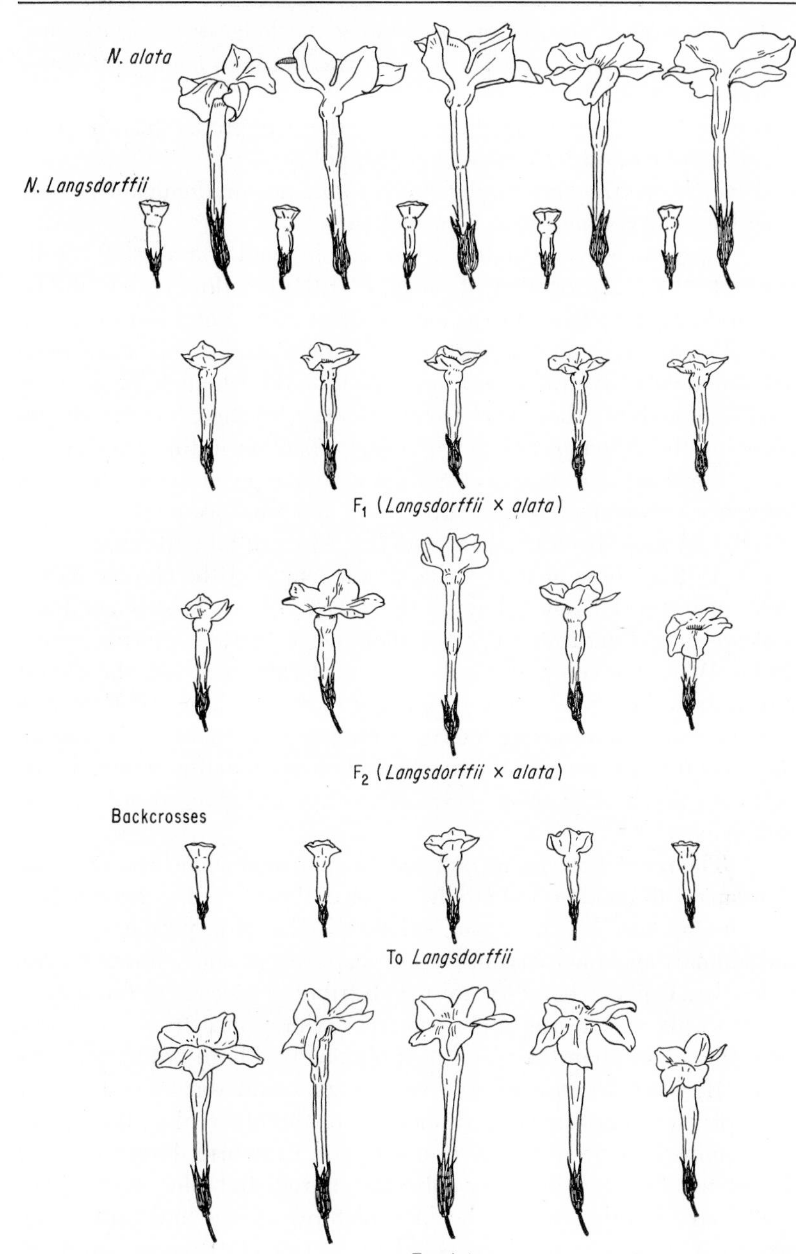

Fig. 11.1, continued.

3. The starriest of the flowers are among the longest; the least-lobed are among the shortest. (The F_1 cross was between a long star flower and a short unlobed one.)
4. If we choose the very smallest flowers they are predominantly green and unlobed and have blue or bluish pollen.
5. If we choose the very largest flowers they are predominantly white and star-shaped and with ivory pollen.

Large size, ivory pollen, white corolla, and star-shaped corolla went into the cross together; if, in spite of the bewildering variability, we can keep our attention riveted on these two contrasted combinations of characters and can envisage all at once size, shape, and corolla and pollen color, then it is easy to see that, on the whole, in back of the amazing variability there is a strong tendency for the character combinations of the P_1 generation to tend to stay together in the offspring.

For these two species of nicotines we may even demonstrate the difference between what we really obtain and what we might have obtained, had there been no such tendency. We can take the three characters: 1) the lobing of the corolla, 2) the length of the corolla, 3) the width of the corolla, and show (Fig. 11.2) the kinds of new combinations we should get in the F_2 were there no restrictions upon recombination. When we compare these theoretical extremes with the closest approach to them found in a population of several hundred F_2 plants, then we realize how strong the restrictions are. In terms of the recombinations *we did not get,* the ones which were actually obtained now look very much alike to us, even when they are glanced at only superficially.

The restrictions on recombination vary somewhat from one kind of organism to another and are due to several factors. The most important one, because it is universal, is linkage. The germ plasms of plants and animals and microorganisms are made up of long, linear macromolecules. Units of heredity are not distributed piecemeal throughout the germ plasm, but are in chromosomes whose ultrastructure is even more threadlike than the views of it obtained with an ordinary microscope. If, when we crossed two species we could somehow stain the germ plasm of one species red and that of the other blue, then when we examined the germ plasms of our F_2 and F_3 hybrid descendants we should not find helter-skelter mixtures of red and blue units. They would not, in other words, be like mixtures of red and blue beads taken out of a box in which equal quantities of the two had been mixed. They would be more like mixtures from a box in which long strings of blue beads and long strings of red beads had been stored together. If, in the hybrid plants, we could see the ultimate threads of the germ plasm we would be struck by the long stretches of red or of blue, and the comparatively few lengths in which red and blue alternate with each other in close juxtaposition along the same thread.

4) The results with back-crosses are readily summarized. They were much less variable than the F_2's and they tended to resemble the recurrent parent. In the first backcross to *Nicotiana alata*, for instance, the plants as a whole did not remind one of *Nicotiana Langsdorffii*,

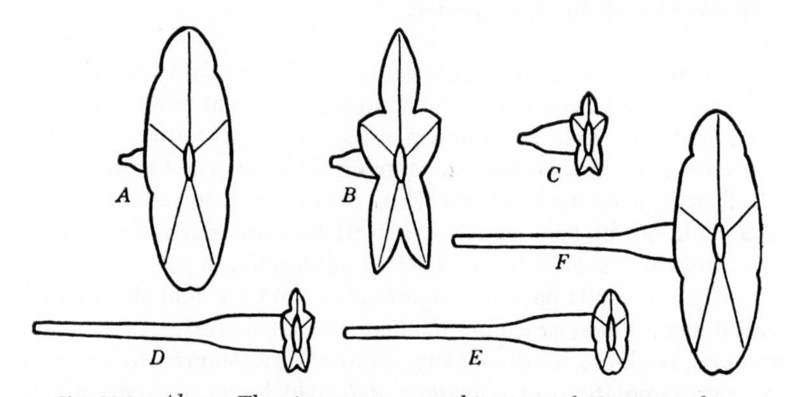

Fig. 11.2. *Above:* The six extreme recombinations of *Nicotiana alata* and *Nicotiana Langsdorffii* which could be obtained were there no restrictions (linkage, etc.) on recombination. *Below:* The closest approach to each of the above extremes which was obtained in an actual F_2. Drawings diagrammatic but strictly to scale from measured specimens. (From E. Anderson, *Introgressive Hybridization*, Wiley, 1949. With permission.)

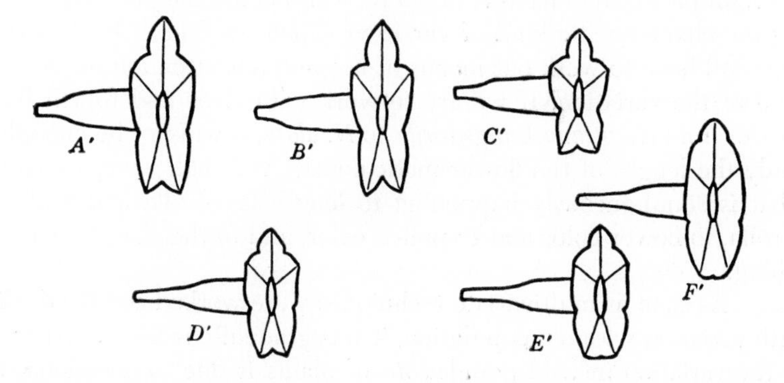

even though genealogically they were one quarter from that species. To casual observation, even by one who knew both species of nicotine, they appeared like rather variable *Nicotiana alata's* rather than like hybrids. It was only when one studied them analytically, noting that all their differences from normal *alata's* were in the direction of *Nicotiana Langsdorffii*, that their hybrid nature became apparent. Then one could see that their variability was due to characters which departed from the average for *Nicotiana alata* in the direction of *Nicotiana Langsdorffii*. One plant would be greener than *Nicotiana alata* and slightly smaller, another would be less sharply lobed and with a shorter corolla. By meticulously going over a population of the first back-cross to *alata* and cataloguing the ways in which each plant differed from normal *N. alata*, one would come finally to have a list of the chief differences between the two species.

The second back-crosses were even less variable than the first back-crosses and even more similar to the recurrent parent; the third, fourth and fifth were more and more similar until with the fifth, the back-crosses were becoming indistinguishable from the recurrent parent. That is, a group of plants which were genealogically only 63/64 *alata* could not be distinguished from 64/64 *alata;* 63/64 *Langsdorffii's* were indistinguishable from 64/64 *Langsdorffii's*.

These results have an important bearing for field studies of hybridization. *So long as we are dealing with back-crosses, hybridization is cryptic.* Back-crosses do not suggest hybridization even to the trained observer. Populations of *Nicotiana alata* which owe virtually all their variation to third and fourth back-crosses from *Nicotiana Langsdorffii* do not suggest that species. Even a scientifically trained person who has had no special experience with back-crosses will look upon this variability as just an ordinary sort of plant-to-plant difference.

If we are to make accurate estimates of the role of hybridization in evolution we shall have to begin by working out methods for detecting the characteristic kind of variation which we find in back-crosses. We shall have to work out means of keeping our attention on the sum total of the variation. If we are to work with third and fourth back-crosses from *Nicotiana Langsdorffii* to *N. alata*, it will not be enough to study the length of the flower meticulously. We shall have to analyze what is simultaneously happening to length of corolla and width of corolla, to flower color and to pollen color, and to the sharpness of the lobing.

As soon as multivariate techniques were worked out for dealing with variation within a population, it was gradually realized that much of the variation in wild populations of plants is due to occasional hybridization followed by repeated back-crossing. Since, in general aspect, the results of such a process are different from what most naturalists understand by the word hybridization, it has been given a distinctive name, *introgressive hybridization* and the process itself is referred to as *introgression*. Introgression is the gradual infiltration of the germ plasm of one species into that of another through hybridization and repeated back-crossing. The study of introgression has demonstrated that the commonest result of hybridization is the increase of variability in one or both of the participating species.

Detailed studies of introgression have now been made in many genera and species of plants, including flowering plants, conifers, ferns, and fungi. Populations of animals are generally much harder to locate, define, and study than are those of plants, so that nothing like as much work has been done on introgression in animals as in plants. Detailed studies have, however, been published for different genera of fish, of birds, and of various kinds of insects.

As a detailed example of introgression and of its precise analysis in the field, we may consider *Oxytropis albiflorus,* a common "loco weed" (or stock poison) in the Rocky Mountains of Colorado. It grows there in aspen groves at eight to ten thousand feet, a low-growing perennial legume, whose flowers have rather the appearance of small stiff upright bunches of wistaria. There is a crown of compound leaves arising directly from the rootstock and, coming up through the leaves and rising above them, a little cluster of compact inflorescences. The flowers are prevailingly an ivory white, though plants with pale blue or pale pink flowers are common, particularly at certain sites. Much more rarely one may find plants with flowers colored bright pink. The initial analyses were made at Dory Hill, where a pioneer graveyard of Gold Rush days is flanked by open pastures. Since there were several flowers on each plant, the statistical treatment of the data was made much simpler by selecting from each plant one leaf and one flower stalk that were typical of the plant as a whole. In this way, flower heads which had been malformed by grazing or similar accidents were largely eliminated.

The first phase of the study was to determine as many characteristics as possible that were relatively constant on any one plant but varied markedly from plant to plant. The traits most readily observed were leaf height, flower height, pubescence of the flower stalk, laxness or compactness of the inflorescence, and the color of the corolla and of its subtending calyx.

The plants obviously varied greatly in the height of the flower stalk and of the leaves, but just as obviously height was also affected by how shady and how well watered the immediate vicinity was. The difficulty of measuring this character was removed by studying, not the absolute height of either flower stalk or leaves, but their comparative height. The first measure taken on each plant was therefore the precise extent to which the flower stalk did or did not exceed the leaves. Data were found to vary—from stalks with flowers several centimeters above the leaves to those with flowers 4 cm below them. In technical terms the leaves were varying from *exserted* to *included.*

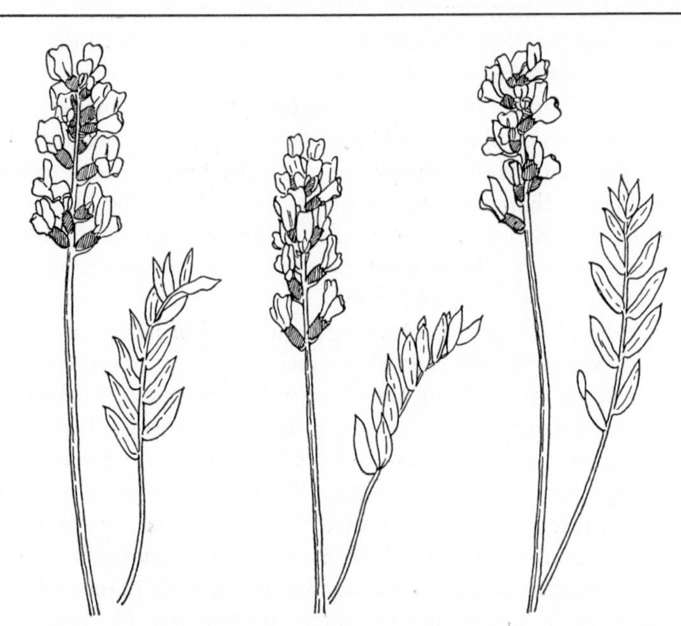

Fig. 11.3. The three white-flowered, low-dense extreme plants from the sample of 50 *Oxytropis* plants. Note that the lowest flower is as low or lower than the tip of the accompanying leaf and that the flowers are set close together. (Redrawn from E. Anderson, "Introgressive Hybridization," *Biological Reviews, 28,* 1953. With permission.)

Another way in which the flowers of *Oxytropis* varied was the extent to which the raceme was made up of flowers closely set together. This was particularly noticeable at the base of the raceme where in some plants the individual blossoms were so isolated as scarcely to touch one another, while in others they were packed in tightly together. After several ways of scoring this condition had been tried, it was finally standardized by counting the number of flowers in the lowest 2 cm of the raceme. This gave values of 6 for the most tightly packed and of 2 for the most widely spaced.

As soon as these two characters, the exsertion of the raceme and its openness, had been worked out, a collection of 50 plants was made and carefully scored for each character. It was then readily shown that the two characters were not varying independently of one another but were tending to go along together. Of the plants with 5 or 6 flowers in the lowest 2 cm, well over half had racemes whose lowest flowers were down among the leaves. Of those plants with 2, 3, or 4 flowers in the lowest 2 cm, over half had flowers which were held above the level of the highest leaflets. There was, in other words, a tendency for dense-

Fig. 11.4. The three tall-open extremes from the same population as those illustrated in Fig. 11.3. Note that the flowers, all of which are colored, are well above the leaves and are widely spaced on the flower stalk. (Redrawn from E. Anderson, "Introgressive Hybridization," *Biological Reviews, 28,* 1953. With permission.)

ness of raceme to go along with included racemes and for openness to characterize exserted racemes.

Science is built upon repeated results; the association of these two characters was immediately checked by making other collections. From adjacent pastures, the most and least exserted plants in the entire area were collected. The correlation was again so strong that it was immediately apparent in such a collection that the most exserted racemes had flowers that were widest apart and the least exserted had flowers which were the densest. A further check was made by collecting plants with the densest and the most open racemes from a pasture and then examining these two extremes for the extent the racemes were held above the leaves. This correlation also held and the point was taken as thoroughly established.

Hairiness of the plant was then studied. It proved difficult at first because the plants were so hairy in so many places and some of the plants obviously had two kinds of hairs. By making repeated trials it was found that the hairs on the calyx (the leaflike organ just below the corolla) varied less from one flower to another, though they varied conspicuously from plant to plant. Under examination with a good binocular microscope it was clear that there were two quite different kinds of hairs. There were some very short black ones too small to be seen effectively with the naked eye and there were much larger and longer ones that ranged from cottony and curled to somewhat silky and straight.

Once we had learned how to grade these two types of hair, no time was wasted on the whole collection. The extreme dense-flowered, inserted plants were now compared with those of the opposite extreme, the lax-flowered exserted ones. The differences in hair type were dramatic. The low-dense extremes either had none of the little black hairs on the calyx or at most a few lines and dots of them. The open-exserted extremes included plants whose calyces were so clothed with tiny black hairs that to the naked eye they looked dark in color. The large white hairs in the former group tended to be curled like cotton batting; in the latter group the hairs were silky and straight.

As these facts slipped into place the two extreme combinations of characters began to appear first to the mind's eye, shortly to be confirmed by careful examination of the relevant plants. The low-dense extremes included few plants with colored flowers; the tall-open included plants which were deeply tinted, sometimes in both the corolla and the calyx, sometimes in just one or the other. We were now ready to make a scrupulously careful examination of all six characters at once in our collection of 50 plants. Each plant was scored for

flower color	denseness of raceme
calyx color	frequency of small black hairs
exsertion of raceme	looseness and curliness of the large white hairs.

These 300 facts (six measurements or scorings for each of 50 plants) were then set out in a diagram using "metroglyphs" to show all the interactions of the six variables. The result shows clearly that the variation resulted from introgression. These six characters are associated loosely together just as characters in the back-crossing experi-

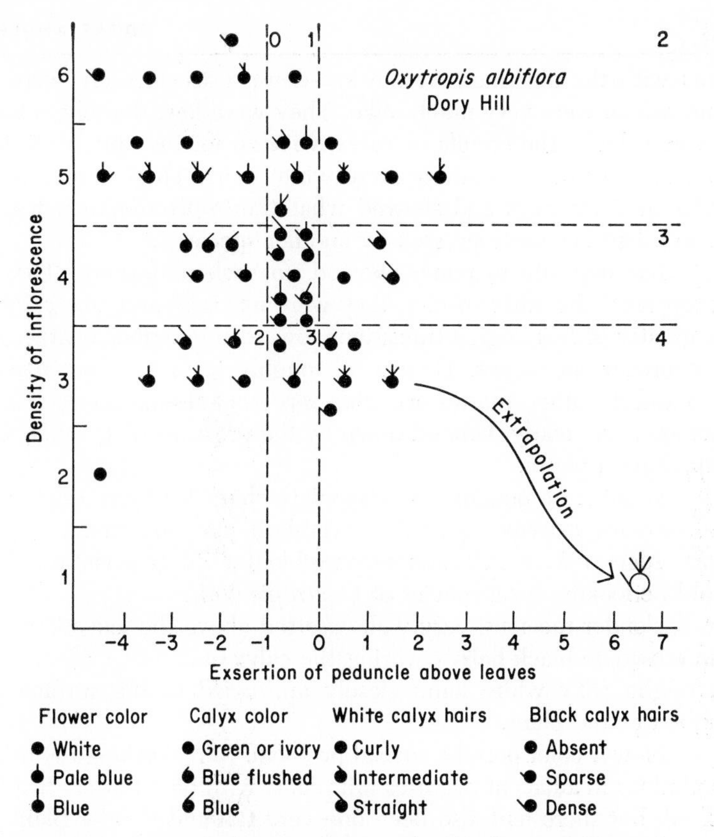

Fig. 11.5. A scatter diagram showing the 50 plants of *Oxytropis* from Dory Hill. Each dot represents one plant, and six characteristics of each plant are simultaneously diagramed. Density of the inflorescence is measured on the vertical axis in 6 grades; the exsertion of the flower stalk above the leaves is measured on the horizontal axis in 12 grades. Four other characters are diagramed by the rays from each dot. A dot with no rays has a low grade for all four characters; in other words it is white-flowered with curly calyx hairs, a green or ivory calyx, and none of the small submicroscopic black hairs. The large glyph at the lower right-hand corner of the diagram shows the kind of plant which would have had to hybridize with the low-dense extremes to create this kind of a population. It has very exserted flowers, and the individual flowers are set wide apart on the flower stalk. It is deep in color with straight calyx hairs, and the calyx is itself deeply colored and is close set on the outside with tiny submicroscopic hairs. (Redrawn from E. Anderson, "Introgressive Hybridization," *Biological Reviews,* 28, 1953. With permission.)

ments with the nicotines. At the low-dense extreme there were four plants which were very much alike. They were low, densely flowered, with no color in the corolla or calyx, with no microscopic black hairs, and with very curled cottony large white hairs. They were generally similar in other ways and showed what *Oxytropis albiflorus* was like before it had been introgressed by another species.

The opposite extremes showed no such uniformity. They did not represent the other species; they were introgressants that exhibited to a greater or less degree transitions toward the various characters of the nonrecurrent parent. They were roughly ¾ or ⅞ *Oxytropis albiflorus* and the other quarter or eighth represented inheritance from the other species, greatly damped down by the presence of so much *O. albiflorus* germ plasm.

Might it be possible to extrapolate character by character from the low-dense extremes, past the variable high-open extremes to *Oxytropis,* species *X,* which was responsible for all this variation? We would be looking for a species of *Oxytropis* with:

1. tall, slender racemes, very well exserted above the leaves
2. microscopic black hairs covering the calyx
3. straight, silky white hairs closely appressed to the surface, over much of the plant.

Flower color posed a special problem. In rechecking the original correlations in adjacent pastures tall plants with blue flowers had been noticed; but there had also been one very tall and slender plant with bright pink flowers. This suggested that we might be looking for a pink or magenta-flowered species. To one familiar with the genetics of flower color in other species, the blue color of the introgressants could readily be explained. Many white-flowered plants with little pigment carry blue color rather than pink. When they are back-crossed to a pink-flowered species, the capacity to produce additional pigment comes in from the nonrecurrent parent, but the blue genes of the recurrent parent predominate in the back-crosses as in the following diagram:

Oxytropis albiflora	*Oxytropis X*
blue	pink
little or no pigment	much pigment

Oxytropis back-crosses
blue (occasionally pink)
little to considerable pigment

Accordingly, the prediction was made that there should be (and probably fairly near Dory Hill) a species of *Oxytropis* with slender appressed silky hairs and bright pink flowers. Furthermore their calices should be colored pink and have a dense undercoat of tiny black hairs. This predicted combination of characters was looked up in the local manual, which indicated that *Oxytropis Lambertii* might be the nonrecurrent parent we were looking for. Search was made for it the following day, and it was found growing in quantity at slightly lower elevations.

Most sciences pass from a descriptive to an analytical phase. When, as in this case—and there have been other examples—predictions could be made concerning a species which the observer had never seen, the study of hybridization was definitely advancing from the descriptive to the analytical phase.

In the loco weeds of Dory Hill it was readily apparent that introgression was taking place most actively in areas which had been greatly altered by man's activities. The most brightly tinted flowers were clearly concentrated in those spots where the former balance of nature had been most strikingly upset.

Dory Hill was no ordinary graveyard. It was on the hill over which passed the packtrains of Gold Rush days, carrying the ore from nearby Central City down to Golden, where the Great Plains abut on the mountains. It was close enough to the actual mining area so that many mining claims had been staked out there in the early days, and little borrow pits peppered the landscape. Although in later years the ore went out by more efficient routes, the old abandoned trails were still partly in use for moving stock up into the high mountains during the summer grazing season. A succession of gravel and blacktop and paved roads had crossed and recrossed the hill to meet the needs of ranchers and summer visitors. The little graveyard, so actively used in gold rush days, had been virtually forgotten. For nearly a century man had been subjecting this hilltop to the ever-changing pattern of his trackways, trails, and roadways. It was at those points where the native vegetation had been most radically altered and the soil most actively and repeatedly disturbed that the effects of introgression were most plainly to be seen.

The connection of introgression with disturbed habitats is indeed a common phenomenon. One of the most instructive examples involves two handsome species of *Iris, Iris hexagona* var. *giganticaerulea* and *Iris fulva,* which are native to the lower Mississippi delta. The first of these is a tall plant with large upright flowers of deep blue marked with white and yellow; the latter is a smaller plant with floppy flowers of bright terra-cotta red-brown. The hybrids are a motley lot; since one species has blue pigment on a white background and the other red pigment on a yellow background, the hybrids include such recombinations as red over white (producing reds and pinks), or blue over yellow (producing smoky shades of gray-blue), in addition to various intermediate purples and wine-reds.

On the lower delta, the farms line the rivers and bayous, property lines run back straight from the river in the old French colonial manner, and the farms are very narrow, scarcely wider than a city lot, but running back for as much as a mile or so. Under these conditions it would be observed that hybridization was often largely restricted to a single farm. One instructive example was studied in detail. The hybrids were in a marshy pasture along a little ditch which ran across several adjoining farms. On one of them the willows and other woody vegetation had been completely removed and the farm had been overgrazed, so that there were bare spots in the pasture, particularly at those places where the cattle had wallowed about when the water level was high. On this particular farm there were hybrids all along the brook; on either side of the property they had spread up to the border fence line but not beyond it. On this one farm they had become almost like a weed, spreading out in great masses through the swampy pasture where the cattle grazed on the competing grasses (and even upon competing shrubs) but left the irises pretty much alone.

The habitats of the immediately neighboring farms had been disturbed, but less violently. In one of them the willows and other shrubs in the marshy area along the ditch had been left free to grow, and it was too shady for the irises. The neighbor on the other side had removed all the shrubs but had not overpastured the area, so that his whole farm was grassy. The pasture with the irises had been having a violent time and still looked it. Here and there were shrubs browsed by the cattle and cut back from time to time by the owner. In the wettest parts of the marsh were muddy areas where cattle had floundered about when the water level was high; some of them were only a foot or so square, the largest like great buffalo wallows. The habitats of the pasture, sun *vs.* shade, grassy *vs.* nongrassy, had been hybridized so to speak. The hybridization of the habitat had produced various new niches in which the hybrid irises not only persisted but were at a selective advantage.

In the marshy area there were a few plants of *Iris hexagona* var. *giganti-caerulea* but they were greatly outnumbered by introgressants, each plant exhibiting in a different way the influence of germ plasm from *Iris fulva.* Some had the yellow signal patch of *Iris hexagona giganti-caerulea* in their flowers; others were without it. Few of the plants had blooms as red as those of *Iris fulva,* but most of them tended in that direction. There were red-violet shades and dark red-violets, there were wine-reds and beautiful red-purples.

Eventually the variety and beauty of these mongrel flowers car-

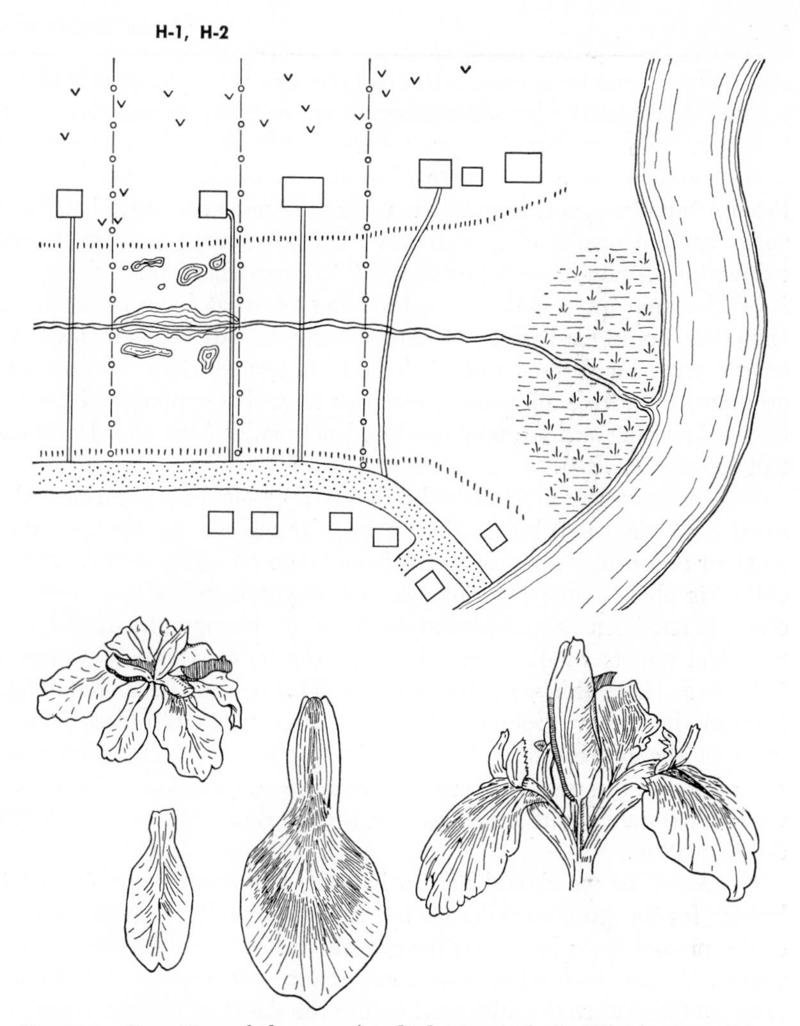

Fig. 11.6. *Top:* Map of the area (studied intensively by Riley) where *Iris hexagona* var. *giganti-caerulea* had been introgressed by *Iris fulva.* At the right is a bayou with a small ditch draining into it forming a marsh in which *Iris hexagona* var. *giganti-caerulea* is growing. A series of long narrow farms have their houses set on the high ground with entrance driveways leading across an ancient branch of the Mississippi River (now abandoned and filled in) to the opposite high ground on which a roadway is located. *Iris fulva* grows in the rear of these houses. There are two major groups of hybrids, H-1 and H-2. In colony H-1 there had been extensive introgression; most of the plants showed transitions towards various characters of *Iris fulva* and a few of them resembled that species quite closely though in measurably different ways. Colony H-2 (aside from two plants) showed only slightly the effect of *Iris fulva.* Note that the hybrids are all concentrated on one farm; along the horizontal ditch they extend right up to the boundary fence on either side. *Bottom:* Flowers of *Iris fulva* (*left*) and *Iris giganti-caerulea* (*right*) to the same scale. One sepal of each species is laid out flat to show differences in size, shape, and color pattern. (Redrawn from E. Anderson, *Introgressive Hybridization,* Wiley, 1949. With permission.)

ried them into an even more advantageous (and even more disturbed) habitat. News of the beautiful iris pasture reached enough New Orleans gardeners so that the plants were mostly all sold, at so much a basket, and began a new stage of evolution as domesticated plants. From this pasture, and from others where the same processes had been going on, the results of introgressive hybridization passed over into cultivation. Amateur and professional iris gardeners throughout the South became interested in the breeding of what have come to be known as Louisiana irises. The original crosses and back-crosses have been repeated and species of iris have been brought into the breeding program. Hundreds of named varieties have been produced by selective breeding and are now marketed nationally (and to a lesser extent internationally).

Introgression in disturbed habitats thus has brought a new domesticated plant into being. Fortunately for science, nearly a score of amateur and professional scientists have taken an active interest in the delta iris phenomenon. During the last 30 years, in one phase or another, it has been described and analyzed in monographs, books, and technical papers by J. K. Small, E. J. Alexander, Caroline Dorman, P. Viosca, H. P. Riley, E. Anderson, R. Foster, and L. F. Randolph. Not only has a new group of irises been domesticated, but various aspects of the process have been precisely observed and scientifically recorded. For this one introgressant there is now waiting for the scholar who may someday put it all together, a critical account of at least one domestication.

Much as we should like to have it, information of this sort is lacking for the great world crops by which we live (and even for most of the ornamental plants that have been domesticated in more recent years). Wheat, corn, rice, beans, sugarcane, sweet potatoes—all such crops as these were domesticated before the dawn of history. However much it would profit us to know the details of their domestication, we can only piece the evidence together indirectly and by inference. Did introgression play as important a role in the domestication of these ancient crops as we know it did for the Louisiana irises? It is a likely hypothesis.

One reason why the story of these beautiful irises of Louisiana cow pastures is important, is that it is already stimulating new kinds of investigation into the origin of cultivated plants in general. Another reason for its importance is the way this simple demonstration calls attention to the dynamics of evolution in disturbed habitats. Other studies of introgression have illuminated these relationships in various ways.

A striking demonstration of the connection between active introgression and severe disturbance of the habitat is presented by two species of sage that flourish on sunny dry slopes in southern California.

One, *Salvia mellifera,* is a fine-twigged bushy plant with tiny blue flowers. The other, *Salvia apiana,* is a dramatic gray-leafed plant, whose much larger flowers are pollinated chiefly by the carpenter bee. Although they do not look very much alike, they are readily cross-pollinated, and hybrids and back-crosses have been grown in experimental plots. They *can* cross with each other, but ordinarily they do not—or if they do, the seeds do not ordinarily come up. Though they grow almost side by side over vast areas along the coast, hybrids are seldom found and introgressants are rare. Careful study of one of these exceptional introgressive populations revealed the dynamics of the relationship.

The base of the steep southern face of the San Gabriel mountains had at one point originally abutted on a level flanking mesa of live oaks. A century ago, where the sunny vegetation of the mountain slopes joined the shady live oaks, a small olive orchard had been planted and later was abandoned. *Salvia mellifera* and *Salvia apiana* were common on the sunny slopes above this point; but the most scrupulous study of their variation showed little evidence of introgression between them. In the abandoned olive orchard, however, and at the junction of the former stand of live oaks, unmistakable hybrids and back-crosses were conspicuous. A tabulation plant by plant showed that on the edge of the olive orchard, the introgressants were at an advantage; they were clearly in the majority.

On the sunny slopes of the mountains, the two species had been growing together along with various other species since prehistoric times. The whole association of plants had passed through the sieve of natural selection. The various kinds fitted in with each other so exactly that there was no place in which a newcomer could survive. Even when the two *Salvias* crossed with one another, there was ordinarily no intermediate niche in which an intermediate hybrid could gain a foothold. When, however, the olive orchard was installed on the level soil where the live oaks had once grown, new kinds of habitats were brought into being.

When the olive orchard was abandoned, various plants from the sunny slopes seeded down there, and among them *Salvia* hybrids at length found a spot where they could grow and develop. Once established, such hybrids were a source, year after year, of variable hybrids and back-cross generations of plants. If any of these new variants did not fit into the strange new habitat of the olive orchard, there were always others that might. In a comparatively short time, by natural processes, a little local swarm of *Salvia* introgressants had been bred and selected. In that strange new environment it was superior to either of the old, established, time-tested *Salvias* of the upper slopes. With new kinds of habitats readily available, new kinds of *Salvias* had rapidly evolved through introgression.

The conservatism of the two *Salvias* on the sunny slopes above the olive orchard is particularly instructive when contrasted with introgression within another association of plants, the chaparral. The California chaparral is a loose association of shrubs and small trees which covers thousands of square miles of rolling country. Many of the species which make it up are evergreen or semievergreen. As we know it now, the chaparral has at the very least been greatly affected by brush and grass fires; the whole association has the ability either to come back from seed or to sprout again from rootstocks after the fire has run through it. Opinions differ as to just when the chaparral came into being. Some experts believe that much of its evolution has taken place since the white man first came to California. Others would set the origin back farther in time, though all agree that it is, as an association of plants, a relative newcomer.

Introgressive hybridization seems to be going on in several of the genera which make up the chaparral; it has been studied intensively in one species, *Adenostoma fasciculatum*. This species is particularly resistant to fire, and in areas such at Mt. Diablo, where there have been repeated and heavy fires, it may make up the great bulk of the vegetation. Its common name is Spanish, *chamise*. In colonial days those areas where the *chamise* dominated the chaparral were sometimes known as *chamisal*—that is, the place of the *chamise*. It is a wide-branching shrub ordinarily about the size of a large lilac bush, though in rocky or gravelly areas it may be no more than knee high or even less than that. Its tiny dark green leaves are so small and needlelike as to resemble those of a heath or even a conifer such as a spruce. In late spring it is covered with bunches of small creamy-white flowers, sometimes in dense little clusters, more frequently in large open sprays like those of a lilac bush. It was the variation pattern of these inflorescences that first called particular attention to the species.

Along the road up Mt. Diablo there are extensive stretches lined with *chamise* and very little else of any size. When they are in bloom there is dramatic variation from one bush to the next in the size and shape of the flower clusters. The stony mountain soil is essentially similar from plant to plant; the bushes are so close that their branches are intermingled; yet there is striking variation from one plant to the next in the flower clusters. On one plant they will be widely spread, so open that each flower is separated from its neighbors, and on the very next bush they may all be quite dense. On some plants the clusters will be

tionary importance of introgressive hybridization. Evolution in the past has proceeded whenever changes in the habitat put new kinds of plants and animals at a selective advantage. In the last 5000 years the chief changes to be reckoned with by most plants and animals have been those introduced by man. It is he who early in his career domesticated fire and made it one of his hunting and land-clearing tools. It is he who has dammed streams and drained marshes, cut down woodlands, scarred the face of the earth, changed the water level, introduced English sparrows into the New World, cacti into Australia, and blackberries into New Zealand.

Seen in the large, the chief evolutionary advance in this 5000 years has been the rapid evolution of plants and animals that will fit into landscapes man has dominated. It is recorded in the weeds of roadsides and croplands, the giant grasses of our vast tropical savannahs, the pantropic weeds which spread so rapidly that their original homes are matters of dispute; it is observable in the intricate mantle of Mediterranean plants that followed the Spaniards into California, and in the European meadow plants of our American pastures and hayfields, as they have rapidly continued to evolve—all of them clothing larger and larger sectors of the earth as it fell increasingly under the ecological domination of man.

By simple analogy we can demonstrate the effectiveness of introgression under such conditions. Let us imagine an automobile industry in which new cars are produced only by copying old cars one part at a time and then putting them together on an assembly line. New models can be produced only by changing one part at a time. They cannot be produced *de novo* but must be built up from existing assembly lines. Imagine one factory producing only Model "T" Fords, and another with two assembly lines producing Model "T" Fords and also modern station wagons. It is evident that if changes can only be brought about by using existing assembly lines these would have to proceed slowly in the factory which had only one assembly line from which to select. In the other factory, however, an ingenious automobile designer given two assembly lines to work with, and dissimilar parts, could combine systems out of either and quickly produce a whole set of new models.

The single assembly line is like evolution without either introgression or hybridization. An auto, like an organism, is the product of a series of operations; a mutation affects only one of them. We know of nothing in the mutation process which will insure that a mutation affecting one step will be in any way coordinated with a mutation affecting another. The double assembly line analogy is like evolution canalized by introgression. When hybridization and back-crossing are carrying elements of foreign germ plasm over into a previously stabilized one, the new elements carried over have already been selected to work harmoniously together. Introgression not only greatly increases variation, but by bringing in together previously integrated changes, it greatly increases the probability that something workable can be assembled out of the mixture.

Living, as we all have since childhood, in the midst of man-dominated landscapes, it is difficult for us to appreciate the extent to which we are surrounded by one of the greatest bursts of evolutionary activity the world has ever seen. Looking across a stretch of calm and stable countryside—our grandfather's farm, shall we say—it takes an effort of the imagination to summarize the changes which have gone on there in the last 10,000 years, to assess the evolutionary change which is still rapidly under foot at the present moment. When we stop to reflect, it is our cultivated crops and our domesticated animals that come most readily to mind. Their evolution has come about (and is continuing) not only through the stimulus of man's dominance but increasingly under his actual guidance. Much more important in terms of evolution, however, are the changes which have been taking place in the whole landscape, not merely in the plants and animals under our direct control.

If grandfather was a California rancher we realize that the orchard and the field crops of the ranch are due to man's efforts. The chaparral in the hills above the ranch and in stretches here and there along the roadways we take for granted as a characteristic part of California landscapes, as indeed it has become. Yet, as we have just seen, the *Adenostomas* of the chaparral are in evolutionary ferment; from the studies that have already been made on other genera in that association—the oaks and the California lilac (*Ceanothus*), for instance—it is fairly certain that the chaparral as a whole is undergoing complex introgression. In looking intensely at the *Adenostomas* we have put our finger on one detail in the man-dominated landscapes that are evolving under the influence of his activities.

To indicate the active evolution going on around us, let us examine the wild lettuce which, all unasked, grows along the roadside at the edge of town. This common weed lettuce (*Lactuca scariola*) is a European plant that quite uninvited travels about with man. An expert glance at almost any weed patch of it will show that it varies markedly from plant to plant in such characters as the size and shape of the leaves and the ways in which they are toothed along their margins.

Where does all this variation come from? Apparently a good deal of it comes from crosses between weed lettuce and the cultivated sorts which flower in nearby gardens. Ordinarily these results are not readily apparent because the most striking characteristics of the cultivated sorts are recessive and do not show in the F_1. Red leaves, a characteristic of a few cultivated varieties, is, however, dominant (or semidominant) in the F_1. When a red-leafed variety comes into fashion, as one does now and then, it is comparatively easy to find an answer to our question about sources of the variable weed lettuces. If we keep a sharp eye out, we find red-leafed plants here and there among the weed populations. Some of them are noticeably more vigorous, indicating that they are F_1's between the wild and cultivated sorts which are exhibiting hybrid vigor. If we collect the seeds from such a plant and sow them, they produce a variable F_2 population combining in various ways the characteristics of the wild and cultivated lettuces.

Introgression from the cultivated sorts into the weeds is apparently quite common and goes on right under our noses a good deal of the time in many parts of the world. Through it, diversity is kept up in the weed lettuces and their evolution can continue to go forward.

In such ways evolution proceeds at an accelerated rate in the plants and animals which travel around the world with us, not only unasked, but frequently combatted. In much the same way as in the wild lettuces, introgression goes forward in the grasses of our roadsides and dooryards, in the plants which line our railroad rights of way and come up in the freightyards of our large cities. It is not only in the crop plants we breed that evolution is going forward; it is equally or even more powerful in the weeds that compete with crops or in the fungal and bacterial diseases which are parasitic upon them. So fast can new strains of oat diseases evolve that in the Corn Belt states, scientific oat breeders seem to be losing the race; new strains of disease are being evolved more rapidly than the experiment stations can produce disease-resistant varieties.

A similar kind of evolution is proceeding in the animal world. The new direction of animal evolution in the last 10,000 years is with the weedlike animals—the rats, the mice, the cockroaches, the ticks, the house spiders, the houseflies. It is the unseen clouds of microorganisms that follow us about—the yeasts, the molds, the bacteria in our fields and gardens, our barns and factories and homes—organisms that populate our very bodies. This is the dramatic evolution in a new direction which has gone forward under man's unconscious influence.

At earlier times in the earth's history other animals than man dominated the landscapes of their time. The giant herbivorous dinosaurs of the early Cretaceous, the largest land animals the world has ever seen, must have made catastrophic inroads upon the vegetation of their own day. Their effect would have been approximately equivalent to that of gigantic bulldozers that fed on vegetation and sometimes fought each other! Landscapes dominated by them would have been as disturbed as they are today in those areas where man with gigantic machines is clearing space for factories, supermarkets, and housing developments.

We know from the fossil record that one of the great revolutions in vegetation occurred during the Cretaceous, when the ferny and coniferous vegetation of the early Cretaceous was succeeded by that of the upper Cretaceous in which flowering plants predominated. We have no detailed information regarding what went on, but it is certainly safe to say that these giant reptiles affected the vegetation of their day in much the same way as we have affected the *Adenostomas* and irises of our own.

Until such studies as those described here were undertaken, there were great differences of scientific opinion as to the importance of the role of hybridization in evolution. Some eminent scientists thought it had been a major factor; others, quite as eminent, were convinced that it was not. Studies such as those made on *Adenostoma* and iris and *Salvia* have moved this question from the zone of argument to that of observation, experiment, measurement, and analysis. It is now generally admitted that in the higher plants at least, hybridization has played an important evolutionary role; there is evidence that it has been of consequence among some animals. There is at present a growing possibility that it may have been of importance in evolution.

REFERENCES

Anderson, Edgar, 1949, *Introgressive Hybridization.* New York: John Wiley.

Heiser, Charles, 1949, "Natural hybridization with particular reference to Evolution." *Botan. Rev., 15:* 645–87.

CHAPTER 12

STANLEY L. MILLER

Assistant Professor of Chemistry
University of California, San Diego

Stanley L. Miller was born at Oakland, California, in 1930. He was an undergraduate at the University of California where he received the B.S. degree in 1951 with a major in chemistry. He continued his study of chemistry at the University of Chicago, where he was awarded the Ph.D. degree in 1954. In 1954–55 he was a Jewett Fellow at the California Institute of Technology. From 1955 to 1960 he was Assistant Professor of Biochemistry in the College of Physicians and Surgeons of Columbia University. He has been in his present position at San Diego since 1960.

At the University of Chicago Dr. Miller came under the influence of Professor H. C. Urey. During this period he carried out his now famous experiment in which he was able to show that a number of amino acids and other organic compounds may be synthesized under conditions that might have prevailed on the primitive earth.

Among Dr. Miller's publications are the following: "A production of amino acids under possible primitive earth conditions," *Science*, 1953, 117:528; "The formation of organic compounds on the primitive earth," *Ann. N. Y. Acad. Sci.*, 1957, 69 (Art. 2):260–275.

The origin of life

CHAPTER 12

STANLEY L. MILLER

University of California

Introduction

The problem of how life arose on the earth is one of the most difficult in modern science. Almost every branch of science will have something to contribute to it before the problem is solved. Knowledge from the fields of biochemistry, organic chemistry, physical chemistry, microbiology, genetics, geology, and astronomy must be brought to bear on the problem. The exploration of space will be of great importance, since this will enable us to examine the biochemistry of living organisms on Mars, if indeed they exist. The presence of life on Mars would confirm the present ideas that life is likely to arise when the conditions are favorable. An examination of the components of Martian organisms should give us an idea of which components of living organisms are essential and which may have arisen by accident, as well as an opportunity to investigate an entirely independent biological and biochemical evolution.

There are few firm foundations on which a theory of the origin of life can be built. We do not know with any certainty how the earth and solar system were formed, what the conditions such as temperature and composition of the atmosphere and oceans were on the primitive earth; nor do we know the nature of the most primitive living organism. Furthermore, we do not know when life arose, except that it occurred some time between one billion and 4.5 billion years ago.

With all these unknowns it is easy to see that there are many ideas on this subject and little agreement. It is not possible to discuss all of these ideas here, but we shall consider the hypotheses that seem most plausible at the present time.

Early Considerations of the Problem

The riddle of the origin of life has occupied man's mind since history began. The problem was not as troublesome for the ancients as it is for us today, since it was quite clear to them that life arose by spontaneous generation. Thus when the Egyptians saw snakes arise from the muds of the Nile, and when the Greeks saw rats arise from piles of garbage on exposure to warmth, they interpreted this to mean that such animals arose spontaneously.

That organisms could arise spontaneously, as well as by sexual and asexual reproduction, was not seriously questioned until the middle of the seventeenth century. In 1688 the Tuscan physician Francesco Redi showed that worms did not develop in meat if the vessel containing it was covered with muslin so that flies could not lay their eggs on the meat.

The demonstration that microorganisms, which had been discovered in 1676, did not develop spontaneously was much more difficult. In 1765 Lazzaro Spallanzani showed that microorganisms did not appear in various nutrient broths if the vessels were sealed and boiled. Objections were raised that the heating had destroyed the "vital force" in the broth and air. This "vital force" was postulated as necessary for life to develop. By readmitting air it was possible to show that the broth could still support the growth of microorganisms. But Spallanzani could not demonstrate that the air in the sealed flask had not been altered, and the doctrine of spontaneous generation persisted widely.

The problem was finally solved by Pasteur (1862), who used a flask with broth, but instead of completely sealing the vessel he drew out a long **S**-shaped tube with its end open to the air. The air was free to pass in and out of the flask, but the particles of dust, bacteria, and molds in the air were caught on the sides of the long **S**-shaped tube. When the broth in the flask was boiled and allowed to cool, no microorganisms developed. When the **S**-shaped tube was broken off at the neck of the flask, microorganisms developed. These experiments were extended by Pasteur and by Tyndall to answer the numerous objections that were raised. Thus, after two centuries of experimentation and many more centuries of belief, the doctrine of spontaneous generation was disproved. For a more detailed examination of these early beliefs see (1).

Shortly before, in 1858, Darwin and Wallace had published, simultaneously and independently, the theory of evolution by natural selection. This theory could account for the evolution of all the plants and animals, including man, from the most primitive single-celled organism.

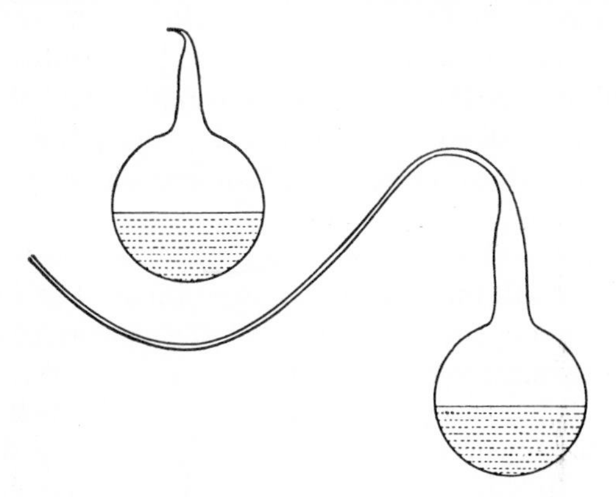

Fig. 12.1. Flasks illustrating Spallanzani's and Pasteur's experiments.

Therefore, the problem of the origin of life involved no longer how each species developed, but only how the first living organism arose.

To answer this question it has been proposed that life on earth was created by a supernatural event. This is not a scientific theory, since by its very nature it is not subject to experimental investigation. Arrhenius (1903) offered a second theory—that life developed on earth as a result of a spore or other stable form of life coming to the earth in a meteorite from outer space or by the pressure of sunlight driving the spores to the earth. One form of this theory assumes that life had no origin but, like matter, has always existed. The presence of certain long-lived radioactive elements shows that the elements were formed about 5 billion years ago. If the elements have not always existed, it is difficult to understand how life could have always existed.

Another form of the Arrhenius theory assumes that life was formed on another planet and traveled to the earth. This hypothesis does not answer the question of how life arose on the other planet. It is doubtful, furthermore, whether any known form of life could survive for very long in outer space and, in addition, fall through the atmosphere without being destroyed. Therefore, although this theory has not been disproved, it is held to be highly improbable. In order to test this theory at any time in the future, it would be necessary to prevent the contamination of space and other planets, particularly Mars, by microorganisms carried on interplanetary rockets. For this reason, space vehicles are being sterilized.

A third hypothesis held that the first living organism arose from inorganic matter by a very improbable event. This organism, in order to grow in an inorganic environment, would have to synthesize all of its cellular components from carbon dioxide, water, and other inorganic nutrients. Our present knowledge of biochemistry shows that even the simplest bacteria are extremely complex, and that the probability of forming a cell from inorganic compounds in a single event is much too small to have occurred in the five billion years since the earth's formation.

The fourth proposal is that life arose spontaneously in the oceans of the primitive earth under favorable conditions. The favorable conditions mean, among many things, that the oceans contained large quantities of organic compounds similar to those which occur in living organisms. This concept had been expressed by many people, including Darwin. However, the first forceful, clear, and detailed argument in favor of this hypothesis was given by the Russian biochemist A. I. Oparin in his book *The Origin of Life,* the English translation of which appeared in 1938 (1).

Oparin argued that if large quantities of organic compounds were present in the oceans of the primitive earth, these organic compounds would react to form structures of greater and greater complexity, until a structure would form which we could call living. In other words, the synthesis of the first living organism would involve many nonbiological steps, and none of these steps would be highly improbable. This implies that the most primitive organism would perform a minimum of biosynthesis since most of the necessary metabolites would have been present in the environment. This type of metabolism is called *heterotrophic.* Photosynthetic organisms that make all their metabolites from carbon dioxide and water came much later in evolution. This type of metabolism is called *autotrophic.* The first organisms were very dependent on their environment, and because of their inefficiency in metabolism and reproduction had a rather tenuous existence.

At the present time the spontaneous generation of an organism cannot take place. Any organic compounds that are formed are rapidly devoured by the microorganisms already present on the earth, and therefore the accumulation of these compounds and their development into more complex structures cannot take place. It is necessary to have a sterile planet in order for life to arise spontaneously, for otherwise the very primitive organisms would inevitably lose the battle for survival to the more efficient and firmly entrenched organisms already present.

Oparin argued that the primary organic compounds could be formed if the earth had a reducing atmosphere of hydrocarbons, ammonia, and water, instead of the present oxidizing atmosphere of carbon dioxide, nitrogen, and oxygen. His argument was based on astronomical theories which are no longer believed, although the conclusion that the earth had a reducing atmosphere was correct.

Urey examined the problem of the formation of the earth and came to conclusions about the primitive atmosphere that were similar to Oparin's. His argument was based both on the thermodynamics of the various chemical reactions that would take place and on a mechanism for the formation of the earth that is currently held to be correct (2). It will be useful to examine briefly some of the present ideas concerning the formation of the earth (3).

The Primitive Earth

The theory that the planets were formed by pieces torn from the sun is no longer seriously considered. Instead of the earth's forming in a molten state, it is presently held that the planets and sun were formed at the same time from a cloud of cosmic dust at low temperatures. Because of the forces of rotation and gravitation, this spherical cloud of dust and gas collapsed into a round disk. The disk, in turn, broke up into sections or rotating cells, and the particles of dust and gases in these cells were pulled together by gravitational attraction until they became solid bodies. The central portion became the sun, while the sections farther out became the planets. It is clear that most of the gaseous material, particularly the hydrogen, helium, nitrogen (as ammonia), carbon (as methane), and oxygen (as water) escaped before the earth was formed. This is true because the earth contains a much smaller amount of these elements—relative to a nonvolatile element such as silicon—than the sun. More of these lighter elements were retained when Jupiter and Saturn were formed because of the lower temperatures at that distance from the sun.

After the mass of dust and gas becomes dense enough, this body has a gravitational field that slows up or else prevents the escape of gases into outer space. In the case of the earth only the two lightest elements, hydrogen and helium, can escape. The rate of escape is strongly dependent on the temperature and the gravitational field, so that in the case of Jupiter and Saturn their low temperatures and high gravitational fields make the escape of hydrogen and helium very slow. Therefore, the present atmospheres of these planets are probably not much different from the ones that surrounded them when these planets were formed. The atmospheres of Jupiter and Saturn are observed to contain methane and ammonia, and the presence of hydrogen and helium has been observed indirectly.

Since the earth was formed from the same dust cloud, it is reasonable to expect that the earth started out with an atmosphere similar to those of Jupiter and Saturn but with much less hydrogen and helium. In the case of Venus, Earth, and Mars, this atmosphere has been altered by the escape of hydrogen. These planets, smaller and closer to the sun, lose their hydrogen rapidly enough to have changed the nature of their atmosphere in geological times.

The loss of hydrogen results in the production of carbon dioxide, nitrogen, nitrate, sulfate, free oxygen, and ferric iron. The overall change has been conversion of the reducing atmosphere to the present oxidizing atmosphere. Many complex organic compounds would have been formed during the overall change, thereby presenting a favorable environment for the formation of life.

It is possible to say approximately what the primitive atmosphere contained by examining the equilibria involved; for a discussion of the equilibria, see (4). As long as there is an appreciable amount of molecular hydrogen present, we can say that the atmosphere will consist of methane, ammonia, nitrogen, and water vapor. Carbon monoxide is unstable under these conditions. Carbon dioxide dissolves in the ocean, and it also reacts with silicates to form limestones ($CaCO_3$). As the hydrogen escapes into outer space, the methane and ammonia are dehydrogenated and this hydrogen escapes. In the end this results in the oxidation of the methane and ammonia to carbon dioxide and nitrogen. Finally, the water is photochemically dissociated to oxygen and hydrogen. This hydrogen escapes and free oxygen appears in the atmosphere, with the result that it becomes highly oxidizing. This does not mean that thermodynamically unstable gases were entirely absent from the original atmosphere, but that they were present only to the extent of a few parts per million. It is asserted in some quarters that the surface carbon of the earth came from the outgassing of the interior, the carbon being in the form of carbon monoxide and carbon dioxide, and therefore the primitive atmosphere contained these more oxidized carbon compounds. Although it is likely that much of the surface carbon of the earth came from outgassing of the interior, this more oxidized carbon would have been reduced to methane as long as molecular hydrogen was present.

prior to sparking gave the same yields as when the autoclaving was omitted.

The mechanism of synthesis of the amino acids is of interest if we are to extrapolate our results in this simple system to the conditions on the primitive earth. It would be possible for the amino and hydroxy acids to be synthesized near the electrodes from the ions and free radicals produced by the electric discharge. However, the major products of the electric discharge are aldehydes and hydrogen cyanide. These compounds react to form amino and hydroxy acids by the following reactions:

$$RCHO + HCN + NH_3 \rightleftarrows RCH(NH_2)CN + H_2O$$
$$RCH(NH_2)CN + 2H_2O \rightarrow RCH(NH_2)COOH + NH_3$$
$$RCHO + HCN \rightleftarrows RCH(OH)CN$$
$$RCH(OH)CN + 2H_2O \rightarrow RCH(OH)COOH + NH_3$$

These are well-known reactions in organic chemistry, the first being the Strecker synthesis and the second the cyanohydrin synthesis. It was shown that most, if not all, of the amino and hydroxy acids were synthesized by these reactions. However, the β-alanine was not formed by this mechanism, but probably by the addition of ammonia to acrylonitrile, followed by hydrolysis to β-alanine. Similarly, the addition of hydrogen cyanide to acrylonitrile would, on hydrolysis, give the succinic acid.

This mechanism accounts for the fact that most of the amino acids produced were α-amino acids. The amino acids in proteins are all α-amino acids, and this raises the question of whether they are present because the appropriate enzymatic and structural functions of proteins can be constructed only with α-amino acids. The answer to this question is not known, but it is possible that α-amino acids are present in proteins because they were the amino acids available for use when life originated, and they have persisted in proteins ever since.

The experiments on the mechanism of the electric discharge synthesis of amino acids indicate that a special set of conditions or type of electric discharge is not required to obtain amino acids. Any process or combination of processes that yielded both aldehydes and hydrogen cyanide would have contributed to the amount of α-amino acids in the oceans of primitive earth. Therefore, it is not fundamental whether the aldehydes and hydrogen cyanide came from ultraviolet light or from electric discharges, since both processes would contribute. It may have been that electric discharges were the principal source of hydrogen cyanide and that ultraviolet light was the principal source of aldehydes, so that the two processes complemented each other (7).

Ultraviolet light. It is clear from Table 12.1 that the greatest source of energy would be ultraviolet light. The effective wavelengths would be $CH_4 < 1450Å$, $H_2O < 1850Å$, $NH_3 < 2250Å$, $CO < 1545Å$, $CO_2 < 1690Å$, $N_2 < 1100Å$, and $H_2 < 900Å$. These short wavelengths are difficult to work with in the laboratory, and so less work has been done with this source of energy. One would expect the results of the ultraviolet light experiments to be similar to the electric discharge experiments, since similar free radicals would be formed.

Groth found no amino acids produced by the 1849Å line with a mixture of methane, ammonia, and water; but amines and amino acids were formed when the 1470Å and 1295Å lines of argon were used. The 1849Å line produced amines and amino acids with a mixture of ethane, ammonia, and water. The mechanism of this synthesis was not determined. Terenin also has obtained amino acids by the action of the krypton lines on methane, ammonia, and water. The yield of amino acids in these experiments was quite low because of the low intensities of the ultraviolet lamps and the low quantum yields.

We can assume that a considerable amount of ultraviolet light of wavelengths greater than 2000Å must have been absorbed in the oceans, even though much of this radiation would have been absorbed by the small quantities of organic compounds in the atmosphere. Few experiments have been performed that simulate these conditions.

The most important experiment of this nature is Ellenbogen's work with a suspension of ferrous sulfide in aqueous ammonium chloride. Methane was bubbled through the solution, and the source of energy was ultraviolet light. This experiment gave an insoluble substance which showed absorptions in the infrared characteristic of peptides. Paper chromatography of a hydrolysate of this substance gave a number of spots with ninhydrin, of which phenylalanine, methionine, and valine were tentatively identified. In addition to demonstrating the synthesis of amino acids, this experiment showed that peptides can be formed under primitive conditions.

Bahadur has reported the synthesis of amino acids by the action of sunlight on concentrated formaldehyde solutions containing ferric chloride and nitrate or ammonia as the source of nitrogen. Pavlowskaya and Passynsky have synthesized a number of amino acids by the action of ultraviolet light on a 2.5 percent solution of formaldehyde containing ammonium chloride. These high concentrations of formaldehyde could not have been present on the primitive earth. If such syntheses could be effected with 10^{-4} or 10^{-6} M formaldehyde, then this type of synthesis might have been important, since formaldehyde would have been synthesized in the atmosphere by ultraviolet light and electric discharges.

oxygen; but, if ATP is available, the acetic acid can be converted to glucose and other metabolites.

When the supply of nonfermentable organic compounds was exhausted, organic compounds would have had to be made by the reduction of carbon dioxide. This photosynthesis was probably similar to that of sulfur bacteria and blue-green algae which carry out the reactions.

$$2H_2S + CO_2 \xrightarrow{\text{light}} 2S + (H_2CO) + H_2O$$

$$H_2S + 2CO_2 + 2H_2O \xrightarrow{\text{light}} H_2SO_4 + 2(H_2CO)$$

where (H_2CO) represents carbon on the oxidation level of formaldehyde (carbohydrates). Because it is much easier to split H_2S than to split H_2O, it would seem likely that organisms should develop photoreduction with sulfur first. When the H_2S and S were exhausted, it would become necessary to split water and evolve O_2, the hydrogen being used for the reduction of CO_2.

When the methane and ammonia of the primitive atmosphere had been converted to carbon dioxide and nitrogen by photochemical decomposition in the upper atmosphere, water would be decomposed to oxygen and hydrogen. The hydrogen would escape, leaving the oxygen in the atmosphere. It is likely, however, that most of the oxygen in the atmosphere was produced by photosynthesis from plants rather than by the photochemical splitting of water in the upper atmosphere.

The evolution of multicellular organisms probably occurred after the development of photosynthesis. The evolution of primitive multicellular organisms to more complex types and the development of sexual reproduction can be understood on the basis of the theory of evolution.

Life on Other Planets

Life as we know it requires the presence of water for its chemical processes. We know enough about the chemistry of other systems, such as those of silicon, ammonia, and hydrogen fluoride, to realize that no highly complex system of chemical reactions similar to that which we call "living" would be possible in such media. Also, much living matter exists and grows actively on the earth in the absence of oxygen, so that oxygen is *not* necessary for life, as is stated so often. Moreover, the protecting layer of ozone in the earth's atmosphere is not necessary for life either, since ultraviolet light does not penetrate deeply into natural waters, and also because many carbon compounds capable of absorbing the ultraviolet would be present in a reducing atmosphere.

It is possible for life to exist on the earth and for living things to grow actively at temperatures ranging from 0°C, or perhaps a little lower, to about 70°C. At much lower temperatures the rates of reaction would probably be too slow to proceed in reasonable periods of time. At temperatures much above 120°C reaction velocities would probably be so great that the nicely balanced reactions characteristic of living things would be impossible. In addition, it is doubtful if the organic polymers necessary for living organisms would be stable much above 120°C, even allowing for the amazing stability of the enzymes of thermophilic bacteria and algae.

Only Mars, Earth, and Venus conform to the general requirements of life so far as temperatures are concerned. Mars is known to be very cold, and Venus may be too hot. Recent observations of the black-body emission of radio waves from Venus indicate surface temperatures of 290 to 350°C. Infrared bands of water have been observed recently on Venus from a balloon at high altitude. The presence of water on Venus would make life possible, but if the radio-wave temperature is in fact the temperature on the surface, then life could only exist on dust particles in the atmosphere. This does not seem likely.

Mars is known to have surface temperatures of from +30° to −60°C during the day. The colors of Mars have been observed for many years by many people. The planet exhibits seasonal changes, appearing green or bluish in the spring and brown and reddish in the autumn. Sinton has observed absorptions at 3.43μ, 3.56μ, and 3.67μ in the reflected light of Mars (16). The 3.4μ adsorption corresponds to the C–H stretching frequency of most organic compounds. The changing colors of Mars and the 3.4μ adsorption are the best evidence, however poor, for the existence of life on that planet. This question will doubtless be settled a few years hence, when space vehicles will be able to bring back data on the presence or absence of life on Mars.

Life in other solar systems. The theory that life arose spontaneously on the earth under favorable conditions implies that life should also arise on planets of other solar systems, provided the conditions are favorable. The possibility that life may be present on Mars, on which conditions are not particularly favorable at the present time, strengthens this argument. It is therefore of interest to consider how many stars may have planets with favorable conditions and therefore probably have life on them. The following argument is by Shapley (17), who concludes that there are at least 100 million planets with living organisms on them.

There are at least 10^{20} stars in the part of the universe observable with today's telescopes. Not all of these stars will have planets because many of them may have been formed in a different way from our solar system or may have had their planetary systems disrupted in some way. It is reasonable, however, to expect that at least one star in a thousand has a planetary system, and this gives 10^{17} stars with planets. Many of these planets will be either too hot or too cold to support life because they are too close or too far from the star. Also, there are stars which vary in brightness and would not have a sufficiently uniform temperature to permit life to develop. But if at least one in a thousand of these stars with planets has one or more planets of the correct temperature, this gives 10^{14} stars with at least one planet of the right temperature. In addition to being neither too hot nor too cold, a planet must not be so massive that the atmosphere is too thick or so small that all the atmosphere escapes from it. It is reasonable to expect that at least one in a thousand of these planets of the right temperature is the proper size to hold a suitable atmosphere, and this gives 10^{11} stars with a planet of the right temperature and a suitable atmosphere for life to arise. Yet even with a suitable temperature and atmosphere, life might not arise for many reasons. But it is reasonable to expect that life arose on at least one in a thousand of these planets, and this gives 10^8 planets on which life may have developed.

It can also be argued that evolution has proceeded more rapidly on some of these planets than on the earth, and that civilizations exist that are more highly developed than ours. Again, using the figure of one in 1000, there would in that event be 100,000 civilizations more highly developed than those on the earth.

There are many ways of making estimates of this sort, but it is likely that the figure of 10^8 planets with life on them is low, and the figure could be 10^{14} or even higher. The figure of 10^8 planets favorable to life is probably a minimum, unless present ideas about the formation of the solar system and the origin of life are grossly in error. It appears then that life on the earth is not a unique phenomenon.

REFERENCES

1. Oparin, A. I., 1957, *The Origin of Life,* 3rd ed. New York: Academic Press. (New York: Macmillan, 1938). The first edition has been reprinted by Dover in a paperback.
2. Urey, H. C., *Proc. Nat. Acad. Sci. U. S., 38:* 351, 1952. Many of these problems were discussed by J. D. Bernal, *Proc. Phys. Soc.* (London), *62A:* 537, 1949; *ibid., 62B:* 597, 1949; and 1951, *The Physical Basis of Life.* London: Routledge and Kegan Paul.
3. The origin of the solar system is discussed in several books. The chemical problems are emphasized in H. C. Urey, 1952, *The Planets.* New

Haven: Yale University Press. The atmospheres of the planets are discussed by Urey in greater detail in *Handbuch der Physik,* 1959, ed. S. Flügge. Berlin: Springer Verlag, Vol. 52, pp. 363–418.

4. MILLER, S. L., AND H. C. UREY, *Science, 130:*245, 1959.
5. Attempts to synthesize organic compounds from CO_2 and water are reviewed in E. I. RABINOWITCH, 1945, *Photosynthesis.* New York: Interscience, Vol. 1, p. 81. The cyclotron experiments are in W. M. GARRISON et al., *Science, 114:*416, 1951, and discussed further in M. Calvin, *Am. Scientist, 44:*248, 1956.
6. A preliminary description of this experiment is given in S. L. Miller, *Science, 117:*528, 1953. The details are given in *J. Am. Chem. Soc., 77:*2351, 1955.
7. The mechanism of the amino acid synthesis is discussed in S. L. MILLER, *Biochem. Biophys. Acta, 23:*480, 1957; and the experiments are reviewed in *Ann. N. Y. Acad. Sci., 69:*260, 1957, and also in *Proceedings of the First International Symposium on the Origin of Life on the Earth,* 1959, ed. A. I. Oparin et al. New York: Pergamon Press, pp. 123–135.
8. The various primitive syntheses are reviewed in greater detail in Reference 4.
9. The case for thermal synthesis is reviewed in S. W. Fox, *Science, 132:*200, 1960.
10. ORO, J., and A. P. KIMBALL, *Arch. Biochem. Biophys., 94:*217, 1961.
11. The polymerization of nucleotides is discussed in R. F. STEINER AND R. F. BEERS, JR., 1961, *Polynucleotides.* Amsterdam: Elsevier.
12. KORNBERG, A., *Science, 131:*1503, 1960.
13. GRANICK, S., *Ann. N. Y. Acad. Sci., 69:*292, 1957; M. CALVIN, *Am. Scientist, 44:*248, 1956; *Science, 130:*1170, 1959.
14. Optical activity and asymmetric syntheses are discussed in G. W. WHELAND, 1949, *Advanced Organic Chemistry.* New York: John Wiley, pp. 246–250. This discussion of the origin of optical activity follows that given in Wald, *Ann. N. Y. Sci., 69:*352, 1957.
15. HOROWITZ, N. H., *Proc. Natl. Acad. Sci. U. S., 31:*153, 1945. Reprinted in *Great Experiments in Biology,* 1955, M. L. GABRIEL AND S. FOGEL, eds. New York: Prentice Hall, p. 297.
16. SINTON, W. M., *Science, 130:*1234, 1959.
17. SHAPLEY, H., 1958, *Of Men and Stars.* Boston, Mass.: Beacon Press. Also available in a paperback. This book discusses the life in the universe from the point of view of an astronomer.

General references. Many books and review articles have been written on the origin of life, but most of them are unnecessarily speculative and vague. References 1, 2, 4, and 17 are recommended. The geological aspects are emphasized in E. S. Barghoorn, *Geol. Soc. Am.*

Mem., *2*, *67*:75–86, 1957. A group of papers appears in a symposium, *Modern Ideas on Spontaneous Generation,* printed in *Ann. N. Y. Acad. Sci.*, *69*:257–376, 1957. An international symposium was held in Moscow in August, 1957; the papers are printed in *Proceedings of the First International Symposium on the Origin of Life on the Earth,* 1959, ed. A. I. Oparin et al. New York: Pergamon Press. The more important papers from this symposium have been published separately in *Aspects of the Origin of Life,* 1960, ed. M. Florkin. Oxford: Pergamon Press.

Index

Abscission, 237
Absorption coefficient, of chlorophylls, specific, 20
Absorption spectrum
  of algae, 24
  of chlorophylls, 20
  of leaves, 17
  of protochlorophyll, 18
Accessory pigments, 23ff.
Acetyl-CoA, 57
Acids
  fatty, 110
  metabolic pool, 121
Actinomycetes, 125, 127
Action spectrum
  for chlorophyll formation, 18
  for photosynthesis, 25, 26
Activated molecules, 16
Adenine, 131, 246
  see also Purines
Adenosine diphosphate, 56
Adenosine triphosphate (ATP), 27, 56, 85, 90, 93, 116, 330, 336
Adenostoma fasciculatum, 306ff.
  introgression in, 307ff.
Aerobes, 45, 46
Albino, 189
Alexander, E. J., 304
Algae
  absorption spectra of, 24
  blue-green, 23, 111, 113, 121
  Chlorella, 12, 24, 28
  green, 29, 124
  high temperature strains, 15
  Porphyridium, 24
  potential use in space travel, 30
  red, 23, 124
  use as food, 29, 30
  use in photosynthesis research, 7, 23, 28f.

Allen, M. B., 33, 37
Amesz, J., 35
Amino acids, 110, 125, 132, 143, 189, 280
  and Krebs cycle, 60
  mechanism of synthesis by electric discharges, 327
  optical activity in, 334f.
  synthesis by electric discharge, 325ff.
  synthesis from formaldehyde and ultraviolet light, 328
p-Aminobenzoic acid, 124
γ-Aminobutyric acid, 128
Amniotic fluid, 276
Anaerobes, facultative and obligate, 46
Anaerobic bacteria, 172
Anaerobic reactions, 55
  fermentation, 55
  glycolysis, 55
Anaerobiosis, 114
Anemia, pernicious, 124
Ant colony, 275
Anthocyanin pigments, 25
Antiauxins, 230
Antibiotic-resistant mutants, 178
Antibody, 164
Antigen, 164
Apical meristem, 215ff.
Apical surgery, 258, 262, 263, 265
Apparatus, photosynthetic, in plants, 12, 16
Aristotle, 4
Arnold, W. A., 36
Arnon, D. I., 36
Arrhenius, S., 319f.
Arthrobacter, 125
Ascorbic acid (vitamin C), 134
Aspergillus diastase, 52
Assimilitory quotient, 27, 30
Athiorhodaceae
  growth factors for, 112f.
  photosynthesis, 112
Atmosphere
  regulation of CO_2 in, by photosynthesis, 8
ATP, *see* Adenosine triphosphate
Autocatalysis, 150
Autotrophic bacteria, 172
Auxin, 251, 266, 267
Auxin-a, 223ff.
Avena test, 222
Axons, 272

Bacillus botulinus and botulism, 46
Back-cross, 288, 291
  defined, 288
Bacteria
  luminescent, 127
  marine, 125, 127
  pathogenic, 114f.
  photosynthetic, 112, 114
    see also Athiorhodaceae, *Chlorobrium, Chromatium*
  purple photosynthetic, 22
  soil, 125
Bacteriochlorophyll, 22
Bacteriophage, 140, 142, 145ff., 158ff., 191
  temperate, 153ff.
Bacteriophage-resistant mutants of bacteria, 178
Bannister, T. T., 37
Bassham, J. A., 36
Beggiatoa, 113
Bell, L. N., 38
Benson, A. A., 36
Bergeron, J. A., 36
Bile pigments, 118f.
Biochemical mutants of bacteria, 177
Bioluminescence, 63
Biotin, 110, 124, 126
Bishop, N. I., 37
Blackman, F. F., 7
Blastomeres, 272
Blinks, L. R., 37
Bogorad, L., 36
Boichenko, E. A., 38
Bone, 275, 277
Bonner, W., 37
Borrelia vincentii, 116
Brackett, F. S., 37
Brenner, S., 192
Bridges, C. B., 188
Briggs, G. E., 35
Bril, C., 35
Brody, S. S., 37
Brown, A. H., 37
Buchner, E., 45
Burk, D., 8, 37
Burlew, J. S., 33

Calines, 239
Callus, 240ff.
Calorimeters, bomb and biological, 43

Calorimetry, 42
Calvin, M., 28, 36, 331
Cancer, produced by viruses, 155
Carbon, path of, in photosynthesis, 28
Carbon dioxide, 276
  absorption of by alkali, 11
  concentration in atmosphere, 8, 14
  effect of concentration on rate of photosynthesis, 13, 14
  fixation of by chloroplasts, 28
  infrared absorption by, *see* Infrared
  measurement of photosynthesis rates by consumption of, 10
  radioactive, 10
  regulation in atmosphere of, by photosynthesis, 8
Carotenoids, in plants, 19, 23, 24
Catalase, 110, 116
Caulocaline, 239ff.
Caventov, 6
Cell, single plant, 261, 267
Cell aggregates, 277, 280
Cell dissociation, 377
Cell division, 261, 267
Cell suspensions, 277
Cellular components, 279
Cellular reproduction, 278
Chance, B., 23, 37
Chaparral, introgression in, 308
Chase, M., 193
Chelation, 130f.
Chemotherapy, 127
Chlorella, 135
  use as food, 29
  use for studies of photosynthesis, 12, 28
Chlorobium, 111f.
Chlorophyll
  empirical formula of, 19
  energy transfer from, 22f.
  extracted, 3, 6, 7, 19f.
  fluorescence of, 7
  formation in plants, 17
  function of, in photosynthesis, 22
  light absorption by, in plants, 18, 24
  natural *in vivo,* 3, 17, 19ff., 24
  reduction of, by light, 19
  spectrum degradation, 113, 121
Chlorophyll *a,* 7, 19, 20, 22f., 24, 25
  complexes of, 22, 24, 25
Chlorophyll *b,* 7, 19, 20, 23, 24, 25
Chlorophyll in leaves
  red absorption band, 17, 19
Chlorophyll units, 22f.
Chloroplasts, 21, 26f., 91ff.
  isolation of, 27
  and photosynthesis, 93, 95ff.
  of plants, 21, 26
  reducing activity of, 27
  relation between ultrastructure and function, 95
  ultrastructure of, 93f.
Cholesterol, 110
Chromatium, 112
Chromosomes, 187, 276
  replication, 203
  theory, 188
Chrysomonads, 124
  see also Ochromonas
Ciliates, 129
  see also Paramecium and *Tetrahymena*
Cis-cinnamic, 233
Citric acid, 130
Citric acid (Krebs) cycle, 59, 84, 86, 87
Clayton, R., 36
Cleavage, 272
Clendenning, K. A., 36
Coacervate colloid, 333
Cobalt, 126
Coconut milk, 242
Coenzyme A, 57
Coenzymes, 116, 239ff.
Coleoptile, 219ff.
Coliphage, 191
Collagen, 272, 280, 283
Collagen fibrils, 282
Collagen molecules, 282
Collagenous fiber, 280
Colon bacteria, 191, 201
Color of leaves, 17
Combustion, heat of, 42
Competence, role of, in human eye, 273
Connective tissue, 282
Control of disease, 164ff.
Control of environment, 8
Corpus, 216ff.
Correlation, 219ff.
Cortex, 258
Cortisone, 117f.
  see also Steroids
Creatin, 56

Creatin phosphate, 56
Crick, F. H. C., 195, 196
Cristae, mitochondrial, 86
Crop production, efficiency of, 11f.
Cross-banding, 282
Cryptomonads, 121
Culture medium, 261, 265, 266
Cyanohydrin synthesis, 327
Cycle of energy, 74
Cystine, 130
Cytochrome oxidase, 61
Cytochromes, 61
 in chloroplasts, 23
Cyptoplasm, 186

Daniels, F., 37
Darwin, C., 319
Death, relation of to growth, 214
Deoxyribonucleic acid, *see* DNA
Derivative spectrophotometry, 22
Developmental biology, 274
Diaminopimelic acid, 110
Diatoms
 vitamin B_{12} requirements, 124
 Navicula, 24
2,6-Dichlorophenol-indophenol, reduction of, by chloroplasts, 28
2,4-Dichlorophenoxyacetic acid, 231ff.
Differentiation, 215ff., 257f., 261, 266f.
Dinoflagellates, 127
Diphosphopyridine nucleotide (DPN), 116
DNA, 100, 102, 177, 188ff.
 artificial, 202
 chemistry of, 195
 hydrogen bonding in, 196ff.
 information in, 198
 nitrogen-15 labeling of, 201
 synthesis of, 202
 radioactive labeling of, 193
 relation of to RNA, 205
 translation of, 204
 Watson-Crick model for duplication of, 332
 Watson-Crick structure of, 195, 196, 197
DNA code, 203ff.
DNA replication, 199ff.
DNA synthesis and ATP, 73f.
Doman, N. G., 38
Dominant forms of genes, 188f.
Dorman, C., 304
Doty, P., 202
Double mutants, 179
Duysens, L. N. M., 35
Dye reduction by chloroplasts, 28

Ear placode, 272
Earth
 early atmosphere of, 322
 formation of, 321
"Eclipse Period," 151
Effectiveness of light wavelengths
 in chlorophyll formation, 18
 in photosynthesis, 26
Efficiency of photosynthesis, 11f.
Egg, 271f., 276
Egg cell, 186
Egle, K., 34
Electric organs and phosphagen, 71
Electron microscope, 81ff., 274, 275, 280, 282
Electron transport system, *see* Energy-transfer mechanism
Ellenbogen, E., 328, 330
Elodea, 9
Elongation, 218
Embryo, plant, 260, 261, 262
Emerson, R., 7, 12
Endoplasmic reticulum (ER), 99ff.
 and golgi complex, 104
 origin of, 100
 relation to nuclear and cell membranes, 100, 102, 104, 106
 rough-surfaced, 100, 102, 104
 smooth-surfaced, 100, 102, 104, 106
 as transport system, 102, 104, 106
Energy
 for biochemical reactions, 336
 degradation, 42, 75
 for growth, 171
 kinetic and potential, 41
 within molecules, 16
 release of, 53
 solar, 31
 transfer of, 16, 22f., 53
  between pigments, 22f.
 yield during aerobic degradation, 58
Energy-transfer mechanism (electron transport system), 85, 86, 87
Energy transformation, 6
Engelmann, T. W., 25

Enrichment cultures, 117ff.
Environment
  cellular, 262, 267, 268
  external, 262, 268
Enzyme patterns, 273
Enzymes
  hydrolytic, 45, 50f.
  localization in cell, 65
  synthesis of, 331
Escherichia coli, 191
Ethanol, 130
Euglena gracilis, 124
Evolution
  of early organisms, 325
  introgression as important factor in, 311ff.
  theory of, 319, 337
Evstigneev, V. B., 38
Eye, 272, 277

F_1, F_2, 288, 291
  defined, 288
Facultative bacteria, 172
Falk, H., 35
Fats, 66, 68
Feathers, 277
Fermentation, 54, 336
  measurement, 46
  respiratory quotient, 69
Fermented drinks, 45
Fern, 274
Ferrichromes, 110
  see also Terregens factor
Ferricyanide, reduction of, by chloroplasts, 28
Fields, 273
Fine structure, 282
Flower color, 188
Flowers, formulation of, 218
Fluorescence, 7, 16
Fogg, G. E., 33
Folic acid, 110, 121, 126, 134
Food
  efficiency of utilization of, 11f.
  formation of, by plants, 3, 9
  shortage of, 9
  storage of, 66
Forti, G., 35
Foster, R., 304
Fox, S. W., 329, 330
Franck, J., 37
French, C. S., 1, 3, 36
Frenkel, A. W., 37
Fruit drop, 237
Fucoxanthin, 24
Fuller, R. C., 33, 36

Gabrielsen, E. K., 36
Gaffron, H., 7, 10, 33, 37
Galls, 250
Gametophyte, 259f., 274
Gastrulation, 272
Generation time of bacteria, 169
Generative condition, 218
Gene mutation, 205
Genes, 187, 272, 276, 282
  definition of, 211
  fine structure of, 159ff., 208ff.
Germination, 219
Gibberellin, 243ff.
Gibbs, M., 36
Glomeruli, 277
Glucose, 121, 132
Glycerol, 121, 133
Glycogen, 66
Glycogenolysis, 66
Glycolysis, 54
Godnev, T. N., 38
Goedheer, J. C., 35
Golgi complex, *see* Endoplasmic reticulum
Good, N., 34
Grana, of plant chloroplasts, 26, 93f.
Granick, S., 331
Groth, W. E., 328
Growing points, 214
Growth center, 264f., 267
Growth correlations, 218
Growth factors
  definition, 110
  in soil, 119
Guanine, 131f.
  see also Purines

Habitats, disturbed, introgression in, 301f., 304, 310
Harder, R., 34
Hardin, G., 198, 200
Haxo, F., 36
Healing wound, 274
Heart, 277
Heiser, C., 314

Helmont, J. B. van, 4
Heme, hematin, 110, 118ff.
Hemoglobin, 110, 187
  sickle-cell, 207, 208
  similarity of to chlorophyll, 21
Hershey, S. D., 193
Heterocatalysis, 150
Hill, R., 27, 28, 33, 35
Hill reaction, 27f.
Hollaender, A., 33
Holt, A. S., 34
Holz, G. G., Jr., 133
Hormones, 239ff.
  plant, 258
Horne, R. W., 192
Horowitz, N. H., 335
Horse, 275
Hummingbird, respiration of, 49
Humus, 6
Hydra, 274, 276
Hydrogen bonding, in DNA, 196, 197, 198
Hydrolysis, energy change in, 51

Immunity, 164f.
Indoleacetic acid, 223ff., 266f.
Indoleacetic acid oxidase, 228f.
Inductors, 273
Infrared
  absorption of by CO_2, 11
  reflection of, by leaves, 17
  in sunlight, 11
Ingenhousz, J., 5
Initial cell, 216
Interaction properties, 282
Introgression
  in *Adenostoma,* 307ff.
  in chaparral, 308, 310
  defined, 294
  in disturbed habitats, 301
  evolutionary role, 311ff.
  in *Iris,* 301ff.
  in lettuce, cultivated and weed, 312f.
  in *Oxytropis,* 295ff.
  in *Salvia,* 305f.
Iris, 273
Iris fulva, 301ff.
  introgression in, 301ff.
Iris hexagona var. *giganti-caerulea,* 301ff.
  introgression in, 301ff.

Jacob, F., 194
Jagendorf, A. T., 37
Jakoby, W. B., 128
James, W. O., 35
Jupiter, 321f.

Kamen, M. D., 36
Kandler, O., 34
Kautsky, H., 35
Keto acids and amination, 60
Kidney, 277
Kinetics of photosynthesis, 9, 16
Kinetin, 246
Kjeldahl method for nitrogen, 67
Kluyver, A. J., 117
Koh, B., 8, 37
Kornberg, A., 202, 331, 333
Krasnovsky, A. A., 19, 22, 34
Krebs cycle, *see* Citric acid cycle
Krotkov, G., 34
Kutyurin, V. M., 38
Kynurenine, 121

Laboratories studying mechanism of photosynthesis, 34ff.
Lactic acid bacteria, 45
Laplace, biological calorimetry, 44
Larsen, H., 36
Lascelles, J., 35
Lateral auxin transport, 226
Lateral bud inhibition, 234
Latimer, P., 38
Lavoisier, A. L., 5
  biological calorimetry, 44
Lavorel, J., 34
Leaves
  absorption of light by, 17
  color of, 17
Lens, 273
Lettuce, introgression in, 312f.
Lewis, C. M., 12
Liebig, J., 6
Life
  definition of, 332
  on other planets, 337ff.
Life span, 214
Light
  absorption of by leaves, 17
  effect on protochlorophyll in plants, 18
  reflection of by leaves, 17

Light intensity, 9f., 13, 14
effect on photosynthesis rates of, 15
Limb, 274, 277
Linkage, 189
Linnaeus, C., 5
Linschitz, H., 36
Lipoic acid, 110
Litvin, F. F., 38
Living system, unique in three ways, 279
Livingston, R., 37
Lochhead, A. G., 125
Loco weed, 295
Luciferase, 63
Luciferin, 63
Lumry, R., 37
Lysis, 191
Lysogeny, 153ff.

Machlis, L., 9, 28, 33
McLeod, G. C., 26
Macromolecules, 279, 280
aggregates of, 282
Magnesium, 130
"Main line" of oxidation, 61
Malaria, parasite of, 117
Mammalian embryo, 276
Manometry, 46f.
for measuring rates of photosynthesis, 10
Marre, E., 35
Mars, 317, 322, 338
Massini, P., 35
Matthaei, J. H., 205
Mayer, R., 6
Mechanism of photosynthesis, 12f., 16
Membrane, unit, 94
Mendel, G., 187
Mendel's laws, modification of, 210
Menke, W., 34
Meristem, 215, 257, 258, 262, 265
Meselson, M. S., 200
Metabolic gradients, 273
Metabolic pool, 114
Metabolism
autotrophic, 320, 335
heterotrophic, 320, 335
Metals, trace, 131
Metroglyphs, 294, 299
Microsomes, 280
Miller, S. L., 316
Milner, H., 36
Mirsky, A. E., 211
Mitochondria, 275, 279
and cellular respiration, 84f.
and enzymes, 63ff.
localization of in cells, 65
as powerhouses, 64
relation between structure and function, 87ff.
ultrastructure of, 85f.
Mitosis, 279
Molecules, activated, 16
Molluscs, 282
Morgan, T. H., 188
Morphogenesis
animal, 271ff.
environmental factors, 275f.
fibrils, 282
meaning of, 275
organs and parts, 277
whole organism, 276
Mortimer, D. C., 34
Moyse, A., 34
Müller, D., 36
Muscle contraction and ATP, 72
Muscles, 277
Mutation, 150, 205ff.
favorable, 207f.
mutagenic agents, 156f., 160
unfavorable, 207f.
in viruses, 155ff., 160
Mutual reactivation, in viruses, 162
Myelin sheath, 98f.
Myers, J. E., 37
Myosin, 272

Negelein, E., 12
Nerve impulse and high energy phosphates, 71
Nerves, 274, 277, 278
Neural crest, 272
Neural plate, 272
Neuron, 275
Nichiporovich, A. A., 38
Nicotiana alata, 287ff.
hybrids of, 287ff.
Nicotiana Langsdorfii, 287ff.
hybrids of, 287ff.
Nicotinic acid, 110, 116, 124
Niel, C. B. van, 7, 37, 117, 123f.

Nirenberg, M. W., 205
Nitrogen-15 labeling, 199, 201
Norman, R. W. van, 37
Notochord, 272
Nucleic acids, 142, 144, 145ff., 152, 155, 157, 159, 160, 162, 164, 279
  function as genetic material, 150f.
  role in virus infection process, 147ff.
Nucleo-cytoplasmic interactions, 273
Nucleotides, 189
  synthesis of, 331
Nucleus, 186
  of bacteria, 173

Ochoa, S., 331
Ochromonas danica, 135
Ochromonas malhamensis, 126
O'hEocha, C., 35
Olsen, J. W., 36
Olsen, R. A., 37
Optical activity, origin of, 333
Organic compounds
  energy sources for synthesis of, 323f.
  synthesis of
    by electric discharge, 325ff.
    under oxidizing conditions, 323
    by radioactivity and cosmic rays, 329
    by thermal energy, 329
    by ultraviolet light, 328
Origin of life
  by spontaneous generation, 318
  theories on, 319f.
    Arrhenius theory, 319f.
    Oparin theory, 320
  time of, 318
Oxidase, specificity of, 52
Oxidation, energy change in, 51
Oxygen, 4, 5, 6, 10, 28
  discovery of, 5
  isotopic, for study of oxygen source in photosynthesis, 13
  measurement of production by photosynthesis, 10
  production of, by photosynthesis, 4, 5, 6, 28
Oxygen debt and muscle contraction, 72
Oxygen electrode, 10
Oxytropis albiflorus, 295ff.
  introgression in, 295, 301
Oxytropis Lambertii, 301

Pantothenic acid, 110, 116, 126
Paramecium, 133
  test for carcinogens, 133f.
Paramyosin, 282
Parthenocarpic fruit, 236f.
Pasteur, L., 117, 318
Pea, garden, 189
Pellagra, 116
Pelletier, 6
Penicillin and biochemical mutants, 178
Peptides, synthesis of, 330
Peptones, bacteriological, 115f., 129
Pfeffer, W., 6
pH change, used to measure rate of photosynthesis, 10
Phage, 191
Phagotrophs, 135
Phloem, 258, 261, 266
Phosphagen, muscle, 57
Phosphate, 131
Phosphate bond, high energy, 56, 62
  in cell work, 70
Phosphorescent Bay, Puerto Rico, 127
  see also Dinoflagellates
Photochemistry, 27f.
  of chloroplasts, 27f.
  in plants, 16, 25
Photophosphorylation by chloroplasts, 28
Photoreceptors, 95f.
Photosynthesis, 112, 324, 336f.
  as an energy source, 30f.
  effect on CO_2 in atmosphere, 8
  efficiency of, 11f.
  energy relations of, 6
  factors affecting rate of, 12ff., 18
  kinetics of, 9ff., 16
  laboratories investigating mechanism of, 34ff.
  partial reactions of, 27f.
  rates of, measurement, 9ff.
  stochiometry of, 6
  see also Chloroplast
Photosynthesis research, objectives of, 31f.
Photosynthetic apparatus of plants, 12f., 16
Photosynthetic phosphorylation, 336
Phototropic curvature, 220ff.
Phycobilins, 23, 26
Phycocyanin, 23, 24

Phycoerythrin, 23, 24, 26
Phylogenetic relationships in bacteria, 182
Phylogenetic tree, 114
Physiological field, 264
Phytol, 19
Pigment content of plants, description of, 20
Pigments
accessory, of plants, 23, 24, 25
photosynthetic, in plants, 16ff., 19, 24ff.
plant, separation of, 19
Pintner, I. M., 124
Pirson, A., 34
Pith, 258, 262, 266, 267
Planets, formation of, 321, 322
Plankton, 124, 128
Plant physiology, 4, 5, 6
see also Photosynthesis
Plants and animals, interdependence of, 3
Plants, classification of, 5
Plaque, 191
Plaque formation, 145
Plasticity, 229
Platinum electrodes, for oxygen measurement, 10
Pneumococci, 116, 190
Polarity, 235f.
Polio virus, 142, 165
Polynucleotides, synthesis of, 331
Polysaccharide, 190
Population, 9
Porphyra, 124
Porphyridium, 24
Porphyrins, 324, 336
Porter, J. W., 35
Power, *see* Energy
Precursor, and role in auxin formations, 225
Priestly, J., 4
Pringsheim, E. G., 33
Pronuclei, 272
Protein molecule, 275, 279, 280
Protein synthesis, 205
Proteins, 56, 67f., 143f., 189
Protist, definition, 109ff.
Protochlorophyll, 17, 18
Protochlorophyll in leaves, action and absorption spectra, 18
Protoplasm, definition, 111
Protozoa, carnivorous, 130, 134
Provasoli, L., 124
Punnett, T., 37
Purines, 110
synthesis of, 331
see also Guanine
Pyridoxal phosphate, 116
Pyridoxine, 110
Pyrimidines, synthesis of, 331

Q_{10}, 15
Quanta, of light, 12, 16
Quantum yield of photosynthesis, 12
Quinone, reduction of by chloroplasts, 28
Quotient
assimilatory, 27, 30
respiratory, 30, 67ff.

Rabinowitch, E. I., 7f., 33, 37
Radioactive labeling, 193
Radioisotopes, 274
Rafn, C. G., 5
Randolph, L. F., 304
Rates of photosynthesis, 9ff.
Recessive forms of genes, 188
Recombination
in *E. coli*, 179
intragenic, 209
restrictions on, 289ff.
in viruses, 157ff.
Reconstitution of viral components, 148f.
Redi, F., 318
Reflection of light by leaves, 17
Regeneration, plant, 261
Reproduction
in bacteria, 169
molecular, 203
Research in photosynthesis, objectives of, 31f.
Respiration
of bacteria, 171
cellular, 84f.
and drying, 49
effect of temperature, 49
energy used for by plants, 11
measurement of, 46
rates of, 48, 49
and size of organisms, 49

Respiratory quotient, 30, 67ff.
Respirometer, 47
Retina, 273
Rhizocaline, 239
Riboflavin, 110, 126
Ribonucleic acid (RNA), 100, 102, 204, 205, 211
Ribosome, 100, 102, 104
Riley, H. P., 304
RNA, *see* Ribonucleic acid
RNP (ribonucleoprotein) particle, *see* Ribosome
Root formation, 235
Root tip, 274
Roux, E., 34
Ruhland, W., 33
Ryan, F. J., 197

Sachs, J., 6
Sager, R., 197
Salvia apiani, 305f.
  introgression in, 305f.
Salvia mellifera, 305f.
  introgression in, 305f.
San Pietro, A., 37
Sapozhnikov, D. I., 38
Saturn, 321f.
Saussure, N. T. de, 5, 32
Scientific problems, solution of, 32
Sclera, 273
Senebier, J., 5
Sensitive plant, 247
Serological types of Pneumococci, 176
Sexual reproduction, 276
Seybold, A., 35
Shapley, H., 338
Shibata, M., 35
Shlyk, A. A., 38
Shoot apex, 257, 261ff., 266
Shrew, respiration of, 49
Sickle-cell hemoglobin, 207
Simonis, W., 35
Slime mold, 274
Small, J. K., 304
Smith, J. H. C., 17, 36
Smith, L., 36
Spallanzani, L., 318
Spectra
  absorption, 17, 19ff.
    of chlorophylls, 20
  action, 18, 25, 26
  derivative of absorption, 22
  fluorescence, of chlorophyll in plants and in ether, 21
  reflection, 17
Sperm, 272
Sperm cell, 186
Spikes, J. D., 37
Spirochete, syphilis, 116f.
Spoehr, H. A., 7, 8
Spontaneous generation, 318
Sporophyte, 259, 260
Stahl, F. W., 200
Stanier, R. Y., 36, 123
Staphylococcus aureus, 115
Starfish, 274
Sterile culture, 258, 262, 265, 267
Steroids, sterols, 133
  see also Cortisone
Stokes, G. G., 6f.
Stoll, A., 7
Strecker synthesis, 327
Subcellular particles, 280
Sulfur, 130
Sunlight, effect on plants, 4
Supramolecular structures, 283
Symmetry
  dorsiventral, 263, 265
  radial, 263, 265
Synergistic action, 230ff.
Synthesis and ATP, 73
Synthesis of specific proteins, 273

Tail, 277
Taka-diastase, heat resistance of, 52
Tamiya, H., 29, 35
Taylor, J. H., 203
Temperature
  effect of, on rate of photosynthesis, 13ff.
  optimum for algae, 15
Temperatures favorable for life, 338
Terenin, A., 38
Terregens factor, 110, 126
Tetrahymena pyriformis, 129, 134
Thermodynamic laws, and cells, 75
Thermodynamics, laws of, 42
Thiamine, 110, 124, 126, 130, 244
Thiamine pyrophosphate, 116
Thioctic acid, 110
Thiovulum, 113
Thomas, M. D., 35

Timiryazev, C., 6
Tissue cultures, 243
Tobacco, flowering, 287ff.
Tobacco mosaic virus, 140, 142, 143, 148, 149, 156, 163
Tollin, G., 36
Torpedo, electric fish, 71, 72
Torrey, J. G., 10, 28, 33
Trace elements, 130f.
Transduction in *Salmonella,* 180
Transfer of energy, 16, 22
Transformation, genetic, 190f.
Transformation in pneumococci, 174
Traumatic acid, 247
Triphosphopyridine nucleotide (TPN), 27
Tritium labeling, 203
Tropisms, 219
Truit, H. J., 37
Tryptophane, 225ff.
  and degradation, 121
Tubercle bacillus, 115
Tubules, 277
Tumermann, L. A., 38
Tumor, 274
Tumor viruses, 155
Tunica, 216
Tunicate, 274
Two-pigment theory of photosynthesis, 25

Ultracentrifugation of DNA, 201
Ultraviolet light, effect on *E. coli,* 173
Units, chlorophyll, 22f.
Urey, H. C., 321
U-tube experiment, 179

Vaccine, 165
Veen, R. van der, 35
Vegetative condition, 218
Vejlby, K. H., 36
Vennesland, B., 36
Venus, 322, 338
Vernon, L. P., 37
Vinograd, J., 200
Vinogradov, A. P., 38
Viosca, P., 304
Virgin, H. I., 36
Viruses, 139ff., 191f.
  bacterial, 191
  beneficial uses, 140
  as cancer-producing agents, 155
  chemistry and structure, 142ff.
  classification, 140f.
  control of virus disease, 164ff.
  "eclipse period," 151
  events of infection by, 145f., 151ff.
  genes in, 191
  host range, 162f.
  infection with "free" nucleic acid, 148, 150
  life cycle, 194
  lysogeny, 152ff.
  mutation, 155ff.
  mutual reactivation, 162
  nutrition of, 117
  recombination, 157ff.
  reconstitution, 148f.
  reproduction, 151f.
  role of nucleic acid in infection process, 147ff.
  separation of components, 146ff.
  size, 141f.
  symptomatology, 163f.
Vishniac, W., 37, 111
Vitamin B, 244ff.
Vitamin B_6, 110
Vitamin B_{12}, 110, 121, 124, 125f.
  absence in green plants, 135
Vitamin E, 134
Vitamin K, 110
Vitamins
  definition, 110
  as prosthetic groups, 53

Wallace, A. R., 319
Warburg, O., 7, 10, 12, 35
Wassink, E. C., 22, 35
Watson, J. D., 195, 196, 197
Wavelength of light
  absorption and reflection of by leaves, 17
  effectiveness for chlorophyll formation, 18
Wessels, J. S. C., 35
Whatley, F. R., 36
Whittingham, C. P., 33, 35
Willstätter, R., 7
Wing, 275
Winkler method, 47
Winogradsky column, 110f., 122
Withrow, R. B., 33

Witt, H., 35
Wolken, J. J., 37
Wollman, E. L., 194
Worms, 274
Wurmser, R., 34

X-ray diffraction, 274
Xylem, 258, 261, 266, 267

Yeast, 45
Yeast extract, 243f.
Yield, quantum, of photosynthesis, 12

Zalensky, O. V., 38
Zygote, plant, 257, 259, 260, 267
Zymase, 45